The Gre

Building Bible

All you need to know about ecobuilding
2nd Edition

ISSN 1479-4616

ISBN 1-898130-02-7

Edited by Keith Hall

Includes extensive listings of green building professionals, tradesmen, product
suppliers and organisations in the UK & Ireland

**Green Building
Press**

www.newbuilder.co.uk
www.greenbuildingpress.co.uk

the Green
building bible

Jo Burt

Acknowledgements

This book would not have been possible without the willing help of numerous people. Thank you Jamie Anderson, Kirk Archibald, Ben Bamber, Dave Barton, Adrian Birch, Graham Bond, Anita Bradley, Damian Bree, Jo Burt, Rosemary Burton, Paul Connell, Bill Dunster, Jerry Clark, Nanik Deswani, David Elliot, John Garbutt, Mark Gorgolewski, Barbara Grantham, Sally Hall, Richard Handyside, Feidhlim Harty, Robin Hillier, Paul Jenkins, Genevieve Jones, Peter Kaczmar, Maya Karkour, Stephen Lowdnes, Chris Morgan, Chris Morton, Edward Moss, Jane Powell, Michael Priaulx, Gideon Richards, Sue Roaf, Nick Salt, Sarah Sayse, John Shore, Craig Simmonds, David Thorpe, Barbara Tremain, Chris Twinn, Pete Walker and Anthony Walker.

I would also like to extend my thanks to the following organisations for their contributions and support; HHP, LILLI, WSSST, Sustainable Homes, CSBT, BioRegional, Centre for Resource Managment , SEDA, SPONGE, FSC, AECB, TRADA, Sustainability Works and TGR.

I would also like to extend my thanks to all of the advertisers who have supported this edition. Their input has enabled us to keep the cover price affordable and because of our strict advertising policy, (see page 22) these businesses add to the usefulness of this book.

I must give special thanks to my wife Sally and our close friend Jerry Clark for their unfailing support, limitless patience and tolerance of a grumpy man through a very difficult year. My son Keith Jnr also deserves a mention for his patience, help and support.

Finally to all those unsung heros (they know who they are) who have been practicing green design and building for far, far longer than I can claim. I dedicate this book to them.

Keith Hall - Green Building Press

the Green building bible

2nd edition

Published by: *Green Building Press*.
The format of this publication, its contents and the listings are protected by copyright and database copyright. No reproduction is permitted without prior approval of the publisher.

Green Building Press
Publishing Editor: Keith Hall
Green Building Press, PO Box 32,
Llandysul, SA44 5ZA
Tel: 01559 370798
E-mail: info@newbuilder.co.uk
Web Site: www.newbuilder.co.uk

Advertising - Jerry Clark 01208 895103
jerry@newbuilder.co.uk

Listing compilation by Graham Bond

Disclaimer

The views expressed in this book are not necessarily those of the publisher. No guarantee is given as to the accuracy of any information contained herein and no liability is accepted by the publisher or the authors for any errors or omissions. The publisher accepts no responsibility whatsoever for any individual or company, for whatever reasons, selected from the listings or adverts held within this book. Readers should obtain references and details of past projects prior to making any decision to employ.

The listings at the back of this book are provided in good faith to assist you in creating your green buildings. However, the publisher accepts no liability for any losses or damages caused as a result of any employment or use of these businesses. Before employing or buying any products from any of the businesses listed in this book, you should satisfy yourself as to the quality and suitability for the task.

Extra copies of this book and other publications from the *Green Building Press* may be ordered on the internet at: **www.newbuilder.co.uk** or by post - send cheque or postal order, made payable to *Green Building Press*, for £9.95 (incl p&p) per copy. Send to *Green Building Press*, PO Box 32, Llandysul, SA44 5ZA.

the Green building bible

Contents

Contributions for future issues should be Apple Macintosh compatible with accompanying hard copy. The Editor reserves the right to reject contributions and advertising or to edit any material offered for future publication if the best interests of the book or readership are not served. All enquiries and contributions should be directed to:- The Editor; Green Building Bible, Green Building Press, PO Box 32, Llandysul, SA44 5ZA **Publishing Editor: Keith Hall** - keith@newbuilder.co.uk Tel: 01559 370798 **Advertising: Jerry Clark** - jerry@newbuilder.co.uk Tel: 01208 895103 © Green Building Press 2005.
Printed on recycled paper by Cambrian Printers Ltd. Tel: 01970 627111 www.cambrian-printers.co.uk No reproduction in any form without prior approval of the publisher. ISBN 1-898130-02-7
Cover design © Green Building Press.
Inset photo - Paul Connel, building designed and built by Paul Connel architect.
Cartoons - Jo Burt

Welcome to the future

Welcome to this, the second edition of the Green Building Bible. Almost a year in the making, this ground-breaking publication builds upon the achievements of the first edition. My primary goal for this edition was to ensure it was inclusive and covered the whole green building movement. I am pleased to say that I think these goals have largely been achieved and after reading the book I'm confident that you will agree.

This book is testament to the fact that there are many desperately concerned individuals out there that have little confidence in the way most of our current homes and offices are designed and built and they see no future in the 'business as usual' approach most of the industry wishes to pursue. Whilst no single person knows exactly what needs to be done to rectify the damage that we are collectively inflicting upon the planet, it is clear from within these pages that there are many things we can do to address the problems. The construction industry is a very conservative beast and it is clear that there are many existing vested interests who are resistant to change. Let's hope that those who read this book will join the campaign to persuade them otherwise.

In compiling this book I hope that I have provided you, the reader, with in-depth and adequately referenced information regarding the many avenues available that you may wish to follow - whether you are just a concerned householder with a family that you care for or an industry leader requiring a briefing on the state of play of this rapidly maturing 'green building' sector. I am not claiming that this book contains all of the answers but I am confident that this is the best attempt to date.

This book provides not only a snapshot of the current state of play in the green building movement but also works as an encouraging, practical and immediately useful hands-on tool for newcomers to the subject, as well as those already in the industry. I wish to add a personal thank you to all those who have contributed to and supported the production of this edition, especially to my wife Sally who is really the backbone of much of my work. Without her expert and dedicated managerial skills, this edition would not have been achieved.

I would also like to offer my personal thanks to the many authors that have provided the core data for this book. I have taken advantage of the great desire for co-operation that exists within the green building industry. This has enabled me to bring together such a diverse range of architects, builders, scientists, manufacturers, product distributors, installers, and end users. It is this diversity and willingness to share that always fuels my willingness to keep publishing this kind of information. This book now takes its place alongside my other publication, Building for a Future magazine, in charting the continued development of the green building industry in the UK.

Publishers are a much maligned breed but my personal active involvement in this sector for over 15 years, coupled with my hands-on background for many years as a time-served carpenter and joiner and house builder have acted as a catalyst for engagement with all of the major green building organisations that are individually delivering the green building message within and around the industry. This engagement has allowed me to combine, for the first time and in one publication, a gauge of the current state of play of the industry.

Throughout this book, in our other publications and on our web site (www.newbuilder.co.uk), you will find a wealth of information, ideas and products to help you play your part in balancing the burden that we and our buildings are placing on the environment. As each year passes by, the opportunities to make a difference are increasing and there are now a growing number of government and local authority initiatives and grants for projects or technology that will improve the environmental performance of buildings.

I am already planning the third edition of The Green Building Bible. If you wish to be involved contact me. If there is a particular subject that you think we have overlooked or one which you would like to see featured, contact me. If you have any comment on this issue, any projects you would like included or are involved with any initiative or organisation that should be included in the future edition, contact me.

There is a profile of all of the authors that have contributed to this book on page 280.

Keith Hall - Publishing Editor
keith@newbuilder.co.uk

A concept of green design and construction

Sustainability and quality of life are highly influenced by the buildings in which we live and work. At their best, buildings can be inspiring, efficient structures which facilitate health and creativity, and enable us to live in harmony with one another and the planet. **John Shore** reports...

Green buildings should aim to cause the minimum possible harm to the environment and users - throughout their design, construction, use, upkeep and eventual end of life recycling. Despite green and sustainable construction becoming increasingly popular, this comprehensive, cradle to cradle philosophy is not yet common currency.

So perhaps the first rule of green design should be to avoid the need to destroy, replace or abandon as unsuitable without proper consideration. Adaptability and loose-fit may be more appropriate than a design which costs the environment dearly by requiring regular modification and renovation. A sustainable house, for example, might be designed to service the needs of many generations of diverse users – from infancy to old age, from lively teenagers sharing space and facilities, to disabled people or elderly relatives. Such long-life green buildings need to be part of a sustainable community infrastructure to deliver their full potential.

Green building, as a concept, is straightforward and makes perfect sense. It means making thoughtful design choices and using ecological materials in ways that create quality, long-lasting environments with minimum damage to the planet. Natural resources can often be used for services – energy – heating – cooling – water etc.

A vision for a green future

Imaginative and enlightened planning is essential if we are to achieve this. Current thinking must adapt to our needs for thicker, insulated walls, equal access to sunshine, decent sized gardens, green spaces and trees, space to work from home, a softer infrastructure, less need to travel...

We need to rethink current housing policy based on simplistic, polarized thinking and outdated concepts. Such unsustainable development builds impoverished communities and additional long-term social costs. People need environments that are worth caring for.

Low energy buildings provide us with an easy way to combat climate change. Cities and urban areas will need to be greened, - less buildings and more nature, - more local fresh food production. Rural areas could benefit from sensitive development, so they become less isolated and more sustainable. Independently serviced buildings would allow use of the extensive existing rural road network. As we begin to develop our use of natural resources, more people will need to live and work in the countryside.

Green buildings will become the new vernacular form if we are not afraid to design with integrity and use materials with a new honesty. Simple, economical forms require less materials, energy and maintenance. The ever-increasing bureaucracy of building should be resisted, in order to encourage local solutions and building diversity. High standards in construction are essential, but building regulation should not stifle innovation or make buildings so unaffordable that they become unsustainable. Enabling affordable land for self-build might be an ideal way to develop green building skills and green communities without the curse of identi-kit houses. Affordable green buildings could help deliver a step-change in the way we live and work, freeing up time for us to create a more caring and sane society. >>>

High Performance

Scandinavian Windows and Doors

Timber from sustainable sources
Low 'U' values
Low embodied energy
Comprehensive design flexibility
Full support and backup service

The Swedish Window Company
Old Maltings House
Long Melford
Suffolk
CO10 9JB
Tel +(44) 01787 467297   Fax +(44) 01787 319982
e-mail: info@swedishwindows.com
www.swedishwindows.com

Challenges for green design

For green buildings to make a real difference, they must be practical designs which we can all have and afford. Cost-efficiency is a pre-requisite for sustainability, because income generation usually has environmental consequences. Green designs do not have to be complex or costly.

Many ordinary buildings are often described as green or ecological without real justification. We should design and build with integrity and responsibility. Complex and costly multiple-layer walls, or a wall or roof of south-facing glazing may not be the most efficient or sustainable building form. The technology needed to make a building autonomous has always been tempting, but unless it can be cost-effective, simple and reliable, it may not deliver any benefit.

Well designed, easy to build, robust buildings that are healthy to live in and perform well year after year without causing harm to the planet are urgently needed. We must rise to the challenge of climate change – but without resorting to building in unecological materials! A building is not just a machine or a lock-up for our posses-sions, but something we intimately live with, that we care for and love.

Key aspects for green buildings

- Cost-efficiency (a pre-requisite for sustainability)
- Conservation of energy and resources
- Ecological foundations and minimal site intervention
- Reduction of infrastructure; roads; pipes; lighting...
- Elimination/reduction of material and resource wastage
- Elimination/reduction of toxic materials and processes
- Use of renewable/biological materials and energy
- Use of safe, recycled materials and products
- Vapour-diffusive – air and wind-tight construction
- Super insulation and ecological thermal energy storage
- Use of natural lighting (for health and energy saving)
- Minimisation of electro-magnetic fields
- Long life – low maintenance, robust design

- Adaptable, inclusive (access for all) design
- Green surroundings – design with nature and climate

Get the design right!

Be clear about your design strategy. A south-facing passive solar building will demand a different approach than an east-west-axis building. Houses which achieve a U value of 0.1 to 0.15 are often described as zero-heat, which means they do not require a conventional heating system. But even when combined with passive solar space heating they still will usually require small amounts of back-up heating for short periods. A zero-heat house will require a thickness of 235-300mm insulation in the wall, 300-400mm in the roof and 200-250mm in the floor, depending on the properties of the other elements used.

Good natural lighting and solar space heating can be achieved without massive areas of high-embodied-energy glass. Glazing should be sized correctly and provide adequate shading and ventilation to avoid summer overheating. Double glazing with a 1.5 'U'value (frame+glass) is now common and can be supplemented with low energy blinds. Insist on non-conductive glazing (super spacers) and pay attention to air-tight-ness, the quality of seals and materials used for doors and windows. Ensure that internal materi-als and finishes are robust to eliminate the need for wasteful renovation. Reduce water use by fitting aerating taps, and showers. Installing professionally engineered dry (composting) toilets may actually be more eco than a rainwater harvesting system used to flush ordinary water closets. Keep pipework compact and eliminate unnecessary pumps, boilers and techno-gizmos. Design to allow the easy reuse of materials in the future – buildings do not have to be irreversible.

Choice of materials

The construction of buildings and their infra-structure are major causes of environmental degradation, pollution, climate change and energy use. A building's design and the choice of materials and processes can minimise the ecological impact during construction and in use, or can influence and cause a (possibly unfore-seen) chain-reaction of damage. >>>

Primary embodied energy of common products and raw materials (approximates)

Material	kWh/m³
Lead	157,414
Copper	133,000
Steel iron ore (blast furnace)	63-80,000
Steel recycled	29,669
Aluminium	55,868
Plastics	47,000
Glass	23,000
Fibre cement slates	5,282
Cement	2,860
Aluminium (recycled)	2,793-3,910
Clay tiles	1,520
Bricks (non flettons)	1,462
Plastic insulation	1,125
Gypsum plaster / plasterboard	900
Autoclaved bricks	800
Concrete 2 : 4	800
Imported softwood	754
Foamed glass insulation	751
Concrete tiles	630
Concrete 1 : 3 : 6	600
Lightweight clinker blocks	600
Local slate	540
Local stone tiles	450
Sand cement render	400
Bricks (fletton)	300
Mineral fibre insulation	230
Home grown green oak	220
Crushed granite	150
Cellulose insulation	133
Home grown softwood (air dried)	110
Sand and gravel	45
Sheeps wool insulation	30

Sources: Centre for Alternative Technology; Environmental Science Handbook; Pittsburgh Corning; Timber Trade Federation; CIRIA; GreenPro.

Green design aims to achieve a sustainable balance between human and environmental requirements. This balance is not just a matter of science and technology – following your intuition may be equally valuable and essential. History shows us that techniques and technologies once considered to be wonderful improvements sometimes prove to do more harm than good.

Green building is now firmly set in the public consciousness. This popularity has encouraged a confusion of claims for green credentials which sometimes are unrealistic or even inac-curate. Many manufacturers argue that green equals energy saving, while drawing a veil over the environmental costs of materials extraction, processing, toxicity issues and the manner of production or the costs of sales and distribution. Care needs to be taken since similar products from different sources may vary greatly in their eco-properties.

Apart from the clear distinction between natural and synthetic building materials, it is useful to consider five main groupings-

● Renewable (timber, wool, etc - from photosynthesis / biology).
● Extracted (earth, sand and gravel - minimal processing)
● Extracted and processed (lime, plaster, slate, stone, brick)
● Extracted/highly processed (cement, steel, glass and plastics)
● Recycled (re-used timber, brick, aggregate, steel, glass, insulation)

Some green designers and builders want to work mainly with renewable, extracted and recycled materials and by doing so, help the building industry evolve and develop along this more natural path. Understanding and choosing materials on environmental grounds is a complex task and the work done by the Centre for Sustainable Construction at BRE is an invaluable resource. Green material suppliers still need to have their products profiled. To date only a few products have been profiled **www.bre.co.uk/envprofiles**.

Material properties

The tables on this and the following pages for Conductivity, Embodied Energy and Thermal Capacity, graphically illustrate important material properties.

Even some green products may involve aspects which you might decide to avoid. A green designer has to consider an incredibly wide range of information and possibilities and then select the best solution. Do local materials really exist and would their use be appropriate for a low-energy, green building – and is quarrying or mining ecological, desirable or sustainable?

In order to lighten the burden we place on the environment, we can create buildings mainly from renewable, 'biological' materials, – which rely on the income rather than capital resources of the >>>

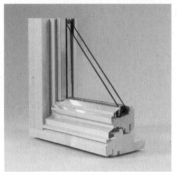

planet. We now have a wide range of green materials and we can use glass, metals and plastics efficiently, where greener alternatives do not yet exist. Non-PVC pipes and cables are available.

Timber frame, recycled paper insulation, straw bale and earth are all becoming popular materials for green building. Each brings its own strengths and weaknesses – no one method or material offers the only solution for all situations. We may need to combine the properties of materials in order to create successful buildings. A strawbale wall, with external timber cladding and internal earth plastering might be a logical strategy. Timber (from sustainable sources) is versatile as a beautiful, structural, easy to work material which may be locally available. New vapour-diffusive membranes enable us to build timber frame buildings with high levels of air-tightness and greatly reduced heat loss. Eco-friendly roofing, thermal storage, foundations and ground floor insulation all need and are getting further development.

Thermal mass and storage

There are two schools of thought on how much thermal mass to include in a building. All buildings include a level of mass, which will take up heat depending on its conductivity, and which can be re-radiated after a time-lag if the ambient temperature falls. The decision on how much to include will depend on site and climate, the building design and the uses the building has to fulfil. (It should be noted that many people living in thermally lightweight structures with appropriate glazing detailing and insulation generally

Thermal conductivity of materials (pre-lambda 90/90)	W/mK
Copper	380.000
Aluminium	198.000
Steel	48.300
Granite	3.810
Limestone	1.530
Dense brickwork	1.470
Dense concrete	1.440
Sand / cement render	1.410
Very packed damp soil	1.400
Sandstone	1.295
Bricks (engineering)	1.150
Dry soil	1.140
Clay bricks (compressed, unfired)	0.950
Brickwork and tile hanging	0.840
Damp loose soil	0.700
Water	0.580
Adobe	0.520
Glass	0.500
Earth blocks	0.340
Thermalite blocks	0.140-0.190
Plaster board	0.180
Recycled wood fibre/ Gypsum plasterboard	0.176
Hardwood	0.160
Clay board (alternative to plasterboard)	0.140
Softwood / plywood	0.138
Oil tempered hardboard	0.120
Chipboard	0.108
Strawbales (dry)	0.080-0.100
Strawboard(very rare)	0.098
Snow (average density)	0.090
Woodwool slab (light)	0.082
Stony soil (normal)	0.052
Bitvent 15 sheathing board	0.050
Foamed glass insulation	0.036-0.046
Cork	0.043
Fibreglass Insulation	0.040
Hemp insulation	0.039
Flax / sheepswool insulation	0.037
Hair	0.036
Cellulose fibre (recycled paper) Warmcel 500 wall insulation	0.036
Warmcel loft Insulation	0.035
Expanded polystyrene Insulation	0.033
Polyurethane foam	0.023
Still air	0.020

Illustration by PHP Architects

16

report no experience of summer overheating).

Studies of heavy-weight buildings reveal the need for constant background heating to provide thermal comfort – hardly a sustainable concept. Since mass has to be heated, too much can be as much a problem as too little. The mass has to be cooled effectively at night, or it will be unable to take up heat the next day. The usefulness of solid materials as a thermal buffer reduces with thickness and is highly influenced by surface area. Hot thermal mass will not cool a building but can contribute to overheating.

A relatively small amount of water could be a simple solution to the provision of thermal storage in lightweight, super-insulated buildings. Water is more than twice as efficient as dense concrete; ecological, non-hazardous and available at zero cost. Phase-change materials allow the selection of heat take-up and release temperatures and are a much more effective thermal buffer than water or glass.

The heat (watts per hour) needed to raise the temperature of one cubic metre of material by 1°C gives an indication of thermal capacity.

Thermal capacity of materials Wh/m³ K

Phase change material (PCM)*	5,000
Glass	1,250
Water	1,158
Cast iron	1,104
Lead	1,040
Steel	1,014
Slate	653
Stone	650
Dense concrete blocks	483
Sasmox gypsum-wood board	458
Alluvial clay-40% sand	457
Plaster on render	440
Quarry tiles	418
Brickwork	374
Earth	356
Lightweight concrete blocks	336
Gypsum plaster	314
Dry oak, beech or ash	252
Woodwool slabs	250
Wood chipboard	224
Gypsum plasterboard	219
Softwood flooring	217
Aerated concrete blocks	140

*Gypsum plaster with encapsulated PCM (room temperature swing 22 to 27oC).

Sustainable energy

Buildings have an unhealthy appetite for energy, and energy consumption is increasing despite use of more efficient technology. There is massive potential for the development of new energy-efficient appliances and for new ways of living and working. Solar and wind energy are available to all buildings and we should make better use of these independent resources. The increasing use of green electricity from the national grid makes it essential and urgent that we harvest more renewable energy for grid connection.

Photovoltaic (PV) electricity panels are gradually falling in cost while gaining in efficiency and can be easily mounted on the roof and walls of buildings. PV is increasingly used to pump solar water heating systems and to feed the electricity grid. Small-scale wind turbines are more cost effective and can work both day and night. New, quiet, slow-speed turbines are becoming available and some can be building-mounted (with great care!) Wind turbines can also be used to heat buildings and pump water without the need for battery storage. A well maintained wind turbine

can have a long service life.

Given appropriate site layouts, it is possible to heat buildings using windows or roofing as passive solar collectors. Green electricity can be used for the small amount of back up heat required. For more energy-dependent buildings, efficient wood chip and pellet stoves can be used. Green buildings have the potential to become energy producers rather than just consumers.

For both healthy living and quality of life, we need to green not just our homes, but also our places of work and our surroundings. We also need to drastically reduce our need for travel and change the way we work to enable more flexibility and the use of local, natural resources. For a society which can develop spacecraft, micro-computers and mobile telephones this should not be too great a challenge.

Building - the bigger picture

In 2004, the Government chose to accept the recommendation of the Sustainable Buildings Task Group that a Sustainable Building Code should be developed. Sustainability will now, surely, become a legislative as well as a moral pressure. When it does it is vital that the requirements have been sufficiently thought out to ensure that the quest to achieve it becomes a stimulus for innovation and creative solutions, rather than a stranglehold that limits development. **John Garbutt** summarises the current thinking ...

In acknowledgement of the fact that so much good work has already been undertaken in this field, the Sustainable Buildings Task Group proposes basing the recommended Sustainable Building Code on the Building Research Establishment Environmental Assessment Method (BREEAM) and the BRE's EcoHomes System. It also recommends drawing on existing advisory bodies to set up a joint venture body within a very short timescale to develop, manage and maintain the Sustainable Building Code. The Sustainable Buildings Task Group's call to act quickly in this matter reflects the importance that is attached to it.

The very nature of BREEAM and EcoHomes means that the new Code would not just focus on energy efficiency but also on water use, access to public transport and recycling facilities to name but a few. However there is one recommendation that comes dangerously close to enforcing restrictive practice rather than the innovative approach the report purports to inspire.

Having gone to great lengths not to reinvent the wheel, it is a pity that the Group then over-tightens one of the spokes and endangers the very principles it seeks to uphold. The proposal to require a minimum 10% recycled content by value in constructions imposes severe limitations, it could stifle research and development into new products and is based on the erroneous assumption that recycled is by default the most sustainable option.

There are of course instances where recycled content could work well for some building materials, recycled aggregate for foundations, for example, since the recycled content does not impair the function of the product. However, all routes to sustainability should be considered and encouraged in balance. The goal is to attain low energy, low carbon structures. Encouraging the use of recycled materials is an important element of environmental awareness and responsible use of resources, but to over-focus the Sustainable Buildings Code on it could be a self-defeating exercise in sustainability terms.

Just as it is important to look at embodied energy in the context of the whole life cycle of a product, it is crucial to take a holistic view of all aspects of a construction in assessing sustainability. This is why the flexibility of the BREEAM and EcoHomes system works well, since it is the overall score of the building that decides the rating, rather than taking a piece-meal approach to individual elements. The fact that the most effective insulants available are not made from recycled material should not preclude them from being considered sustainable. In reality they could conserve more energy, and enhance the environment over the life of the construction to a far greater degree than their recycled counterparts.

It is clear that when the Sustainable Buildings Task Group comes to fruition the obvious next step would be to use it as a model for the next changes to Approved Document L in 2010. Most would agree that regulating on a broader basket of issues is the right way to go and not before time. The danger is that in trying too hard to be 'green' we over-complicate and ultimately over-look the basic principles that will enable us to achieve the vital goal of sustainability. We need to keep things in perspective, taking into account the long term view, and we need to keep >>>

things simple, so that everybody can achieve the targets.

There is a need to examine all aspects of a buildings life cycle and encourage developers, specifiers and contractors across the board to take a holistic view. This is a relatively new concept, and one that the industry is only just beginning to embrace. Readers of the Green Building Bible should lead from the front by adopting the new standards and demonstrating that sustainable building does not automatically lead to increased costs, taken in the context of the building's whole life cycle, or to constraints in design flexibility. But they should also fight for the right to seek the best methods of achieving this.

The foreword to the Sustainable Buildings Task Group's report talks about the opportunities that have arisen to rebuild our communities because we're tearing down the building mistakes made in the 60s. We need to get it right this time by keeping the big picture in mind and not

end up with limitations on our space, materials or scope to develop the most sustainable solutions. ❖

Cara Naden produced a report on the popularity of and future for the proposed Code for Sustainable Building Practice (CSBP) which is championed by the Deputy Prime Minister, John Prescott. The report was comissioned by Building for a Future magazine. It can be read in full on the Green Building Press website. Follow the link from: **www.newbuilder.co.uk/bffmag/autumn04/index.asp**

© Green Building Press

Advertising Policy of the *Green Building Press*

Advertising space will only be offered to companies whose products or services (in our opinion) offer clear environmental advantages over similarly available products for the same purpose.
In particular we will not accept adverts for products that:
* include ozone destroying gasses
* are wasteful of energy or high energy consumer
* contain components that are considered harmful to human health, either by passive or active exposure
* are racist or sexist in nature

The product selection criteria used for our GreenPro database forms the basis of our advertiser selection process.

Buyers want homes to be eco-friendly

A survey in the summer of 2004 shows the homeowner is willing to pay more for greener housing

Home buyers want to know how their homes rate for energy efficiency and running costs, with 84% prepared to pay an extra 2% on the purchase price for an eco-friendly home, according to the report.

The survey, which was carried out before the government announced in the summer of 2004 that building regulations would be changed to cut energy consumption in new homes by 25%, showed that buyers were critical of the lack of information about how their houses would perform.

Of those polled, 87% of buyers wanted to know whether their homes were environmentally friendly and 66% said they were not given adequate information about the technical specifications of a new home.

The priorities were lower running costs, enhanced air quality and daylight, use of low-allergy and environmentally friendly material, and water efficiency.

The research carried out for Cabe (Commission for Architecture and the Built Environment), the Halifax bank and WWF, showed that prospective buyers were badly informed about what features to look for.

In fact, earlier WWF research had suggested that there would be no extra costs for making homes more eco-friendly. Cuts in energy and water use of about 30% and 40% respectively are achievable for little or no extra cost to house builders.

Robin Nicholson, Cabe commissioner, said: "If you are buying a car, you get any number of specifications allowing you to make easy comparisons on fuel consumption and value for money. We should get the same quality of information on the environmental performance of homes. This survey reflects a much higher priority placed on environmental issues by home buyers than we had all assumed."

The findings prove that the public wants the sort of information promised by the government's home seller's information pack, which home owners and sellers will be required to make available to prospective buyers by January 2006.

Paul King, director of WWF's One Million Sustainable Homes campaign, said: "This research provides powerful evidence of a growing concern about environmental and design issues."

He added: "People understand that sustainable homes are good for their pocket, for their health and for the planet."

The government plans to bring in building regulations during 2005 which include a pressure test for new homes to check that they are airtight, so that heat does not easily escape. ❖

A total of 912 would-be home buyers took part in the online survey, conducted by Mulholland Research & Consulting.

From a report first published in The Guardian July 26, 2004 by Paul Brown, environment correspondent

Material selection

Many building materials use large amounts of energy and produce toxic wastes during manufacture. Some are not healthy to use or to live with, and many are difficult to dispose of safely as well as having adverse effects on the environment when land-filled or incinerated.

Mark Gorgolewski reports ...

When selecting materials for environmentally sensitive construction it is important to consider their environmental impact over their full life, including:

- manufacture
- construction
- operation
- maintenance
- demolition
- disposal

In each phase consideration should be given to the energy used, resources consumed, waste generated, potential for recycling and emissions generated. In addition, materials need to be durable and perform well throughout their life to limit the environmental impact of their maintenance and replacement.

Tools to make meaningful comparisons are limited at present, thus the guidance below and the eight-point plan are intended to outline the general approach that can be taken for the specification of materials and components to reduce their environmental impact.

Life cycle assessment

Life Cycle Assessment (LCA) or cradle to grave analysis is a method of measuring the total impact that a product or process has on the environment. All the inputs (resources in) and outputs (waste - emissions produced, etc.) over the full life of the material or component are measured. LCA is a useful tool to assess the environmental performance of materials and components and to compare products, but only if the information and methods used to compile the LCAs are consistent. Often the problems relate to what is included (or what boundaries are set). Energy used in transportation is a good example. Some LCAs account for transportation of the material to the factory but not to site, whereas some will also include the energy used to transport the workers to the factory manufacturing the component.

The BRE and others are developing consistent rules for LCAs of building materials. However, until there is comprehensive data available on a wide range of building products and materials it is important to review carefully the information provided by an LCA, and use it as one of several ways of assessing the environmental impact of a building material or component.

General guidelines

Choosing materials for improved environmental specification is complex, and requires balancing of many issues which often conflict. It is not practical to rank materials as their environmental impact is linked to the purpose they are used for in the building. However, when choosing materials for a project, environmental performance should be one of the principal procurement criteria. The following are a set of general guidelines that can be used:

Use materials efficiently - try to minimise the volume of materials used and avoid wasteful specification. Using less material can reduce the overall environmental impact of the building.

Choose durable materials - replacement of a component during the life of a building adds life-cycle environmental impact. So durable, long-life components are often beneficial.

Choose low maintenance materials - maintenance such as painting, and even cleaning can be very environmentally damaging over the life of the building, and once the building is complete the designer usually has little control over this. It is therefore beneficial to minimise the need for regular maintenance such as painting and replacement of floor coverings by using appropri-

ate materials.

Use materials from renewable sources where possible - to avoid depleting stocks of non-renewable materials it is often preferable to use renewable materials.

Choose reused or recycled materials where appropriate - reuse and recycling can save on primary non-renewable resources, but care must be taken as in some cases the energy used in transport and reprocessing of recycled materials can be high, and negates the benefits (see recycled materials web sites at end of this article).

Use materials close to their natural state - materials closer to their natural state will tend to have had less processing which often means less energy use, less waste and less pollution.

Use of local materials - using local materials can reduce the need for transport and benefits the local economy and society. However, it is important to consider other factors and ensure that the material has not been moved around the country for processing before being returned to its starting point, for delivery to site.

Source from manufacturers who have a proven environmental management record. - some manufacturers have developed materials and products that are aimed at reducing environmental impact. Others have ISO 14001 environmental management systems in place to control their environmental impact. These manufacturers deserve support.

Source from manufacturers who readily provide environmental data - some manufacturers take environmental control of their processes seriously and will be able to provide appropriate environmental information on their products in their literature. However, be aware of green-wash, as some manufacturers are making very general or unsubstantiated environmental claims.

Minimise waste through co-ordinated design and site practices - much waste occurs through poor co-ordination of sizes etc. during design. Consider how to co-ordinate dimensions to >>>

Follow the eight point plan!

When making environmental choices the main questions to ask about any material or component, are:

1. What is it made of - is it renewable or scarce?
2. What processing did it undergo - was this polluting or energy intensive?
3. How far did it come - was there a lot of road transport involved?
4. What effect will it have on those installing it and those using the building?
5. Does it require a lot of maintenance that may be environmentally damaging?
6. What will happen to it at the end of its useful life?
7. Does it have a unique positive function that over-rides its environmental impacts?
8. Is there a better option?

reduce material use, and minimise waste.

Avoid PVC - the campaign for reducing PVC use continues and various alternatives for windows, guttering, underground drainage pipes, flooring, and cladding are increasingly available. See the Greenpeace web site for alternatives

Use low emissions paints and finishes wherever possible - this is a complex area and general guidance is difficult. However, where possible low emission paints should be used, and preferably water based and mineral based. Good timber stains, based on oils and waxes, are available. Look for paints with the EU eco-label - see website contact at end of article.

Ensure that all timber comes from well managed sources - timber has a vital role to play in green building, yet the timber industry is still having a huge effect on the environment. The information available can be confusing and contradictory, making it difficult to take an informed stance. Certified timber by the Forestry Stewardship Council (FSC) is still the preferred option. Alternatives include locally grown timber or Pan European Forestry Certification (PEFC) timber (see web sites below).

Encourage reuse or recycling of materials at the end of their life - appropriate design and construction practices can help components be easily extracted at the end of their useful life in such a way that they can be reused or recycled.

There will often be conflicts and trade-offs between the various principles listed above and the decision about each material or component will have to be considered independently. The specifier must use their judgement to make an appropriate choice for each particular case. ❖

Sources of further information on material selection

- GreenPro, the on-line eco-building product database at **www.newbuilder.co.uk** contains listings of over 1000 building products available in the UK that have ecological merits,
- For recycled materials and materials containing some recycled content see 'Reuse and Recycle' later in this book.
- Green Building Handbook, Woolley, T., Kimmins, S., Harrison, P. & Harrison, R. E&FN

Spon, 2000
- Ecology of Building Materials by Bjorn Berge, Architectural Press
- BRE Green Guide to Specification - available from the Building Research Establishment **www.bre.co.uk**
- Handbook of Sustainable Building by Anink, D. Boonstra, C. & Mak, J., James and James, 1996
- Greenpeace web site for PVC alternatives **http://archive.greenpeace.org/~toxics/pvcdatabase/**
- BRE Environmental Profiles of the principal construction materials - **www.bre.co.uk/profiles**
- Environmental handbook for building and civil engineering projects vol 1 and 2, from CIRIA, **www.ciria.org.uk**
- List of EU eco-label products including some construction products **www.eco-label.com**
- London Hazards Centre for information about emissions from paints and other products **www.lhc.org.uk**
- Forestry Stewardship Council **www.fsc-uk.demon.co.uk**
- Pan European Forest Council **www.pefc.org**
- UK Woodland Assurance Scheme **www.forestry.gov.uk**
- Forum for the future **www.forumforthefuture.org.uk**
- Healthy Flooring Network **www.healthyflooring.org**
- Certified Forest Products Council visit **www.certifiedwood.org**
- For more information on ISO 14001 visit **www.iso14000.com**
- Hockerton Housing Project **www.hockerton.demon.co.uk**

Most of the publications above are available from The Green Shop **www.greenshop.co.uk** *01452 770629*

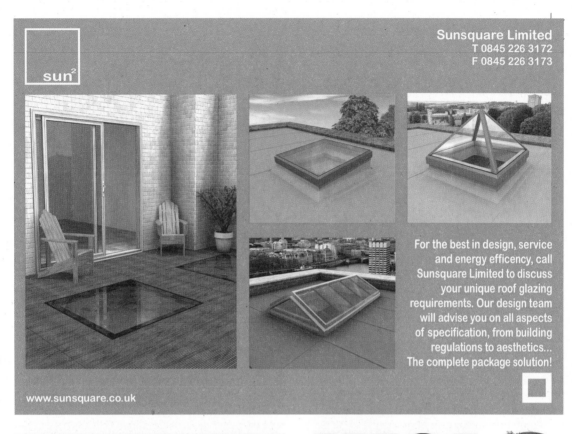

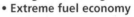

Conserving fuel and power

It has been a long time coming, but in recent years the government has acknowledged that action is crucial if we are to preserve the environment and achieve a sustainable future for ourselves and the generations to come. It has followed this through with legislation aimed at cutting CO_2 emissions, and has set challenging targets to be met by 2010 and 2050. But having seen the light, have they also found the way to reach it? **John Garbutt** summarises the current thinking about building regulations for the conservation of fuel and power.

It is widely recognised that there are four main global environmental sustainability issues: global warming, non-renewable resource depletion, toxic pollution and ozone depletion, and that these global issues far outweigh any local environmental sustainability issues in their need for immediate attention and potential impact from inaction.

Recent studies have shown that the first three issues are essentially one. The extraction and consumption (burning) of fossil fuels is by far the most significant contributor to global warming, non-renewable resource depletion and toxic pollution.

60% of fossil fuels are used to heat buildings in the UK, half of this in housing. Therefore it is argued that environmental sustainability comes down to two main issues: reduce fossil fuel use and specify zero ODP products.

By far the most economical method of reducing fossil fuel use is to reduce space heating demand. The investment for renewable energy sources only becomes convincing once space heating demand is minimised as capital costs may be prohibitive to most. Furthermore the renewables industry arguably does not have the capacity to meet mass market demand.

There are two main methods of reducing space heating demand: reduce heat losses through the building fabric and reduce heat losses from unintentional air-leakage.

There is a whole raft of incentives that can be used to achieve this aim. The 'way' of course, is through legislation, and one of the biggest legislative weapons in this instance is the use of building regulations to make our buildings, both domestic and non-domestic, much more energy efficient.

To this end Approved Documents L1 & L2 to the Building Regulations for England & Wales are currently being reviewed with a new version due to be implemented late in 2005. If the proposed amendments go ahead it is claimed that they would "lead to an improvement in the energy efficiency of new buildings (and hence a reduction in the carbon emissions they would otherwise produce) of around 25%".

The 'truth', however is a slightly different matter. The construction industry has struggled to implement the current 2002 edition of ADL. The main problem appears to be the sheer lack of capacity at present within the building control system to ensure that the current Approved Documents L1 & L2 are being adhered to, let alone when new elements and tighter targets are introduced.

The Office of the Deputy Prime Minister (ODPM), which is responsible for Approved Documents L1 & L2, is exploring the possibility of self-certification by construction companies and of extending the current competent persons scheme in order to combat this apparent shortfall. These are steps that may ease the situation but, in order to be effective, will themselves require regular monitoring and evaluation. To compound the problem further the European Energy Performance of Buildings Directive has to be absorbed into UK law by January 2006, and will add considerably to the administrative pressures already being experienced. One thing is certain, there is an awful lot of work to be done to put all of the necessary inspection and accreditation processes in place before the new Approved Documents come into force.

But what else can we expect from this latest review of the Approved Documents? The recent Consultation document indicated that Approved Documents L1 & L2 are likely to be split further into 4 parts, with newbuild and refurbishment being treated separately for both dwellings and non-domestic constructions. This would give Approved Document L1a for new dwellings, Approved Document L1b for dwelling refurbishment and extensions and similarly Approved Document L2a and Approved Document L2b for buildings other than dwellings. The thinking is that the documents themselves should give only

minimal information with supplementary documents providing the detailed guidance.

Regardless of what other changes are made to the Approved Documents L1 & L2, there will no longer be a simple Elemental or Target U-value method of compliance, as the Energy Performance of Buildings Directive demands that performance standards are set for buildings as a whole, rather than for construction and services elements. This, in itself, is a logical next step towards optimizing energy performance. the danger lies in the possible abandonment of reasonable enforceable minimum U-values for the building envelope, trading off the efficiency of the fabric of the building against elements such as renewable sources of energy. New methods of calculation will be introduced and compliance for new-build will be demonstrated using only these methods. These calculations will consider a very wide range of performance issues e.g. fabric U-values, air-tightness, heating system efficiency, lighting, etc etc etc.

The new method of calculation for new-build dwellings appears to be relatively straightforward, based on the Standard Assessment Procedure (SAP) modified to include the ability to account for renewable energy supply. A target figure based on CO_2 emissions will be set for all new dwellings to comply with. The building size and form will therefore affect the parameters needed, including U-values and air-tightness, in order to achieve the target.

It is likely that there will be one complex calculation method for new-build non-dwellings, but the actual method has to be confirmed. Compliance targets will work in much the same way as for current Approved Document L2 calculation methods. Approved Document L2a (new-build) will contain a set of notional values for the parameters in the calculation method. These notional values have been set at the current Approved Document L2 elemental method standards. By assigning these notional values to the elements of a building, a user will apply the calculation method to produce a base target. The base target is then reduced by a factor to reduce energy use from 2002 levels and a factor to encourage renewables and the resulting figure is the actual target. The performance of all elements can then be varied and, provided that the final building beats the target when it is put through the calculation method, compliance is achieved.

In recognition of the fact that energy use should be minimised before renewables are considered, fall back or worst allowable values are given for building fabric U-values and air-tightness. These have been set at the Elemental Method U-values from the current Approved Documents L1 & L2.

Wall U-value	0.35 W/m².K
Roof U-value	0.25 W/m².K
Floor U-value	0.25 W/m².K
Glazing U-value	2.20 W/m².K

However, given the deliberate promotion of renewables in the draft Approved Documents, there is some concern that these worst case values are not tight enough. There is a grave two-fold risk in not having fall back standards that achieve the aim of preventing the inappropriate trading off of the thermal efficiency of the building envelope against elements such as renewable sources of energy.

I have already covered the notion that designers could end up creating buildings that have relatively poor fabric measures and compensate with the specification of oversized renewable energy sources. The overall capital cost would be much greater and it would be difficult to cost-effectively improve the fabric performance at a later date.

The second consideration is that fabric measures by their very nature tend to be long term assets (60 to 100 years minimum). Heating systems, including renewables, tend to be relatively short term (10-20 years). Most buildings that incorporate renewable energy supply will still require a secondary heating system. What happens to a building's Approved Document L compliance when the renewable supply breaks down and the owner can't afford to replace it or have it fixed. Reliance is placed on the secondary system which will almost certainly have a much greater CO_2 impact.

The obvious solution would be to assume the CO_2 emissions of the secondary heating system in proving compliance for the building, but this would ignore the benefits of renewable supply. This being politically unacceptable means that

the fall back U-values must be tightened to a level which obviates the possibilities illustrated above. It is suggested that the following would be appropriate:

Wall U-value	0.30 W/m².K
Roof U-value	0.22 – 0.14 W/m².K
(depending on position of insulation)	
Floor U-value	0.25 W/m².K
Glazing U-value	2.00 W/m².K

The nature of the calculations themselves and the many possible different permutations bring much greater complexity to the whole process than already exists. No longer will anyone be able to use a straightforward set of U-values to be certain of complying. Far from the apparent freedom of trading off the thermal efficiency of the building fabric against other CO_2 efficient elements, people would be forced to design by complex calculation methods, which could prove extremely problematical. In reality a designer may have to make 5 to 10 attempts at a calculation to get to a stage where the building in question complies with Approved Document L.

The complexity of calculating (let alone achieving) compliance and the potential for inadequate guidance spell bad news for the smaller builder/designer. What is required is a set of robust simple rules embedded in the Approved Documents which, if used, would guarantee compliance with Approved Document L in 99% of cases when the building in question is put to the test via the calculation methods.

The 'light' of course at the end of all of this, is that with modern materials and expertise it is perfectly feasible to make those cuts in CO_2, and it may even be possible to do it within the targeted timescale. However, we need to keep things simple, so that everybody can achieve the targets. ❖

Unfortunately, by the time you read this article the consultation process for the new Approved Documents L will have closed. However, if the cost and complexity of these changes concerns you, it may still be worth addressing your concerns to: PartL.Consultation@fabermaunsell.com

For information, the full consultation package can be downloaded from:

www.odpm.gov.uk/stellent/groups/odpm_buildreg/documents/page/odpm_breg_029821.hcsp

PEN Y COED INSULATION

DYFI ECO PARK, MACHYNLLETH

WARMCEL

The insulation giving you the sustainable solution to energy efficient building

HOUSE OF THE FUTURE, CARDIFF

Pen y Coed Insulation have over 10 years experience in the installation of Warmcel on 1000's of projects that range from factories, schools and large scale housing developments to architecturally acclaimed unique buildings.

Warmcel is so efficient that heat of 1000ºc cannot be felt below a layer on your hand. Warmcel has excellent fire resistant properties

SERVICES OFFERED INCLUDE:

- **U - Value calculations**
- **Detailed specifications**
- **New-build installation**
- **Retro - installation**

PEN Y COED INSULATION is a division of PEN Y COED CONSTRUCTION & INSULATION Ltd a company that specialises in the design, detailing and construction of energy efficient buildings.

PEN Y LAN, MEIFOD, POWYS, SY22 6DA

TEL/FAX: 01938 500 643
email:- penycoed.construction@btinternet.com

Every house a power station?

In October 2003 at the Better Buildings Summit, Deputy Prime Minister John Prescott called on the building industry to 'put high quality design and environmental efficiency at the heart of the built environment'. He wanted "More innovation, better design, better planning, higher standards - more of the "wow" factor and a more can-do attitude" adding "Industry, government, environmentalists, planners, architects, and local residents must push for the highest standards, not the lowest common denominator. Together we can make it happen." **David Elliott** wonders whether we should hold our breath ...

We've all heard this sort of thing before, but maybe now there really is an opportunity to do new things. So what new technological options are available?

PV solar is all the rage

It's expensive still, but the current grant systems help in this respect. A solar roof, after all, is an unusual building component in that it earns its keep! In the USA, the state of California now requires new housing developments to install solar PV panels - it's much cheaper, by about one third, to build PV into the new houses than to retrofit it to existing buildings. Let's hope we adopt this initiative in the UK soon. At the opening of the new Sharp PV solar cell manufacturing plant in Wrexham, Clwyd in 2004, Peter Hain, the secretary for Wales and one time energy minister, said that his cabinet colleagues were discussing the change in building regula-

tions as part of the government's plan to catch up with the solar revolution in Germany - which is where most of the output from the Wrexham plant is destined. He admitted that "there is no doubt the Germans have stolen a march on us in a big way. I believe that we should change building regulations so that by law every new house and development in Britain should have photovoltaic electricity production and solar panels for water heating".

Maybe consumers will be happy to pay a bit more for homes with advanced energy features like PV built in. Let's hope that, if so, the developers also make sure to deal with the basic insulation and energy efficient design aspects....

Combined heat and power (CHP)

Next along the advanced technology path is hydrogen - since PV only works during the day, why not generate hydrogen by the electrolysis of water using electricity from PV cells on the roof, and store it as a high pressure gas, and then use it in a fuel cell to produce electricity when its needed? Tony Marmont has installed a pioneering system like this on his 50 acre farm in Leicestershire - using power from his existing wind turbines, micro hydro plants and PV solar array.

Okay for the pioneers who can afford such systems but will ordinary consumers be willing or able to afford to have complex systems like this, with electrolysers and fuel cells installed in their homes allowing them to generate some or even all their own power? Well, we may get some idea from the response to the domestic scale natural gas fired micro-combined heat and power units currently being consumer tested by British Gas and Powergen. These are small Stirling engine units which can fit in your kitchen and produce electricity as well as heat (see Building for a Future, Vol 13, No 3 at **www.newbuilder.co.uk**).

Hydrogen electrolyser/fuel cell units would be more complex, and at a time when there is much talk about the difficulty of finding plumbers to do simple jobs, consumers may find it a little worrying to have exotic new systems like this installed - keeping them running and properly maintained over time might be a bit of a headache, at least until the technology is developed fully.

Of course, total self generation by 'stand alone' systems is not really very sensible except in very remote locations. Where grid links exist, you can import power to top-up when your system can't meet your needs, and export any excess power at other times. It may even be possible to use roof top micro-wind turbines in this way - there are several on offer now. But this new approach does require a new attitude on the part of homeowners. They would have to think of themselves as running mini-power stations. Some may love that, others may not. Perhaps fiscal incentives would help?

Domestic scale systems are of course not the only option. Woking Borough Council has adopted a different approach - using medium scale gas fired micro-CHP units to feed power and heat to groups of houses via a private wire system and district heating network. Power from PV solar arrays and a fuel cell is also fed into the mix, and the overall system is run and maintained by an energy service company set up by the council. This local 'self gen' system is very popular locally, since it provides cheaper power than from the conventional grid supplies. But, even if, as at Woking, we only go part way down the domestic 'self-gen' road, there is going to be a need for a lot more skilled maintenance people running around in (electric/hydrogen powered) white vans! ❖

A comprehensive introduction to and study of combined heat and power can be found in Building for a Future magazine, Vol 13, No 3 Winter 2003/4 'The Dawning of the CHP Age"

Building sustainability

Building sustainability is about more than satisfying environmental criteria. There is a growing body of opinion that, unless a more comprehensive view is taken, the wrong decisions may well be made regarding the retention or replacement of buildings, and in selecting new designs. **Anthony Walker & Sarah Sayce** report ...

A recently completed research project 'Buildings: a new life', emphasised the need to achieve a balance between environmental, social and economic considerations while recognising that conflict often arises between the different stakeholders, particularly when intergenerational issues arise, and this is exacerbated by the varying quality of information available in the different fields.

Some factors allow clear and accurate measurement, such as energy consumed, use of renewable resources, recycling of waste water and rainwater. Others are more difficult to define and recent interest in the significance of 'intangible assets' illustrates this point. Those which can be subjected to simple mathematical analysis have attracted attention and provide simple and easily measurable results, but even here over simplification, such as the omission of embodied energy in some measures of energy consumption by a building, can result in a gross distortion of the true picture. It is therefore difficult to make an assessment and to strike a balance between such simple statements and the more subjective values of the intangibles.

We therefore need to introduce other concepts, such as the triple bottom line (TBL) of economic, social and environmental criteria in an attempt to encapsulate these differences and achieve a comprehensive understanding. A formula to assist in this has been suggested by Sarah Sayce and colleagues in their work for the Construction Conference on the business case for sustainability and it is based on the idea of the 6L's of sustainability: longevity, lovability, likeability, location, loosefit and low energy.

Under these six headings a wide range of interests is covered which can provide a greater depth of information on which to base measures of sustainability. The points are considered in greater detail below.

Longevity
It may seem obvious that a building and its components need to be durable and capable of a long life in order to be sustainable but there may be instances where a building is designed to have a short life but to be easily transportable or disposable, for example temporary accommodation in disaster areas or for short term employment. However, unless a building has a satisfactory degree of adaptability, the durability of its fabric may not necessarily be an advantage.

Lovability
The extent to which the building owners, the users and the community 'love' the building can have a significant effect on its sustainability. There is evidence that listing a building can lead to a greater appreciation of its importance by users who will take pride in its fabric. It is however also one of the main areas of conflict - where a building which is loved and respected by the community which does not have to use it, is considered uneconomic or disfunctional by those who do.

Likeability
Likeability is intended to establish a functional satisfaction with the building where it is appreciated not so much for its emotive qualities as for its ability to fulfil the occupiers' needs.

Location

Where a building is located is clearly of considerable importance in considering its sustainability. If it does not fulfil a local need it may well become unoccupied and fall into decay. Location is often associated with measurable qualities such as the energy used in transport to and fro, leading to the idea that locations close to major travel interchanges might be assumed to be good. It should be noted here that Richard Florida, in his work on sustainable communities reported in his book 'The Rise of the Creative Class', considers that the intrinsic qualities of place can create a bigger regeneration effect than, for example, the re-location of a major employer.

Loose fit

Loose fit reflects the concept of adaptability, not to be confused with flexibility, which may be bought at the price of complexity and high cost but never used. Many buildings, by providing a 'loose fit' to one particular form of use, have proved very adaptable to alternative uses when they arise.

Low energy

Despite concerns that have been voiced about the potential over-emphasis of environmental factors, these remain of fundamental importance to the global sustainability interests of a community but they are often of relatively low importance to the occupier of the building where energy costs constitute a very small fraction of the total costs of the business. Staff satisfaction is very important to an employer and if that means the use of energy for heating and cooling, then that will take precedence. Unless the basis for these diverging views is understood there is little prospect of making significant progress in these areas.

In both the study 'Buildings: a new life' and the subsequent publication 'Building Sustainability in the Balance', by Sayce, Walker and McIntosh, these concepts are examined to identify the inherent conflicts which, if left unresolved, can lead to an unsustainable conclusion. Using the survival of a building as a simple measure of sustainability, it quickly became clear from

initial studies and an extensive survey, that the commonly considered issues of energy conservation or use of renewable resources were not seen as affecting the life of a building by the majority of those involved in decisions about its future. In the first place there was a divergence of interests between the internal and external stakeholders, the first representing the interests of those who own and rent the building and the second being the surrounding community, both local and global. It was appreciated that some stakeholders may have a foot in both camps. For example a shopper as a member of the community is an external stakeholder but when using the shopping centre is, in effect, an internal stakeholder. Despite these anomalies the distinction generally held good for the purpose of identifying potential conflicts, which multiplied with the use of a finer measure of different interests and intergenerational aspects.

Six case studies were undertaken and further issues affecting sustainability were noted. In particular legal constraints can mean that a building, which in other respects is not worthy of retention, is maintained because of the obligations of the owner to other parties. In one case the need to maintain a quantum of social housing within a specific location prevented the redevelopment of an obsolete building which subsequently, and with some ingenuity, was given a new use as an hotel; it now meets the criteria of sustainability.

The Rodboro building in Guildford is a good example of a number of these issues and reinforced the findings of the research project. Originally designed in the early twentieth century as an industrial structure housing the first assembly line car production plant in the country, it soon became too small for its purpose and was converted first to a showroom and then into retail space on the ground floor with offices above. The fabric which was mainly of brick was durable, had a relatively 'loose fit' and so was adaptable to other uses. Its location suffered badly from the construction of a gyratory system which cut it off from its natural flow of customers and it fell into disuse, but the affection in which it was held by the community (or its lovability) led to demonstrations against proposals by the local authority to demolish it and in due course it was listed grade II in the 1980's. The building lay empty for several years while the local authority considered alternative uses, including an art gallery until, with the economic growth of the 1990's, it found a new use as a large public house with the upper floors converted to a music school and studio. Furthermore the conversion to a leisure use sparked off other conversions close by and acted as a catalyst to the economic revival of the area.

The point of this example is to show that making use of the embodied energy already captured in the construction contributed to a low energy concept, although no specific energy saving devices were incorporated. Another point

is that its central location contributes to a reduction in private transport energy consumption and its ability to adapt to changing needs has been clearly demonstrated, together with the lovability and likeability factors.

The use of concepts such as the 6L's or the matrix proposed in 'Building Sustainability in the Balance', provide a means to identify and combine the many issues that need to be resolved and balanced in achieving a sustainable future. To ignore any one of these is to prejudice the long-term outcome and possibly to prevent sustainability.

It is clear that economic issues are of paramount importance to any building owner. If the owner cannot achieve a sustainable economic position to avoid continuing liabilities, if nothing

else, they may wish to dispose of the building. In areas of very low return historically this has enabled buildings to survive such as the weavers' houses in Fournier Street in Spitalfields, which provide current generations with a wealth of historic interest. However the growing pressures on all land means that such preservation by neglect is unlikely to be viable in the future.

Social sustainability is of increasing importance both through legislation and by virtue of a growing interest in the principles of Corporate Social Responsibility policies and Socially Responsible Investment. The two combined are driving an interest in buildings that reflect these approaches and thus are creating a demand by both occupiers and investors. Measuring and fulfilling these objectives is still a moveable feast and the subject of much debate as to how such standards can be measured.

Finally environmental sustainability is in effect the tip of the iceberg that has achieved considerable interest, research, legislation through Building Regulations and other documents and a wide range of published material. Little of this reflects the diverging interests that can arise. Prefabrication by reducing time on site and waste seems a clear-cut benefit to the community until the intergenerational issues of providing longer-term employment in the maintenance of the buildings within the local area are taken into account. Once this is done some prefabricated systems, reliant on specialised components or building skills, may deny the long-term sustainability of local economic performance. As yet we do little to address these conflicts. Indeed it is not that the environmental issues are of less importance but rather that examining them at a single moment does not necessarily take account of the long-term environmental issues.

The debate must continue. To ignore any one of these is to prejudice the long-term outcome and jeopardise a sustainable future for our children. ❖

Building Sustainability in the Balance is available from www.propertybooks.co.uk

An airtight case for green building

If you live in a typical UK home, expensive, heated air is constantly escaping, making your fuel bills unnecessarily high, giving rise to uncomfortable draughts and damaging the environment. **Paul Jennings** reports ...

Elsewhere in this book, you will read plenty of tips and hints about how best to increase insulation levels and reduce energy losses through the fabric of your building. However, regardless of how much insulation you put in, if you fail to address air leakage – i.e. draughts – your energy-saving expectations will never be fully realised. Sustainability is ultimately about reducing the carbon dioxide emissions that are causing global warming and driving climate change, giving us increasingly extreme and unstable weather conditions. As insulation levels continue to increase, an ever greater proportion of energy losses from our homes will occur through air leakage. If you don't address air leakage you might as well rip this book up and stuff it in the cracks!

The science of draughts

Draughts are uncontrolled air movement – and they make us uncomfortable. The wind blowing on our buildings can force cold air in, around windows and doors and through a wide range of other gaps and openings, or warm air rising within our homes escapes at high level creating a suction which pulls cold air in through these same holes. Neither is satisfactory, yet at the same time we always need ventilation in our buildings to provide a healthy living environment.

We often tolerate draughts because we think they provide the necessary ventilation – wrong!! Draughts are uncontrolled currents of air whilst ventilation is controlled and deliberately induced, using openable windows, trickle vents, extract fans etc. Most UK buildings have too much air leakage (draughts) when the wind blows and not enough ventilation on calm, still days.

Ventilation is the controlled replacement of degraded indoor air with external air and all buildings need ventilation. We need ventilation to breathe, and we need ventilation to get rid of indoor pollutants – cooking and other smells, but particularly water vapour. Minimising the buildup of moisture helps prevent condensation and mould growth, and discourages dust mites. A relative humidity of between 50% and 65% will provide the most comfortable and healthy living environment. If we have open flued appliances, such as wood-burning stoves, we need more ventilation for safety, and if people smoke we need lots more ventilation.

Why minimise air leakage?

As well as allowing costly warm air to escape, air leakage gives rise to uncomfortable draughts, degrades the effectiveness of insulation by as much as two-thirds, and allows potentially damaging moisture to penetrate our walls. Air leakage is bad, ventilation is good. The slogan "build-tight, ventilate-right" has been used for several years to encourage us to improve our buildings and reduce this shameful waste. Indeed, it has been suggested that it is impossible to build a building too airtight, although it is clearly possible to fail to design sufficient and appropriate ventilation.

As insulation levels installed in UK buildings have risen, particularly in recent years, then the waste of energy through escaping warm air has become more significant. Fig. 1 illustrates how the proportion of energy lost through air leakage has increased to the point where it can be more than half of all energy losses. This is likely to be even more significant for green designers and builders as they tend to adopt insulation levels substantially above the minimums required by building regulations.

Airtightness testing

A 'blower door', also known as a 'door fan', is the principle tool used for measuring airtightness

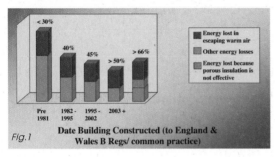

Fig.1 **Date Building Constructed (to England & Wales B Regs/ common practice)**

and identifying leakage in dwellings and other new or existing buildings.   It consists of one or more calibrated fans that are mounted in an open doorway using an adjustable door panel system. A series of steady-state pressure differences are then applied using the fan.

Once steady state conditions have been achieved, the airflow measured through the fan equals the sum of the air leaking through all the different gaps, cracks and openings in the envelope of the building or volume under test, adjusted for temperature difference.

By measuring the corresponding imposed pressure differentials, the leakage characteristics of the volume being tested can be established. Door fan testing is used to:

- provide an acceptance test for new dwellings, offices or other buildings
- identify leakage sites and provide quality control on remedial sealing works, if required
- check the performance of ventilation, extraction or MVHR systems
- establish ventilation rates in existing properties, for example to investigate the cause of condensation problems

Leakage in buildings

Our experience of testing houses and other buildings across the UK, together with test results published by various national bodies, show that the UK construction industry may well be in for a nasty shock when air leakage testing becomes more widespread.

UK builders, with certain honourable exceptions, have not yet grasped the nettle and learnt how to construct and finish airtight dwellings and

other buildings. Yet airtightness requirements are increasingly being included within standard specifications for new developments, particularly in the non-domestic sector, even before the revisions to Part L are finalised. The result can be an uncomfortable squeeze, where builders are required to attempt to remedy leakage problems and carry out additional acceptance tests just before handover – often at considerable (and sometimes unrecoverable) cost.

Test results published by BRE clearly show that improved airtightness in our buildings is essential – UK offices are around 2 to 4 times leakier than equivalent buildings in Scandinavia or North America, whilst industrial buildings are found to be more than 4 times as leaky. In housing, recent experience of testing supposedly airtight timber framed houses encountered many of the same problems found when testing the TRADA low energy house at Energy World in Milton Keynes more than a decade ago!
The leakage sites to be found in dwellings and other buildings can be subdivided into two types:

- structural leakage sites
- services leakage sites

Structural leakage sites occur at joints in the building fabric and around window and door openings. Loft hatches and access openings (usually non-domestic) also fall within this category. There may also be leakage through cracks in masonry walls – poor perpends in blockwork inner leafs being the most common cause – and some diffusion through materials. These are the hardest to retrofix. Good detailing at the design stage is therefore essential. Builders also need appropriate training so they understand how to build airtight buildings to achieve a good test result.

Service penetrations occur where pipes and cables pass into the building. These can be sewerage pipes, water pipes and heating pipes. As well as electricity cables there may also be television aerials and cable television connections. The worst problems tend to occur when these two types of leakage problems interact. Fig.2.

Once there is a failure of the airtight barrier where a hollow intermediate floor is supported from the external wall, a connection exists from a cavity in the external wall (which may be filled with insulation) through hollow internal partition walls to pretty much the whole of the building. Hollow floors and walls are inevitably used to run services – and just as inevitably tend not to be sealed where the services run from one element into another. The result is that electricity sockets and switches, light fittings (especially spotlights), television aerial and cable television connections, heating and plumbing pipes, waste pipes and soil stacks all become points at which air will leak into the dwelling. Even such minor items as room thermostats and heating controllers will permit air leakage around or through them. Moreover, if one such leakage site is sealed, most of the air will still escape at another site, since they tend to connect and to have a similar resistance to the movement of air through them.

Whilst it may be possible to laboriously seal all these sites and thereby cut the air leakage significantly, cold air will still get into hollow floors and walls, cooling internal surfaces and giving rise to discomfort.

Another major source of problems is the boxing-in of services, particularly water and waste pipework and soil stacks. Also riser shafts in non-domestic buildings. Once services are out of sight it is all too easy for sealing works to be overlooked and forgotten, even if they were specified in the first place. There is no culture of airtight construction on UK sites, and until this is achieved, detailed planning and preparation, rigorous site supervision and air leakage testing will be essential to achieve satisfactory buildings. In fact, air leakage testing provides an effective, rapid and reasonably priced method to check the quality of buildings. ❖

Resources

Air testing: www.retroteceurope.co.uk

Volume.10 No. 3 of Building for a Future magazine covered the subject of airtightness in-depth including a number of case studies. It can be viewed free of charge at: www.newbuilder.co.uk /bffmag/ as a downloadable pdf file or hard copies are available at £5.00 per copy.

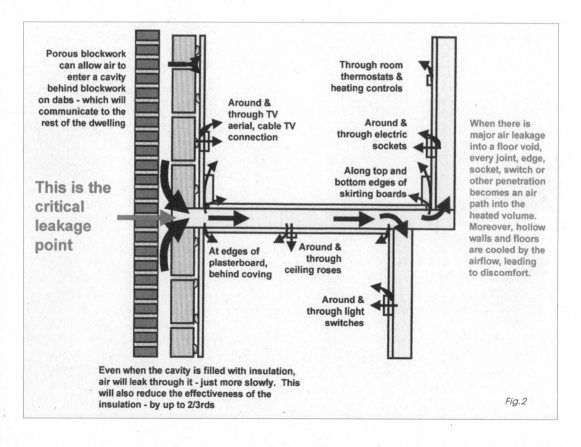

Porous blockwork can allow air to enter a cavity behind blockwork on dabs - which will communicate to the rest of the dwelling

This is the critical leakage point

Around & through TV aerial, cable TV connection

Through room thermostats & heating controls

Around & through electric sockets

Along top and bottom edges of skirting boards

When there is major air leakage into a floor void, every joint, edge, socket, switch or other penetration becomes an air path into the heated volume. Moreover, hollow walls and floors are cooled by the airflow, leading to discomfort.

At edges of plasterboard, behind coving

Around & through ceiling roses

Around & through light switches

Even when the cavity is filled with insulation, air will leak through it - just more slowly. This will also reduce the effectiveness of the insulation - by up to 2/3rds

Fig.2

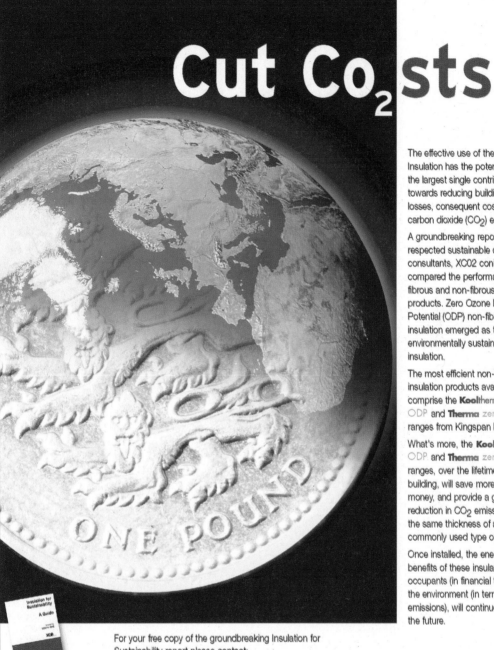

Reuse and recycle

Much of the environmental impact of buildings is associated with consumption of resources and generation of waste. The use of recycled materials and reused components in construction can lead to lower environmental impacts and reduce the materials disposed in landfills. However, the practical, environmental and economic aspects of using these construction materials are often not properly understood. **Mark Gorgolewski** reports ...

It is important to consider, in particular, the environmental impacts and transport implications of the recycling process.

Recycling and reuse are intuitively seen as good environmental practice for four independent reasons. They can

- reduce the amount of primary resources required.
- reduce the amount of waste that requires ultimate disposal back to Earth.
- lead to reductions in the total non-renewable energy used.
- lead to reduced greenhouse gas (and other) emissions.

There are many reasons why construction professionals do not embrace the wider use of recycled materials and reused components. There may be issues of economics, technical considerations, or perception, but they are often exacerbated by a lack of information and clear guidance.

Specifying recycled materials

Materials for recycling and reuse in construction can come from the following:

- waste from the construction process, e.g. broken bricks and tiles.
- waste occurring during manufacture of construction materials and components, e.g. blast furnace slag, waste gypsum from production.
- waste from other industries, e.g. pulverised fly ash, desulphurised gypsum.
- extracted materials and components during demolition and renovation, e.g. steel, and some masonry recycled as aggregate.

Using materials with recycled content, saves the environmental impacts that would be caused by using primary materials, and can also reduce waste. Where possible appropriate opportunities should be sought to specify recycled materials. However, recycling generally involves some re-processing and may need significant amounts of transport, both of which require energy. Thus, using recycled materials will only be beneficial if the recycling processes do not use more natural resources and energy or generate more waste than the production processes of similar products using virgin resources. It is important to question manufacturers of recycled products about this. Nevertheless, large savings can often be made in primary resource consumption and landfill space required for waste.

Increasingly, new materials and products are becoming available which are manufactured from recycled materials. Products such as cellulose insulation and some blocks are manufactured from waste from other industries. There are also opportunities to recycle demolition waste on site, such as crushing concrete and using it as aggregate to replace primary aggregates (see case study).

Increased interest in environmental issues has also led many major manufacturers of building

products such as mineral wool and gypsum boards to increase the amount of both production waste and site waste used in manufacture. Thus, it is worth asking manufacturers about the recycled content of their products.

The Waste Resources Action Programme (WRAP) was set up by the UK government to reduce the amounts of waste going to landfill (see web site references at end of this article). It is funding various projects to increase the amount of recycling in construction, including help for suppliers to get their recycled materials certified as suitable for use in construction.

Reused components (reclaimed)

Reuse can range in scale from whole buildings to small components such as bricks, tiles or even screws. Reusing components preserves both the value of the materials and also the value added when manufacturing the finished component. The impacts of disposal of the component and manufacture of the replacement are avoided. Thus, as long as the reused component can serve the same purpose as a new component, reusing components is intuitively regarded as more beneficial than recycling as there is little or no reprocessing.

There is a healthy market for some reused construction components such as bricks, roof slates, hardwood flooring, timber beams, and architectural features. There is also an increasing demand for components such as reclaimed metal claddings and steel beams. However, many perfectly useable construction products such as window frames, sanitary ware and radiators are not reused in the UK due to a lack of demand. Practice in other countries has shown that such components can be readily reused. If designers and clients in the UK were to begin to specify these products then a supply chain is more likely to be created.

Case Studies

Example - Wessex Water headquarters

The construction of this £20m headquarters building addressed many sustainability issues, including waste. The project generated only about 30% of the waste to landfill that would be expected for a project of this size and led to a cost saving of £10,000.

This was achieved by implementing a waste management plan that included appointing a waste management contractor to assist in sorting and segregating the waste that arose on site. It was found that 65% of the waste was timber, metal or cardboard which when segregated could be readily recycled.

The strategy required efficient processes on site to ensure segregation of materials, and the co-operation of the workforce, which was a challenge. A small recycling team was used to check that waste was correctly placed in the appropriate containers.

Using heavy material such as stone can have a low impact if used close to the location of the

quarry. However, the transport impacts may be high if they need to be moved a significant distance.

The EU Ecolabel can help in the selection of some construction products such as paints and insulation.

Example - Aggregates

Sand, gravel and crushed rock from quarries or dredging are the most commonly used aggregates in construction in the UK. The main environmental impacts are due to extraction and transport. They are non-renewable resources and suitable locations for quarries are increasingly difficult to find. The government has recently introduced an Aggregates Tax on primary aggregates to encourage more use of recycled aggregates. In addition, disposal of masonry

waste at the end of the use of the building is becoming more difficult and costly with the impact of the Landfill Tax.

Crushed demolition concrete and masonry, and other waste materials such as slate waste, ferro-lime (slag), asphalt road planings and power station ash are increasingly being used as a replacement for primary aggregate for many construction uses. 18% of UK aggregates now come from recycled sources.

The benefits of re-cycling crushed concrete are both economic and environmental and include:
- reducing the demand for primary aggregates.
- reducing the demand on landfill space.

- reducing liability for Landfill Tax.
- reducing delivery and waste disposal vehicle movements.

In practice the choice of aggregates depends on local availability. On larger sites, on-site crushing and reuse are the best option as transport is avoided. Increasingly, recycled aggregate is becoming available from local suppliers who collect masonry demolition waste for off-site crushing. Such recycled aggregate can be used for engineering fill, capping materials, sub base for roads and car parks, and hardcore and general site cover. In addition, it is also possible to use clean, graded crushed concrete as aggregate in structural components. However, transportation distances should be kept to a minimum, as it is inappropriate to move these heavy materials over large distances.

Example - Berlin

The environmental authorities of Berlin are working with the local industrial and recycling organisations to the following agreements:
- waste disposal of construction and demolition waste is only possible for the non-recyclable fractions.
- re-use or recycling must be used unless it is not possible.
- hazardous materials must be properly segregated.
- construction and demolition waste should be sorted on site, or if not possible, separation should be done at a sorting/treatment plant.
- minimum standards are set in technical requirements for recycled mineral waste.
- there should be transparency of process during the waste stream from source to re-cycling and use or disposal.

Other examples of recycling and reuse

Langley Park - At this major housing site, the demolition contractor, under the direction of Laing Homes, sought to re-use materials from the demolition works. 500,000 clay roof tiles were removed from the buildings, cleaned and packaged. A further 40,000 tonnes of demolition waste was crushed and used on site as bulk fill.

The Environmental Building, BRE, Watford used recycled aggregates from a demolished building on the BRE site and was constructed using 80,000 reclaimed bricks. Before construction began another building was demolished with 96% of the demolition materials being reused or recycled.

Comely Green Place, Edinburgh - This housing development of 95 flats uses concrete blocks containing 85% recycled material and roof tiles composed of 85% slate waste.

London Remade - London Remade aims to change the way the Capital manages its waste through a programme designed to develop and diversify markets for recycled materials. It is a partnership comprising the business community, regional government & London Boroughs, the waste management industry and the not for profit sector. They are working with London design professionals to identify opportunities for the use of recycled materials in the design and manufacture of products.

Conclusions

The largest environmental benefits are achieved when using reused components. Specifying these leads to significant environmental benefits. However, due to the variable and inconsistent supply at present there is a premium to be paid for many reused components such as second hand bricks and roof tiles, and it may be difficult to secure sufficient quantities from one source for larger projects.

Standardisation of components would greatly enhance the match between those retrieved from old buildings and those required for new buildings. Many architects would like to reuse old elements but find it difficult to locate suitable supplies. Equally many demolition contractors would like to sell whole building elements for re-use, but the timing of the demolition contract rarely coincides with demand for those elements. Supply and demand of reclaimed construction products is currently too erratic for a stable market to exist. However, this barrier is not insurmountable, and the imposition of 'green' taxes such as the Aggregates Tax acts as a stimulus to increase demand.

When sourcing reused components, approaching demolition contractors directly may be the best option to secure cost-effective supplies. Salvage yards will need as much notice as possible to source larger batches. Various web

sites offer services to advertise reused components. ❖

Sources of further information on recycling and reuse

- The GreenPro products database at: **www.newbuilder.co.uk** holds links to most recycled and reclaimed building products and manufacturers plus articles on application
- National Recycling Forum **www.nrf.org**
- Salvo reclaimed materials database **www.salvo.co.uk**
- For recycled materials see **www.ecoconstruction.org**
- BRE materials information exchange **www.bre.co.uk/waste**
- The reclaimed and recycled construction materials handbook, CIRIA (1999)
- CIRIA recycling website **www.ciria.org.uk/recycling**
- Aggregates Information Service **www.trl.co.uk/viridis/**
- Waste Resources Action Programme **www.wrap.org.uk** Various Digests from the Aggregates Advisory Service list potential sources and further information (available from the above web site)
- Sustainable Aggregates Information Service **www.aggregain.org.uk** or 0808 100 2040
- BRE Information Paper IP 5/94 - The use of recycled aggregates in concrete, (1994)
- Use of waste and recycled materials as aggregates: standards and specifications, Collins, R.J. and Sherwood, P. HMSO, (1995).
- BRE Digests 443 - Recycled Aggregates (1998)
- Centre for Resource Management, BRE, Garston, Watford. WD25 9XX Tel: 01923 664471. Before you skip it, click it! **www.smartwaste.co.uk**

Insulation - measuring against common standards

Insulation is a fundamental component to any energy efficient and sustainable building. The type of insulation and its thickness needs to be considered. But what is the most environmentally sustainable option? Recent reports suggest that over the lifetime of a building the energy saving potential of insulation should be the dominant factor in its specification, and that the lifetime differences between various products are small. The most important factor is to ensure that the insulation is correctly installed. **John Garbutt** reports...

In the past few years choosing an eco-friendly insulation was quite simple. All you needed to do was select one that did not use CFC or HCFC blowing agents in its manufacture or avoid those that were an irritant in use. However, with the successful phase-out of ozone destroying gasses by EU law (based on the Montreal Protocol)[1] and the clearing of mineral wool of suspicion of being a possible carcinogen by the International Agency for Research on Cancer (IARC)[2] it is becoming a less clear-cut decision (if we ignore price).

So how can we choose the most environmentally sustainable products to insulate our buildings? Many might argue that "natural is best" but others will counter with "natural cannot promise durability". It is true that some insulation applications are accessible enough for us to replace them occasionally throughout the lifetime of the building if we so wish but, likewise, some application decisions are 'whole building life' choices. Let's take a look at some of the other environmental issues that may apply to building insulation.

Embodied energy (manufacture and transport)

In recent years insulation materials among many others, have been compared on the basis of embodied energy. However, I believe that it is the balance of the embodied energy, construction elements and the 'in-use' energy consumption over the lifetime of a building that is more important. Indeed, due to the fact that insulation by its very nature is there to save energy, it has become widely accepted that the embodied energy of any insulation material is insignificant compared with the energy saved by it over the lifetime of the building in which it is installed.

Having said that, we should not be complacent. The above statement will only hold true whilst we continue to design buildings with quite high levels of energy consumption. All this will change when our buildings have low or zero heating requirements or zero CO_2 production. The former can only be achieved by using

Insulation for Sustainability

A Guide

A study by
XCO2 for BING

XCO2

insulation wisely at appropriate thicknesses and by detailing our buildings properly to ensure air tightness, the latter if we discover more efficient ways of generating renewable energy. What's more, we have to do the low or zero heating part first in order to do the zero CO_2 part efficiently. Only when our buildings get to low or zero heating levels will the embodied energy of the materials used become significant.

Embodied energy is also an inappropriate tool to use to compare the full 'embodied impact' of any product. It measures just one facet of the harm that the manufacture of a product can cause.

Arguably, the best available measure of embodied impact is the rating system used in the BRE's Green Guide to Building Specification[3]. This publication rates products from A to C on a basket of embodied impacts, including embodied energy. These ratings are based on generic life cycle assessment (LCA) data. You will find that almost all insulation materials, for which data is given, get the top rating of A. The exceptions are cellular glass, extruded polystyrene and high-density (>145 kg/m³) mineral wool; this is a clear reflection of the fact that the embodied impact of insulation materials is relatively insignificant. However, it does illustrate that it is important to consider the density of the insulation material, as more dense insulants may have a low embodied impact per kilogram, but not per m³ or m².

It should also be noted that when the impacts for insulation are combined with the impacts for all other materials that make up, say, a wall

or a roof, the different ratings of insulation products become largely irrelevant as they are masked by the impacts of the other materials in the construction. A fact which illustrates my earlier point.

It is perfectly possible for a wall insulated with extruded polystyrene to get an overall A rating, even if the insulation itself does not, (some might argue that this is a failure of the rating system but we have to start somewhere). It is equally possible for a wall insulated with an A rated insulation material to get an overall B or C rating. It is the rating for the whole construction that counts as far as the Green Guide data is concerned.

The production and publication of embodied energy/embodied impact data by insulation manufacturers is therefore, if anything, an issue of corporate social responsibility (CSR) rather than environmental sustainability. Some manufacturers have now produced independently certified LCA data. Most of those have done this work with BRE Certification. However, the production of such data is effectively meaningless unless manufacturers are able to demonstrate a commitment to reducing the environmental impacts of their production processes. It will be interesting to see how manufacturers deal with DTI requirements that all publicly quoted companies report on CSR performance as of January 1, 2006.[4]

Accurate and unbiased embodied energy / embodied impact figures for insulation materials are difficult to find other than in BRE LCAs, and therefore should be treated with care. No embodied energy / impact data is presented here because I found it very difficult to ascertain if the data available is comparable and used consistent methodologies. >>>

Energy in-use must be optimised first.

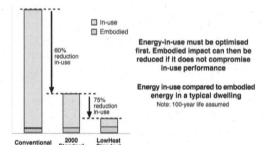

In-use
Embodied

60% reduction in-use

75% reduction in-use

Conventional | 2000 Standard | LowHeat Standard

Energy-in-use must be optimised first. Embodied impact can then be reduced if it does not compromise in-use performance

Energy in-use compared to embodied energy in a typical dwelling
Note: 100-year life assumed

Delivering what is promised

It is widely accepted that reducing "in use" energy consumption of buildings is the key to their global environmental sustainability. Therefore, a major parameter on which to compare insulation materials must be their ability to deliver their specified thermal performance over the lifetime of a building. This is one of the key themes of an independently produced report on the sustainability of insulation materials funded by BING (the European trade association for manufacturers of rigid urethane insulation products)[5], which brought to bear the concept of risk factors. These are all factors which could detrimentally affect the thermal performance of individual insulation materials, sometimes in very different ways, and hence the global environmental sustainability of buildings. These risk factors may include the impacts of:

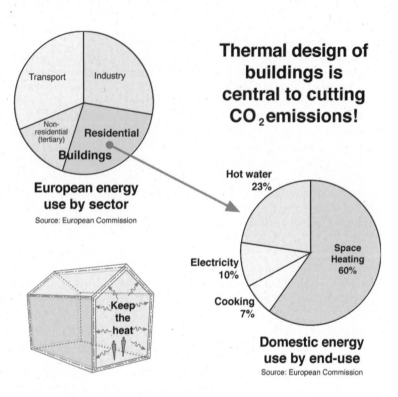

Thermal design of buildings is central to cutting CO_2 emissions!

European energy use by sector
Source: European Commission

Domestic energy use by end-use
Source: European Commission

- liquid water or water vapour;
- air-movement; and
- compression or settling.

Whilst it may be true that all insulation materials will perform as promised in a laboratory, the real test is what happens on site. Installation practices are notoriously uncontrollable and all materials will perform badly if installed without due care and attention.

Once the global issues have been considered it is then time to consider less pressing, but still important, issues such as recycled content, local sourcing, disposability etc. The key to the national level environmental sustainability of any product is a balance of all these issues. However taking just one issue and over-focussing on it could be counter-productive.

Recycled content of products is about to go through something of a revolution in the UK construction industry. The Government have funded a body called The Waste & Resources Action Program (WRAP) to promote materials that have a recycled content. It gives very specific rules as to what counts as recycled content and what does not. These rules follow the definition cited in the ISO standard on Environmental Labels and Declarations[6].

Some insulation already contains recycled content. However, when examining the recycled content of insulation materials please bear in mind that recycled content is the proportion, by mass, of recycled material in the product. Only pre-consumer and post-consumer materials should be considered as recycled content.[7] This means that surplus material cut from the edges of products during their manufacture and shredded and added back in at the start of the process don't count.

Thermal performance

Adherence to common rules for thermal performance claims should also be checked. The EU Construction Products Directive has created a set of harmonised product standards for insulation which demand that the thermal performance of all products is quoted in a comparable way that takes account of ageing and statistical variation. It is called the Lambda 90:90 method. All major UK insulation manufacturers have adopted this approach to quoting thermal performance. However, at the present time there are a number of smaller scale products for which there is no harmonised standard available and therefore no consistent method that takes account of statistical variation. No doubt these will be brought into the fold soon but until then inconsistency will reign. It is worth noting that the introduction of the harmonised product standards added about 10% to the thermal conductivity of the insulation products that are covered (i.e. made them 10% worse).

Fire

Another, often overlooked aspect of the performance of insulation materials is their performance with respect to fire. This is quite a complicated area but roughly speaking there are two facets to consider: reaction to fire and fire resistance. Reaction to fire is measured by the 'Class O' type rating system enshrined in building regulations or the risk categories shown in the Building Standards in Scotland. These ratings can be achieved by reference to the new Euroclass system for reaction to fire or by the tried and tested BS 476 Parts 6 and 7. There is a debate in the insulation industry at present as to which route is best.

What has caused this confusion is the fact that the new Euroclass rating system for reaction to fire is arguably irrelevant when applied to 'naked' insulation products, as the system was developed for wall and ceiling linings and insulation is rarely used as such. The reaction to fire test has slightly more value when used for products tested 'in-application', since insulation products are then tested mounted as they would be in practice, for example behind plasterboard.

Proponents of the Euroclass system suggest that 'naked' products lie around building sites all the time and that the products are exposed when, say, holes are cut in walls but I cannot understand how testing a product as a wall or ceiling lining can relate to packs of products lying on the ground.

Regardless, the test still gives no indication of a product's ability to resist fire. It is this crucial distinction that can make all the difference to the ability of a building to withstand a fire and maintain structural integrity long enough to enable occupants to leave safely, and allow emergency services more time to get the blaze under control and salvage the building. Mistakenly choosing a material based on its reaction to fire without taking into account its resistance to fire may therefore at best be costly, and could at worst prove fatal.

The crux of the issue is that some materials have excellent fire resistance qualities but relatively poor reaction to fire ratings, whereas others have the best reaction to fire ratings but relatively poor fire resistance properties.

So, if the Euroclass system is not a reliable guide to the fire performance properties of insulation products, what is? The answer may well lie in large scale insurer approved test regimes such as the Loss Prevention Certification Board (LPCB) 'in-application' test, LPS1181: 2003 or those carried out by Factory Mutual (FM). ❖

Refs.

1. All insulation materials (in the UK) are now free from CFCs and HCFCs and have been since Jan 1, 2004. As the issue of CFC and HCFC use is now historic, no mention is made here of these blowing agents.

(2) IARC decision.

(3) Green Guide to Specification, an Environmental Profiling System for Building Materials and Components. Third Edition. Anderson J, Shiers D and Sinclair M. 2002.

(4) The consultation process for this closed in August 2004

(5) Insulation for Sustainability-A Guide XCO2 conisbee for BING 2002. www.xco2.com

(6) BS EN ISO 14021: 2001. Environmental labels and declarations – self declared environmental claims (Type II environmental labelling). BSI. London. 2001.

(7) Pre-consumer waste is material diverted from the waste stream during a manufacturing process. Excluded is reutilization of materials such as rework, regrind or scrap generated in a process and capable of being reclaimed within the same process that generated it. Post-consumer waste is material generated by households or by commercial, industrial and institutional facilities in their role as end-users of the product, which can no longer be used for its intended purpose. This includes returns of material from the distribution chain.

Charts taken from Sustainability-A Guide XCO2 conisbee

Home sickness

The average person in Western countries spends up to 85% of their time inside buildings or in transport taking them between buildings. These buildings have changed dramatically in the last 30 years due to increased energy efficiency as a result of the 1970's oil crisis and by the multitude of new chemicals, materials and gadgetry developed within this period. **Anita Bradley** reports on how these changes are affecting our health...

Over half of UK energy usage goes on buildings and so energy efficiency has become so important – not only to save fuel, but also to prevent further environmental degradation. The way we build, the materials used, the installations needed, and the way we maintain these structures has given rise to the incidence of 'Sick Building Syndrome' (SBS), officially recognised as an illness by the World Health Organisation since 1986. 'Sick Building Syndrome' is a general malaise of multiple symptoms of an unknown or unclearly recognised aetiology. It should not be confused with 'Building Related Illness' (BRI) in which both the disease and its cause is known – such as legionella, asbestosis, or humidifier fever. Although the two share common features, the former is more difficult to pin down and rectify. Difficulty in identifying SBS lies in the vast array of conditions presented, the subjective nature of the complaints and the lack of solid evidence as to causes. People can react very differently to specific conditions and symptoms vary with time and location.

Symptoms associated with SBS include:
- headache
- loss of concentration
- nasal irritation
- dry or watery eyes
- lethargy
- skin irritation
- throat problems
- possibly more acute conditions and diseases.

It is a chemical, biological and mental/psychological phenomenon which, if ignored, can lead to expensive remedial action, absenteeism, lower productivity, and loss of well-being.

It has been estimated (WHO) that up to 30%

of refurbished and a significant number of new buildings suffer from SBS. Any aspect and any type of use of a building can produce SBS with several possible causes having been identified:
- contaminated land
- radon and other gases
- asbestos and lead
- contaminated water
- volatile organic compounds (VOCs)
- electromagnetic fields
- moulds, dust and other allergens   >>>

Our homes are a battle ground where natural and synthetic possessions and building fabric contend for space. The secret is to ensure that a reasonable balance is achieved between the two. How? Pot plants are a good balancing agent. Remember, natural products can also contain substances that can cause allergies, asthma or allergic reaction, as can animals and moulds/fungi. So pay attention to the provision of adequate ventilation. This can alleviate the buildup of toxins in the air of the room. It will be false economy to seal up all the draughts if the consequences of this is an unhealthy family.

- micro-organisms and body matter
- lighting
- heating, ventilation and air conditioning (HVAC)
- poor architectural, engineering design and specification
- inadequate facilities management
- negative ion depletion
- psychosocial factors.

Indoor air quality

The Building Research Establishment (BRE) found that air inside buildings could be up to 10 times more polluted than the air outside. In the late 20th Century, industry and commerce has produced around 70,000 new synthetic materials and chemicals. Of these, less

PVC and other chemical products. Pollution comes from paints, preservatives, insulation, adhesives, carpets, soft furnishings, furniture, cleaners and air fresheners. Other sources include timbers, ply, particle board and such like, which may have been treated with preservatives, glues, paints and varnishes. Fire retardant chemicals add to this burden.

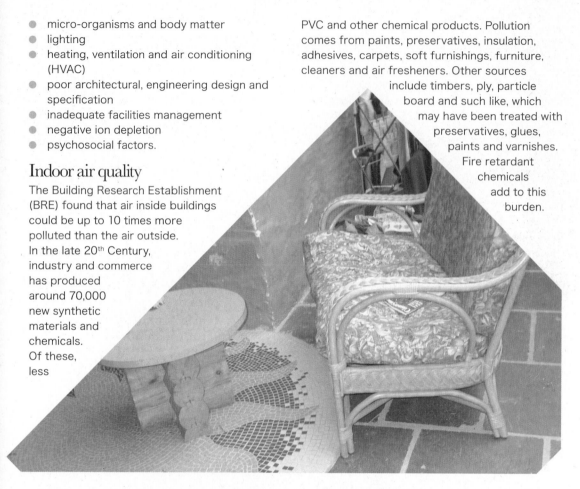

Hard floors are the darling of the anti dust mite brigade and can certainly play a major role in the reduction of possible toxins from carpets in the home. There is plenty of evidence to be found that blames carpets for not only containing chemicals but also harbouring dust etc (foot traffic). The British love of carpet though is not without reason. They make our feet feel warm and give a cosier feel to the room. So the choice is yours!

than 2% have been tested for safety to humans and up to 70% have not been tested at all. Around 1,000 new chemicals and materials are marketed each year without the full cost to human or ecological wellbeing being considered. We take in this chemical cocktail via breath, skin, water and food.

Indoor air contains microscopic particulates – perfumes, bacteria, viruses, animal dander, dust mites, respiration particles, pollen, mould; combustion products – carbon monoxide, nitrogen dioxide, sulphur dioxide, hydrocarbons; and volatile organic compounds (VOCs) – benzene, formaldehyde, chlorine, synthetic fibres,

Due to increasing a building's energy efficiency newer construction techniques and materials have meant that buildings have become virtually air tight. In such buildings the external walls have been designed to minimise leakage of air conditioned air to the outside but have also stopped fresh air permeating to the inside. Sealed windows and artificial air conditioning plants (heating, ventilation and air conditioning – HVAC) are thus needed to maintain warmth or coolness within. However, this trend seems to be allowing a build up of noxious air. HVAC plants have recently been identified as a potent cause of SBS and thus there are strict fitting and main-

The alternative treatment for dry rot, wet rot and woodworm...

ProBor™ wood-preservatives are based on Boron, a naturally occurring mineral. They are water-based and offer exceptional protection against wood-destroying organisms.

ProBor™ preservatives have a deep penetrating action that gives a distinct performance advantage over conventional preservatives.

Call **01403 210204** or visit **www.safeguardchem.com** for further information, including case studies and our **FREEGUIDES** to dry rot and woodworm control.

  DB|20|50

Wood preservatives for professionals.

Safeguard Chemicals Ltd . Redkiln Close . Horsham . West Sussex . RH13 5QL . United Kingdom
Tel: +44 (0) 1403 210204 . Fax: +44 (0) 1403 217529 . Website: www.safeguardchem.com . email: sgrdchem@aol.com

tenance guidelines to keep them working at an optimal level for efficiency and health. Microbes and bacteria were found in ducts and filters. An article in the prestigious British medical journal 'The Lancet' reported the trial of using UV light to kill bacteria within HVAC plants with a high degree of success.

Building techniques that allow the building fabric to 'breathe' are best but not always the desire of the building financier. The notion of the building as a 'third skin' is ideal wherever possible. (This is an idea from the 'Building Biology' movement: the first skin is that stretchy stuff that protects the body; clothes form the second protective skin; and the building fabric is thus seen as the third protective skin.)

Another factor that may help reduce the effects of SBS is that of 'Indoor Surface Pollution' (ISP). This is presented in a BRE paper addressing the importance of ISP in building management and suggests ways of reducing it. The method involves defining ISP by a 'Fleece Factor' (the area of carpet, curtains and other fabric, divided by the volume of the space) and the 'Shelf Factor' (the length of open shelving or filing space divided by the volume of the room). Above all, the recommendations in this paper stress the need for good hygiene. The need for extra, or specialist, cleaning is reduced or made easier by careful design, furniture selection and office/space layout. (*G.J.Raw: 'The Importance of Indoor Surface Pollution in Sick Building Syndrome', BRE Information Paper IP 3/94. Feb 1994*).

Electromagnetic field pollution

Electromagnetic fields occur both in nature and the man-made environment. In nature these fields are very low and occur due to climate, terrestrial factors, cosmic radiation and from the body's own electrical activity. Such fields are generally very low in strength and frequency and are usually beneficial or essential to health. Man-made fields (EMFs) are part of a controversy regarding their effects on the health of people exposed to them. The fields in question are non-ionising in their action and are produced whenever there is a flow of electricity. An EMF is made up of an electric field component

(measured in volts per metre – V/m) and a magnetic field component (measured in Teslas – T). Electric fields form wherever there is a voltage and its strength is dependent on the magnitude of the voltage. A magnetic field arises whenever there is a current flowing. Both components reduce with distance from source. The frequency, shape and strength of these fields are important factors in determining the effect they have on health. Sources of manufactured EMFs are power lines, electrical wiring in buildings and appliances.

Studies have been carried out into EMFs since the possibility of health problems started in the 1960s. These first studies were on occupational exposure. The first study of general exposure began in the late 70s when two American researchers found a suggestive link between power line EMFs and childhood leukaemia. Since then many more and varied studies have been conducted to ascertain if there are health risks arising from exposure to a myriad of EMF sources. Studies have suggested links with cancers and leukaemia, depression and suicide, immune disorders, and allergy.

Over half the elevated levels in buildings come from wiring configurations and appliances. The wiring regulations do not specifically concern themselves with EMFs, but, according to Powerwatch, (*see resources at end*), in following their implementation the fields produced would be minimised. Large commercial buildings can have very low fields because the wires are housed in appropriate metal trunking; but some buildings can have high fields because currents flow along 'earthed' pipework. Electric fields can still be high if a metal conduit is not used. The use of 'ring' circuits give off high magnetic fields and therefore 'radial' wiring is the preferred method. Electric fields can be shielded quite cheaply, but the magnetic field is extremely difficult to eliminate therefore this is best designed out or by shielding them wherever they are generated.

Britain has been well behind other countries in acknowledging the risks, especially for the magnetic field component. The UK's National Radiological Protection Board (NRPB) sets maximum exposure levels as 1,600uT. For comparison, Switzerland 1uT; Sweden 0.2uT; and parts of Italy 0.2-0.5uT.

The magnetic field levels at which certain diseases have been shown to occur at are:

Miscarriage	1.6uT
Childhood leukaemia	0.3/0.4uT
Adult brain cancer	0.2-0.6uT
Depression	0.2uT
Suicide	0.2uT

(*source: 'Health effects of EMFs – evidence and mechanisms', Professor DL Henshaw. HH Wills Physics Laboratory. University of Bristol*)

However, in 2004 the National Radiological Protection Board (NRPB) recommended the adoption of reduced level of exposure to the magnetic field component of EMFs in the frequency range 0-300GHz. This is for general public exposure. The limit recommended is 100uT (down from the previous 1600uT) and is the level adopted by the International Commission on Non-Ionising Radiation Protection (ICNIRP). The frequencies covered include TV and radio broadcasting, mobile telecommunications and the electical supply. Whilst this reduction may seem large it is not so low as to prevent illness as supported by many researchers and scientific papers. Professor Henshaw of Bristol University (an expert in this subject) states that these proposals should go much further. "The proposals to limit public exposure to magnetic fields to 100uT, 250 times higher than the 0.4uT where doubling of the risk of childhood leukaemia is acknowledged, looks ridiculous when viewed alongside the well established practice for chemical carcinogens where levels are set at least 1000 times below the level where evidence of harmful effects have been found."

According to Powerwatch the ideal magnetic field level should be less than 0.01uT and the electric field should be less than 5V/m. Levels of exposure of 0.03uT and 10V/m can be reasonably achieved. The average exposure is 0.04-0.05uT for exposure from both outdoor and

indoor sources.

Several organisations offer testing and advice on EMFs (*see resource guide at end*).

Noise

Noise is not always considered in studies of SBS, but it can contribute to the condition and cause suffering or disturbance for the building occupant. Sources of noise in buildings are air-conditioning plants, outdoor noise filtering indoors, office equipment and 'people' noise. Air conditioning systems can be disturbing if they are functioning badly, poorly maintained and ill designed. Air rushing through vents is a source of noise but the vent size can be increased for the same output, which will lessen levels. Ductwork can carry noise around a building, so insulation and good design are essential. However, noise control is not just about lowering levels as a space that is too quiet can also be troublesome. Continuous soft noise is another factor to be avoided. CIBSE state an upper limit for office work of 46dBA (where decibels 'A' refers to the particular decibel scale on sound level meter). Many offices exceed this level.

Lighting

The links between lighting and sick building syndrome are well known. Glare, flicker, lack of contrast, inadequate illumination and unsuitable spot lighting can all add to a users burden. Many offices or developments are of deep plan design and therefore are unable to be illuminated by daylight to the interior. The use of fluorescent lighting is common place and therefore a common problem. Their use can give rise to eye strain and headaches among other symptoms. ('Fluorescent Lighting: A Health Hazard Overhead', London Hazard Centre). If these lights cannot be avoided then regular maintenance or the use of full spectrum fluorescent is preferable.

Another aspect of lighting design in relation to sick building syndrome is the ability of the occupant to alter their exposure to meet personal comfort. Different tasks require different lighting. CIBSE recommends 500 lux for general office work and 750 lux for deep plan offices or where close work takes place (such as at a drawing board or reading).

Tinted glass is not recommended as we need light levels to maintain our physiology such as the endocrine system. Deprived of lighting cues, our body changes to a 25 hour cycle rather than the 24 hour cycle. Lack of light (essentially bright sunlight) can cause depression, anxiety, fatigue and the modern diagnosis of Seasonal Affective Disorder (SAD). Adjustable and well-designed shading devices are the most desirable solution to both lighting problems and to reduce glare and heat gain.

Ions

Ions are essential to life and health. They are atoms that can be either negatively (-) or positively (+) charged. Negative ions are the benefices of health and are shown to reduce headache, nausea and dizziness. They also make a person more comfortable and alert. Lack of negative ions (i.e. an abundance of '+' ions), are associated with depression, lethargy and anxiety. Many buildings can give rise to a shortage of beneficial ions through materials and equipment; metal ducts for HVAC plant attracts the ions as they pass through, static electricity attracts these ions as does tobacco smoke and dust particles. Static can be reduced by the avoidance of synthetic materials, 'earthing' of all electrical equipment, and good building hygiene. A high density of people can also alter the ratio of negative to positive ions. There are fewer negative ions when the indoor temperature is greater than 22 degrees C, and where there is a high relative humidity. Typical office air contains only 50 negative ions per millilitre whereas clean outdoor air can carry as many as 1000. ❖

Miscellaneous

There are several questionnaires available for identifying SBS and each have their own merit. One such questionnaire is GJ Raw; 'A Questionnaire for Studies of Sick Building Syndrome'. (A report to the Royal Society of Health Advisory Group on Sick Building Syndrome) (BRE Report CI/SfB(U4)1995).

Healthy building
Useful contacts

www. hc.org.uk (*London Hazards Centre*)
www.nrpb.org (*National Radiological Protection Board*)
www.epa.gov (*Environmental Protection Agency USA*)
www.electric-fields.bris.ac.uk (*Human Radiation Effects*)
www.wen.org.uk (*Women's Environmental Network*)

www.healthyflooring.org (Healthy Flooring Network)

Building Research Establishment, Tel: 01923 664000 www.bre.co.uk

London Hazards Centre, Tel: 020 7794 5999

Powerwatch, 2 Tower Road Sutton, Ely, Cambridgeshire CB6 2QA

Further Reading

Baggs, S & J. The Healthy House. Thames and Hudson. 1996

Becker, R. Cross Currents: The Startling Effects of Electromagnetic Radiation on Your Health. Bloomsbury 1990

Philips A & J. Killing Fields in the Home. 1999. (This book and other excellent titles are available from Powerwatch at the address above.

Rousseau D, Rea WJ, Enright J. Your Home, Your Health and Well Being. Hartley and Marks 1989

Smith CW & Best S. Electromagnetic Man: Health Hazard in the Electrical Environment. The Bath Press 1989 (A classic which is currently out of print but is essential reading).

The following books are available from The Green Shop, www.greenshop.co.uk 01452 770629

Pearson, D. The New Natural House Book. Conran Octopus. 1998

Saunders T. The Boiled Frog Syndrome: Your Health and the Built Environment. Wiley Academy. 2002

Water, Electricity and Health -protecting yourself from electrostress at home and work by Alan Hall ISBN 1-869890-94-9 Hawthorn Press

Sick home?
Remedy by design

Healthy building design appears to be a sub-section of environmental design which remains low on the scale of importance for most architects and builders. **Chris Morgan** reports ...

This is strange for three reasons. Firstly, whilst pollution is accepted as a major problem, at a design level, the response is conceived largely in terms of energy efficiency. Pollution happens 'out there' in the world, and we try to reduce this, but there is little grasp of the effect this pollution is having on us, personally.

Second, the awareness of health and of healthy lifestyles is quite advanced. Gyms, vitamin pills, organic food and alternative therapies all attest to a broad appreciation that our health is not all it might be, and yet the places where we spend the vast majority of our time, homes and workplaces, escape any critical analysis beyond the most immediately apparent.

Third, there have been scares. Most people now know that asbestos is dangerous, like lead in paints and pipes, and the media have picked up on concerns about electricity pylons, chemical treatments for rot and others. But like most things, these are considered isolated cases, and there is little sense of a generally, comprehensively harmful built environment. The rise in awareness of 'sick building syndrome' has made some headway in this regard, but in most peoples' reality, it is still not an issue.

And yet for those who investigate, it is shocking to discover the extent to which we have exposed ourselves to a wide range of untested combinations of known carcinogens, mutagens and other harmful elements, and in such close proximity to ourselves and our loved ones.

There is some resistance to such investigations, manufacturers are understandably reticent about any possible health risks associated with their products, and it is notoriously difficult to make clear links between symptoms and the plethora of possible causes. However, a great deal is now understood about what is likely to be both good and bad for health, and it is possible to design and build homes and workplaces which are broadly free from pollutants and actively beneficial in supporting the health and comfort of occupants.

1st Step: remove the pollutants
Non building related

Many pollutants have nothing to do with the building. Smoking is a significant pollutant, as are the many external fumes and particulates which can come in through open windows and air entry systems: agricultural spray drift, car and industrial process exhaust fumes, dust, pollen, then there is electromagnetic radiation from pylons, and even radon from the ground itself in some places. Clearly there is a limit to what can be done to avoid these pollutant sources, but in some cases, the addition of 'buffer' spaces filled with plants and water, acting as conditioners for the incoming air for the rest of the building, can help.

Services and maintenance

Water

Increasingly, the water that comes into our homes is likely to contain not only beneficial minerals and other 'impurities' but also a great number of potentially harmful pollutants such as nitrates, metals, synthetic (and some volatile) organic compounds, radon and controversial additives like chlorine and fluoride.

For those concerned, various types of water filtration system are available, each tending to deal better with some and not other pollutants.

Air conditioning

Some years ago, research in Denmark showed that the biggest source of pollutants in offices was not occupants, not smoking, not even the off-gassing of materials, but the air intake ducting and machinery itself. In other words, the equipment specifically installed to keep the air clean and healthy was the single biggest polluter. In most UK homes this should not be an issue, but it is relevant wherever there is a forced air supply.

Electropollution

The radiation effects of electrical equipment and cabling are much debated, but the links between electrical, and electro-magnetic fields and health are becoming harder to ignore, particularly at high voltage levels. Electric fields are produced whenever there is a voltage (for example, in an electrical appliance and the cable to it, even if it is switched off), while electro-magnetic fields are only produced when current is flowing – the appliance is switched on. Both fields reduce in strength with distance away from the source, so the most common advice is simply to keep a distance, for example, between the plug, cable and electric alarm clock from your head while sleeping.

Electric fields are quite easy to shield through the use of metal trunking or sheathing, but electro-magnetic fields are harder to avoid. The standard ring mains around a room is one source of the relatively high magnetic field in a room and one way of avoiding this is to produce a 'radial' or 'star-shaped' wiring arrangement, but this can lead to more costly wiring installations. The UK is a long way behind other countries in recognising the risks attributed to electro-pollution.

Fumes

Some of the most lethal pollutants are from incomplete combustion fumes from boilers and stoves, leaky flues, or flues where there can be backdraft in the wrong wind conditions. Needless to say that these should be checked as a priority.

Decoration, fixtures and fittings

Decorating your home can be bad for your health! Paint stripper, and most old paint is of real concern, and conventional paints and varnishes etc. are some of the worst offenders for environmental pollution in their manufacture, and in terms of their effect on the health of occupants. The main concern is from the solvent fumes (the bit that dries off) but even water soluble paints may need to be avoided. Natural, non-toxic paints are available and while some are more expensive, switching to these is one of the simplest ways of reducing pollution and safe-guarding your health.

A great deal of furniture and fittings now available contain toxic chemicals not only internally, but in the coatings which are applied to make them stain-free, fire-proof, 'low maintenance' and so on. Chemicals, such as formaldehyde, benzene and phenols are found in plywood and particle boards (chipboard and 'mdf'), plastics, resins, glues, adhesives, synthetic textiles, flooring such as laminates, vinyl, insulation, carpets, curtains and furniture. Many of these chemicals 'off-gas' slowly over months and even years, and their effect can be traced in all areas of the body, particularly the nervous system.

Avoidance is the simple solution and it makes sense to keep to items which are as close to natural as you can find – linoleum not vinyl, timber not chipboard, screwed not glued, oiled or waxed not varnished and so on. Common sense – and a dash of scepticism – can take you a long way in this regard.

The building fabric

One of the most insidious pollutants is the chemical treatment of timber, for example in the roof rafters, or sometimes all over in the case of some timber frame buildings. Even in old properties, such treatment is rarely necessary, and in return for 'peace of mind' your property has been made thoroughly toxic to human, as well as insect or fungal life. It is possible to avoid all chemical treatment of timber if the building is designed properly and still ensure durability.

2nd Step: create comfort

Once you have removed the pollutants from your home or workplace, the next step is to create the ideal conditions for comfort. Even without any pollutants, it is possible (and quite common) to design things so badly that the health of occupants will be at risk under certain conditions. The green building designer's job is to do the opposite.

The big three - heating, ventilation and humidity

Heating

The health effects of heating are the least appreciated aspect of health promoting design. A great deal is known about heating and thermal efficiency, particularly amongst the environmental design community, but, from the point of view of human health, the only sensible heating system is a radiant, or largely radiant one.

Human thermal comfort is far more than having a thermostat fitted at 20°c. The most comfortable thermal environment for humans will be created when the surfaces of the room are a little warmer than the air, when the air is relatively still (not too many draughts, or convective currents) and there is sufficient thermal and moisture mass in the building fabric to moderate both temperature and humidity swings.

The conditions described above are almost impossible to create with a convective (warm air) system, and these systems may have a number of other disadvantages which negatively affect the health of occupants such as dust scorching. A low level radiant system, ideally at wall level, not in the ceiling, and with perhaps some 'top-up', quick-response radiant system if needed is the ideal.

Ventilation

At its most basic level, fresh air is needed to replenish the oxygen we use up in breathing and exhaust the carbon dioxide we produce. However, required ventilation rates have developed in order to account for other aspects. Air extract is needed to cope with pollutants and odours produced by people, materials and services. Extract is also needed to deal with (usually excessive) humidity and micro-organisms.

In a building with few pollutants and with

humidity dealt with passively by the building fabric, the need for ventilation is much reduced. This is not recognised by the regulations yet, but the argument has been successfully submitted in Norway to reduce ventilation levels without health risk to occupants, and to save energy, both in servicing, and in heat loss.

This brings us to another consideration of ventilation, that in extracting air, we are usually extracting warmth, hence the rise in the use of heat exchange extract fans. Given the increase in fabric insulation levels, the percentage of heat loss through ventilation has increased and so these fans perform a valuable function. However, they are effectively covert convection heating systems and, again from a health point of view, might warrant further investigation.

Humidity

The need to moderate humidity in buildings goes far beyond the risks associated with damp and mould, to well understood aspects of human health. Put simply, humans need a fairly balanced relative humidity of roughly between 40% and 65%. Beyond these, there are very close corre-lations with increased health risks, as clearly pictured in the diagram, below.

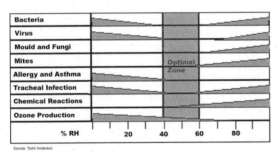

Source: Torkil Anderson

Air conditioning helps to moderate humidity, but like chemical preservatives, this comes with a possible health risk attached. It is possible – and preferable - to moderate humidity passively through the use of the building fabric and materi-als which naturally absorb and desorb moisture. These materials are known as 'hygroscopic' materials and can perform a valuable role in the design of internal air quality, helping to maintain a comfortable and healthy balance of humidity with no running costs or energy input. Clay is by

far the most effective material for achieving this, but other natural materials like timber and lime also work, as long as they are not coated with impervious paints or varnishes. Another method, for those not building new, might be by the installation and use of passive vents that open automatically when there are high humidity levels.

Other aspects

Lighting

Natural light changes and in so doing links people back to the natural passing of time which is increasingly valuable as we now spend so much time indoors. Rooms with windows in more than one wall and orientation will help to enhance this changing pattern of light.

Natural light in buildings create the right conditions for health and contentment. South facing glazing can bring sunlight and combat SAD disorders etc.

Light surface finishes will reduce the need for supplementary lighting, and when design-ing artificial lighting, it is worth considering an emphasis on task lighting or mood lighting. This can be more energy efficient and likely to be more pleasant to use and control. Lighting with poor flicker should be avoided and daylight bulbs can be helpful to overcome the lack of daylight in areas where this is unavoidable.

Noise

Excessive noise is obviously to be avoided, but low level background noise often associated with machinery, and noise from sources that cannot be controlled are considered to have the greatest potential to stress people. Many noises can be attenuated but not all, and in many cases, this can conflict with other requirements, such as the need for fresh air, so design strategies need to be considered early.

Plants

Plants use the carbon in the carbon dioxide we breathe out, and give off the oxygen we need, 'fresh' air is largely fresh because of the activities of plants, so it is not surprising that putting plants inside a house will have some beneficial effect on the quality of the air. Beyond that, it has been found that some plants have an extraordinary capacity to absorb some of the pollutant gases which we produce as part of our modern lifestyle, so their targeted use will have benefits. Plants (and the earth in which they tend to be planted) also help to moderate humidity so should have a more important place in our homes, beyond 'looking nice'.

Conclusion - priorities

Prioritising issues is important as it is easy to lose perspective. Everyone will have their own list, but consider the following as a starter.

1. We spend a lot of time asleep, in one place.

Houseplants can play a role in helping trid toxins from the atmosphere .Eco-Friendly House Plants by D C Wolverton
Available from The Green Shop, 01452 770629

Sleep is the body's time for recuperation on a number of levels. If you can only make one place 'healthy' make it your bed and bedroom.

2. Children, whose cells are developing quite differently from adults are at much greater risk from the effects of toxins. They also spend more time closer to the floor than adults, so pay particular attention to floors and childrens' bedrooms, as above.

3. Arguably the worst offender for health in many peoples' homes can be the unassuming wall to wall carpet, not only because of the materials and treatments it contains, but its capacity to store dirt and harbour dust mites and their faeces. Beyond steam cleaning, if you are experiencing health problems and suspect carpet, replace with wooden floors, linoleum, tiling or similar. Smaller rugs which can be washed do not tend to pose the same threat.

4. The great majority of applications of chemicals for protection against infestation, rot, mould and so on are unnecessary. If you have a problem, consider contacting a specialist (not one trying to sell you a chemical treatment) who will probably be able to assess the situation independently and offer remedial solutions, such as better ventilation, better drainage and so on, without the need for chemicals - environmental controls.

Lastly, a word or two on perspective. Wendell Berry wrote that "No place can be considered healthy until all places are healthy" This serves to remind us of the interconnectedness of these things, and of the fallacy of describing a house as 'healthy', particularly when, as an architect, you cannot control what goes on inside.

Studying buildings and health can turn you into a sort of building-related-hypochondriac. One cough and you begin to eye the skirting boards suspiciously, whereas there may just be a virus going around at school. If you live an otherwise healthy life, it is likely that you will survive your home and workplace(!), but as with most things, why take the risk, when there is a much more comfortable and healthy way to live? ❖

Green building FAQs

Robin Hillier has put together a range of commonly asked questions that homeowners who want to green their home or buy a new green home might ask...

There are many questions that need asking, which might well include is it really necessary to build at all? Remember that the act of building will use resources of labour and materials, and will have an environmental effect of some sort regardless of how eco-friendly it is proposed to be. It may be that as a nation we need to reconsider some aspects of how we live, and that the basic assumption that smaller housing units are required to meet the demand for independent living could be re-assessed. Alternatively more emphasis could perhaps be put on the refurbishment and conversion of existing housing, which would reduce the environmental impact overall. Assuming however, that the decision has been made to build new, here are some basic questions you may wish to ask.

How much 'energy in use' will my house require, and of what type?

All houses in Britain need to moderate the effects of low temperature in winter by providing an environment which is warmer than that outside, and to a lesser extent to moderate summer over-heating as well. If a house is well insulated, with high performance external joinery and glazing, is designed to minimise the exposed surface area: floor area ratio, and to maximise passive solar gain especially in winter, it will require less energy in use. These factors should be prioritised. Reduce carbon based energy sources (eg 'traditional' sources such as coal, gas, wood,) as these will produce CO_2 as they are burnt

and will contribute to global warming (although wood burning in sustainable quantities can be claimed to be carbon neutral as timber is renewable unlike coal and gas, and new plant growth absorbs CO_2 from the atmosphere). Increase sources of energy which are not carbon based, including solar, wind and water, which could be produced nationally (eg. wind farms) or locally (eg. solar panel on roof).

What is embodied energy and why do I need to consider it?

All buildings use materials which require energy to manufacture and transport, and more energy to build. The question is whether it is worth trying to reduce the amount of energy 'embodied' in the initial house construction currently estimated at 10% of total lifetime energy use and, if so, by how much?

The issue is one of assessment and balancing the embodied energy use of a material against its function, and comparison with other, perhaps more benign alternatives where they exist.

How can I ensure that my new house will be healthy and safe to live in?

Many building materials in common use today are manufactured using increasingly complex chemicals, and a surprising number of toxic substances are used within our houses. The big two for housebuilders are:

A. Timber treatment - relatively little timber treatment is used internally in both the USA and mainland Europe. The British construction industry however, with appropriate encouragement from manufacturers, has now got used to immersing most structural and semi structural timber in our houses with timber preservatives and proclaimimg this to be a benefit. Not only is this expensive and unneccesary in most internal situations, but the manufacturers' claims that the toxins are locked in the timber and can therefore not affect the inhabitants is somewhat undermined by an American report (Poisoned Playgrounds: Arsenic in 'Pressure-Treated' Wood - 2001) available at:
www.cehca.org/arsPlayEquip_notable.htm
detailing levels of arsenic in the ground around

timber play equipment which exceed safe limits. If preservatives are so safe then we wonder why the government has (from this year) banned the use of CCA (copper chrome arsenic) within houses?

B. Paints, waxes, stains and internal finishes - there is a long and venerable history relating to internal finishes throughout the centuries - the struggle to find ever more durable and colourful effects has led a long path from products based on milk, lime, blood and other natural materials, to highly synthesised petro-chemical products with dangerous artificial solvents which are both more toxic and persistent than natural alternatives such as linseed or tree oils. These dangers are now well recognised, and the petro-chemical paint industry has responded by introducing even more complex chemical cocktails into low solvent paints. Thankfully there are now many companies producing natural finishes with non-petrochemical contents. It is worth noting that petrochemical finishes are the products of an intensive high energy industrial process which produces large amounts of waste so dangerous that it can only be held in tanks - whereas natural finishes use low energy manufacturing processes and produce small amounts of waste which can be composted.

What construction method should I use given my desire to build a low energy house?

Broadly speaking there are two schools of thought - one says that a low energy house should be of traditionally built heavy masonry to give thermal mass and a consequential diurnal and seasonal delay in temperature variation, together with loads of extra insulation to keep the overall heat loss low. These houses will often have small windows in order to maximise the insulated areas. The disadvantages of this approach are that the walls tend to be very thick to accommodate both the heavy weight structure and the insulation and can quickly become expensive to build as a consequence.

The other school of thought argues that modern living does not require the benefits of thermal delay as a house will more often than not be empty during the day whilst the occupants are

elsewhere, at work or school etc. These houses tend to be built of a relatively lightweight timber frame construction, have a low heating load since lots of insulation can be installed directly into the depth of the timber frame, and will have a rapid response to the heating system as they will heat up within a few minutes of returning to a cold house, since the heating system does not have to transfer much energy into heavy mass walls. They tend to be designed with larger areas of glazing on the basis that sunlight is enjoyable, and can contribute to the heating requirement whilst saving money on electric lighting. The disadvantages of this approach are that they may, if not designed properly, overheat quickly in summer, and rely heavily on ventilation to cool them down.

The two approaches as described above are extremes, and the reality is that decisions can be made during the design phase which can incorporate the best of both worlds - and timber based structural systems are now being introduced into the UK which incorporate sufficient mass to overcome the worst disadvantages of lightweight building methods. Decisions should be made as part of the design process, to take account of lifestyle, site location and topography, self build skills (if required), and budget.

How should I heat my low energy house?

The million dollar question. The UK climate is just cold enough in winter that even a highly insulated house with solar panels will need top up heat for space heating, and a reliable source for year round water heating. This can be sourced from a 'traditional' heat source (gas boiler / electric heaters) or from a variety of 'alternative' sources (solar / heat recovery and ventilation / heat pump), or from some combination of both combined (e.g.. wood burner with electric backup). The difficulty here is the need for hot water on demand which requires either a high energy heat source or else patient and sometimes dirty living! In reality, budgets may dictate either:

● an 'efficient' traditional gas fired central heating system (condensing boiler, good controls) with high insulation levels, which has relatively high capital cost but provides modern standards of comfort, loads of hot water, and can easily produce space heating bills of less than £50/annum

- a mixed alternative energy system e.g. a solar panel supplementing a ventilation heat recovery unit with excess heat routed to the hot water cylinder. Will normally require some back up heating, possibly an efficient wood burner, even in a well insulated house.

An all electric heating system should not be considered except in the most exceptional circumstances, since electricity is a high grade energy source and should ideally be used only for tasks which other fuels cannot supply eg. lighting, pumps, electronic goods and computers. Signing up with a 'green' electricity supplier is not the panacea often suggested, since demand far outstrips supply – a situation which is likely to worsen rather than improve. It is worth noting that the Building Regulations make no allowance for 'green' electricity in energy scoring calculations, as it is assumed that future users could switch supplier.

These are suggested starting strategies for thinking through how to heat a low energy house ... these are not intended as recommendations, and the final choices should be based on site conditions, user requirements, and affordability!

Should I spend my money on solar panels or on more insulation? If insulation, what type?

For a new build house the decision should nearly always be to spend money on insulation first, and alternative energy installations second. The payback period for a specification of 250mm, rather than the more normal 150mm thick insulation could be around 5-10 years depending upon lifestyle etc. whereas even the solar trade admit that it is likely to take 15-20 years to recover the costs of a hot water solar installation, and considerably longer for an electricity producing panel. And the better insulated a house is, then the longer the payback period for alternative energy systems is likely to be!

The choice of insulation depends partly upon budget and also on the importance given to embodied energy and whether or not you

consider it important to use a hygroscopic (breathable) material such as cellulose or sheepswool, which will allow moisture from inside the building to escape to the outside rather than condense within and possibly damage the house structure. A very detailed article is available by request from Impetus Consulting at http://www. impetusconsult.co.uk/projects/publns.html

If budgets allow then it could be viable to design a 'zero' energy house by specifying lots of insulation in conjunction with lots of mass (see the earlier question on construction method), all integrated with lots of alternative energy. It should be noted that 'zero' here really means zero running cost / zero carbon as there is no such thing as a zero energy house - every house needs energy, whether from the sun, wind, earth, or from the people living in it.

What is airtightness all about?

As better insulation standards become more commonplace eco-designers are increasingly targeting air tightness as the key to successful in-use energy reductions. This is rarely reflected in reality - build quality and detailing, even in recently built eco-houses - can often be poor enough that draughts are a noticeable feature. The idea is simple enough: to cut down on unwanted ventilation (draughts which cause discomfort and unwanted energy loss) and ensure adequate ventilation in a controlled manner to ensure health & comfort.

Airtightness testing (by CPC Retrotec). The eco-renovated farmhouse (home of the Editor!) achieved an ACH

of 3.9 which is not bad for a 300 year old stone building.

It requires, however, high standards of detailing and construction which are rarely achieved. A Building Regs standard house might target 8-10 ach (air changes per hour at 50 pascals pressure) and the built reality is probably a far lower performance than this; a typical low energy house would aim to achieve about 2ACH - but may well not perform as well as this, and a bespoke SIPs (structurally insulated panel) system such as Tekhaus claims to achieve about 0,2 air changes per hour (ACH)! It is worth noting however that unless airtight construction is combined with a well thought out and implemented heating and ventilation strategy then condensation may become a major issue for the inhabitants.

Signs are that air tightness will soon become a higher priority under new building regulations, and air tightness testing may well become mandatory for new houses.

What about water saving - is this not a high priority for green buildings?

Yes - but you don't have to care about the planet to justify saving water - a rainwater recycling installation will probably take about 5 to 10 years to recover the cost at today's water prices. Rates and metered costs are predicted to rise sharply to cover the massive costs of not only maintaining the existing infrastructure, but of building new alleviation measures to prevent flooding caused by land use and climate changes.

A simple solution for gardens is to install oversize butts for irrigation. More sophisticated systems for storing and re-using rainwater in toilets and washing machines can be designed to provide up to 45% of total domestic water requirements (see article in Building for a Future magazine Vol 14, no 1, Summer 2004 www.newbuilder. co.uk) . Although technically quite feasible, it is currently relatively expensive to clean and filter rainwater sufficiently to make it potable, and would need specialist technical advice.

I understand the issues - but how do I afford to do all this stuff?

The act of procuring a house, whether by commissioning a builder or an architect to design and manage the whole process, or by physically self building, should ideally be carried out in the spirit of adventure. There is a need to explore all the options available, with regard to selecting the most appropriate designs, configurations, materials and technologies - to suit the immediate, local and global environment, the skills available for construction, and most importantly - to suit the inhabitants. The end result should ideally reflect the rigours of a journey through design which can be an exciting experience for all involved, and should produce above all a place that makes best use of the site, the resources available, and is a delight to use and live in.

The cost of all this? You do not need to be rich to make best use of orientation, breezes, views, daylight and sunlight. ❖

EcoHomes

EcoHomes is an environmental assessment scheme for new and refurbished residential dwellings, developed and managed by BRE (Building Research Establishment). It was launched in April 2000 and, after a slow start, the take-up rate is now exceeding all but the most optimistic expectations. Most significantly, an EcoHomes 'Pass' rating has been designated an essential requirement of the Housing Corporation's Scheme Development Standards, which most social housing developments must comply with. There is a growing trend amongst planning authorities to set EcoHomes targets as part of Supplementary Planning Guidance. **Michael Priaulx** takes us through the scheme...

The EcoHomes assessment consists of seven sections relating to environmental impacts: Energy, Transport, Pollution, Materials, Water, Land Use and Ecology, and Health and Well-being.

- Within each section are further issues e.g. within Energy there is Carbon Dioxide Emissions, Building Envelope (i.e. insulation standards), Drying Space etc. Each of these issues is worth one or more 'credits', which can be achieved if certain criteria are met. In most cases, all dwellings on the site must comply.
- A weighting factor is applied to each section to give an overall % score. (One result of this is that each credit is not worth an equal amount, varying between 0.48% (Materials) and 2.14% (Pollution)).
- The overall score relates to a rating of Pass, Good, Very Good or Excellent. 70% achieves an Excellent rating. The rating structure is shown in Table 1 on the next page.

Confused? You won't be when you have gained a little experience, but there is no doubt it is baffling at first. What is crucial is that if you have a target EcoHomes rating for your development, you are well advised to consult a trained assessor at the earliest possible stage, even pre-planning, to ensure that the design can achieve sufficient credits. (Alternatively, you can download and read very carefully the BRE EcoHomes Guidance document, although keep a day free in your diary... I'm not joking, it is a very big document.) This is very important because if you are expecting to gain credits for cycle storage by installing a few Sheffield stands in the pavement, you won't. If you think your assessor will turn a blind eye to the flat in the corner with no balcony and poor daylighting, forget it.

Which brings us to the mechanics of getting an assessment. A document is produced by BRE called the Developer Sheets. It provides tick boxes and tables to be completed, and lists the documentation which must be provided. NHBC have compiled a shorter version which enables the assessment to be started more easily. This document is completed and provided to a licensed assessor who will issue a 'certification report' to BRE. A quality assurance process is carried out by BRE, and then BRE issues the certificate for the appropriate rating.

Collating the information to enable certification can be a time-consuming process and should not be underestimated. You should incorporate the relevant issues into the specification and drawings as they are produced – ensuring sufficient detail to demonstrate compliance with the EcoHomes criteria. Most assessors will provide guidance but this should be confirmed as not all companies provide an equivalent service.

EcoHomes is intended to be applied at the design stage. Post-construction reviews can be undertaken although these are not mandatory except on land owned by English Partnerships (the Government's national regeneration agency).

It is proposed by BRE that EcoHomes will be reviewed every year – the latest version was issued in June 2003. Bespoke EcoHomes assessments are applied by BRE where a development is not purely residential, or is a special case such as sheltered accommodation. EcoHomes can apply to major refurbishments of existing houses, and an EcoHomes scheme specifically for

Table 1: Rating Structure for EcoHomes 2003

CATEGORY	Number of Credits Available	Environmental Weighting Factor (i.e. % per section)
Energy	20	30
Transport	8	
Pollution	7	15
Materials	31	15
Water	6	10
Land Use and Ecology	9	15
Health and Well-being	8	15

existing dwellings is currently under development with the Housing Corporation, but this will not be launched before 2005.

So is it economically viable to achieve an Excellent rating? To convert a standard Building Regulations house to an Excellent EcoHomes dwelling at a late stage in the design, via a large number of bolt-on measures, will undoubtedly cost a lot of money. However, if the ambition to obtain the EcoHomes rating is incorporated right from the conception of the project, then the costs can be hugely reduced. There are no mandatory credits and the spread of environmental impacts covered means that almost any type of development has the potential to score well if the correct measures are incorporated. Despite this, an Excellent EcoHomes rating is still quite a rare achievement, with only eighteen developments awarded the rating to date.

Which aspects of my development will score well?

A range of sustainable measures which could be incorporated into the design of a residential development have been considered. It is stated how well these would be likely to score under EcoHomes, although this will be variable. It is important to remember that credits in different sections are not equally weighted.

Minimising CO_2 emissions due to space heating is not necessarily vital to obtain a high rating. In new homes, space heating demand is low. Energy demand is largely due to lights and particularly appliances, which are dealt with discretely as separate issues e.g. white goods. Therefore there is less difference than you might expect between the best and the worst homes with respect to this issue. It should be remembered, however, that many of the other sections do relate indirectly to CO_2 emissions.

Passive solar design and sunspaces will typically only achieve maybe one more credit for CO_2 emissions - the SAP calculation is not strongly affected by solar gain. Electrically heated dwellings do not score well as credits will be lost for CO_2 emissions and, more significantly, for NOx emissions, although ground-source heat pumps can attain CO_2 emissions comparable with a gas condensing boiler. The performance of CHP will be very variable depending on the system - on a mixed-use site with a high heat demand, several additional credits could be achieved.

Wood-burning stoves score well, as wood is deemed to have zero CO_2 emissions. Photovoltaics could potentially achieve several credits as they are replacing electricity which has higher CO_2 emissions than gas.

'Green' electricity from the grid is not awarded any additional credits.

Thermal mass will not generally gain any credits as the SAP calculation does not take it into account. You may be getting benefit when global warming kicks in and everyone else is plugging in their cooling units, but unfortunately this is not considered. Super-insulation will achieve five credits for the building envelope, although this can usually be achieved just by meeting best practice U-values - the Building Regulations Elemental Method is sufficient for many dwellings.

Solar hot water heating will typically achieve only one extra credit for reduced CO_2 emissions, again due to the relatively small solar input assumed by the SAP calculation.

Green/ brown roofs get one credit for reducing peak surface water runoff from the roof by 50%, but beware as the increased mass required to support the roof may lose credits in the Materials section. There may be ecological benefits depending on the type of roof used.

The materials section might be expected by some to have a higher weighting (it is worth 15% overall) but in general the impacts of a dwelling in use considerably outweigh the impacts of the materials used for construction. Use of reused or recycled materials will achieve credits, but new materials can achieve an equal number of credits if carefully selected.

Timber frame tends to perform better than masonry in terms of environmental impact. However, masonry construction can also obtain maximum credits if the correct materials are used. Off-site construction is not in itself considered by EcoHomes.

Credits can be achieved if timber with suitable documentation is used, but only if it is reused or recycled timber, or certified by FSC or PEFC.

Minimising internal water consumption gets credits. This can be done through rainwater or greywater use, but unless you also have efficient fittings then the benefits of this will be severely compromised. One additional credit is achievable for specifying a rainwater butt for external irrigation.

The location of the development is important, but the five credits which are available for public transport and local amenities can easily be made up elsewhere.

Fundamental to the Land Use and Ecology section is that a brownfield site can have a higher ecological value than a greenfield one. To score well, a suitable ecological survey is necessary on all but the most barren pieces of land, and you will need to protect and enhance the existing ecology. This will typically require protecting existing trees where possible, and planting some native species and installing bird boxes.

Health and well-being is an important element of sustainable development and is given equal importance to many of the other issues (15% in total). Daylighting, sound insulation, and a private external space are considered.

Environment-friendly finishes, e.g. paints with low VOCs, are not currently considered due to the lack of a verifiable benchmarking system.

Impacts during the construction phase are also not covered at present, although they may be considered in future versions of the scheme.

Tools

Eco-profiling

The Green Guide to Housing Specification (BRE 2000) awards ratings ('A', 'B', 'C') to construction types for each major element (e.g. external wall, roof), for a 'typical' residential dwelling. An example of a construction type for an external wall would be brickwork outer leaf, insulation, aerated blockwork inner leaf, plaster and paint – this is an 'A' rated construction type in fact. These ratings are based on a range of environmental issues such as climate change (reflecting embodied energy), freight transport, toxicity and resource use, based on the typical source and recycled content of the materials used in the UK, over a 60-year period (i.e. including any replacement during this period). Use of an 'A'-rated construction type can enable credits to be achieved in EcoHomes.

Eco-profiling has a number of advantages, the main one being its user-friendliness. Anyone can quickly determine the environmental performance of a construction type with minimal knowledge of either construction methods or environmental issues.

Some manufacturers have had eco-profiling carried out on their individual products by BRE. This can be used to determine a bespoke rating for the product. This is a positive step as it enables manufacturers who allow BRE to scrutinise their processes with respect to sustainability to gain benefit under the EcoHomes scheme.

If an element is reused – e.g. as part of a refurbished building – it will automatically obtain an 'A' rating. However, if only a portion of an

Sustainable Homes commissioned some research on EcoHomes costs on behalf of the Housing Corporation, published in December 2002 (based on the EcoHomes 2002 scheme). For a 'typical' dwelling built to the 'essential' 2002 Scheme Development Standards requirements, the additional costs were:

With maximum points for site credits:

Pass/ Good	no cost
Very Good	+ £1,430
Excellent	+ £1,760

With no points for site credits:

Pass	+ £30
Good	+ £111
Very Good	+ £1,680
Excellent	+ £3,040

element is reused or recycled then it may not alter the rating as the impacts of the other materials used may still be high. Where construction types are not included in the Green Guide, BRE will review them individually as part of an EcoHomes assessment – the full specification of that element must be provided to enable an accurate calculation to be carried out. Some major construction types have been overlooked e.g. beam and block ground floor with a screed finish. Very few 'unusual' construction types have been included: if you are trying to assess your straw-bale house for EcoHomes then you will struggle without BRE's input.

The main disadvantage of the eco-profiling system is that, to create a universally applicable tool, assumptions have had to be made. A generic source is assumed for each material based on the typical case. Therefore, the actual impact of transportation of a material e.g. whether it is locally sourced and manufactured or not, cannot be taken into account. It would be difficult to do this anyway, as all raw materials would need to be taken into account, and timber and aggregates are really the only materials where transport impacts are likely to be greater than manufacturing impacts. Other possible sources of inaccuracy are that a typical recycled input has to be assumed, and the 60-year life cycle does not give full credit to very long-lived construction types.

The Green Guide to Housing Specification is a useful tool although the limitations of the methodology should be borne in mind. ❖

References and sources of further information

BRE EcoHomes: **www.bre.co.uk/ecohomes**

Housing Corporation:
www.housingcorp.gov.uk/resources/sustain

English Partnerships: **www.englishpartnerships.co.uk**
- search for 'environmental standards' to view minimum development requirements.

Green Guide to Housing Specification – Jane Anderson & Nigel Howard (BRE 2000).

NHBC EcoHomes: **www.nhbc.co.uk/energy**
NHBC sponsored the development of EcoHomes by BRE and have seven licensed assessors based in Milton Keynes, London and Edinburgh, and have been involved with more than one hundred assessments.

© Green Building Press

Zero Energy Standards

So what's it going to be like in the UK towards the middle of this century – when severe rationing of fossil fuels seems inevitable ? How are we going to keep our computers and trains running on the limited stocks of renewable energy available within our national boundaries ? Will we have enough green electricity to power all the heat pumps and air conditioning needed to make a lightweight building in a London summer of 2080 seem bearable? **Bill Dunster** reports...

Whatever the improvements in technical efficiency in the renewable energy sector – the answer is a firm 'no'. The first luxuries to go will be mass air travel, followed by a steady reduction in foodmiles, and more people choosing to live within walking or cycling distance from their jobs. However, with half current UK carbon emissions coming from buildings, and the other from our collective lifestyle and workstyles, it is essential that we plan the renovation and replacement of

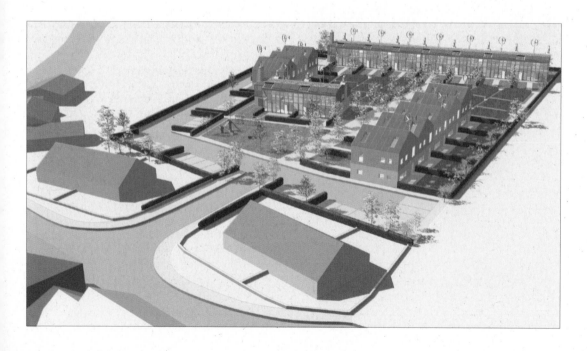

our urban fabric to stay within the limited stocks of renewable electricity and biomass available within our national boundaries. If we wish to create a politically stable society that does not need to spend vast resources competing abroad to secure more than its fair share of the dwindling international supplies of fossil fuel – we need to set benchmarks limiting the consumption of our scarce resources as soon as possible.

It is not enough to sponsor a turbine in Wales with the pretense of powering offices in London unless the offices have already adopted all sensible load reduction measures. Similarly it is not sensible to make claims that a new residential community in the Thames Gateway, powered by the waste of an entire London Borough, is zero carbon, as one day that borough will need its own local 'waste to energy' scheme to maintain public services. It is far better to generate renewable energy on site to minimise the drain on limited national stocks.

There is much debate about how green to go in the construction industry, and how fast. Debra Brownhill, of the 'BRE Ecohomes' scheme admits that the highest standard of 'Excellent' only produces a 35 % carbon saving over the building regulations legal minimum. The volume housebuilders have been slow to adopt even the lowest ecohomes standards, making it difficult for the BRE, as a private sector company funded by the industry, to introduce higher standards. Even the World Wildlife Fund with its million sustainable homes campaign finds itself supporting these low environmental performance standards in an effort to maximise take up of its campaign. If millions of new homes really were built to ecohomes very good standards – national carbon emissions will continue to rise steadily.

Unfortunately this very British advocacy of gradual incremental change isn't going to keep the lights on in thirty to fifty year's time without resorting to the abominable nuclear energy scenario – and the inevitable security headaches that come with the threat of melt downs, terrorism, and radioactive waste disposal over millennia.

Probably the best idea is to limit national demand by encouraging a stepchange reduction in our built fabrics demand for heat, power and cooling. Step change zero fossil energy

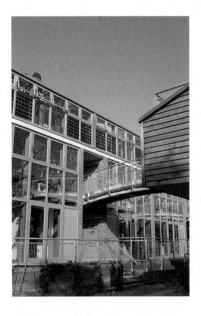

developments are only expensive because hardly anybody is building them – each small scale project is a prototype. The government sustainable community programme plans to build an additional 180,000 homes a year for the foreseeable future to reduce property values in the south east – many of them on land already owned by the government agency English Partnerships. ZEDfactory research has shown that it only takes somewhere between 2000 and 5000 new homes and workspace a year built to ZEDstandards for the economies of scale to cut in, creating no additional premium for achieving ZED infrastructure capable of making a national renewable energy scenario viable. This is a critical moment in the evolution of the UK construction industry, and decisions taken now will dramatically affect the quality of life for most ordinary people in the UK.

If we could somehow agree to adopt the Stepchange initiatives proposed by ZEDstandards, and replicated in Germany by the Passivhaus movement – a ZEDproducts buyers club could be formed enabling even the smallest projects all over the UK to take advantage of centrally negotiated volume discounts. As these economies of scale ramp up, there will be no additional cost premium for a ZED step change specification, and the reactionary industry lobby against change will have no further grounds to complain about cost – all achieved avoiding difficult government mandatory legislation. Coupled to a public promotion of the health and quality of life benefits of the environmental approach, it will be possible to create considerable demand for this new industry specification. ZEDfactory already has an unsolicited database of over 1000 people wanting a ZEDhome, and with only a handful of units being built a year – it is easy to demonstrate that demand exceeds supply by a healthy margin.

With the latest government white paper indicating that North Sea oil and gas are likely to be exhausted within ten years, complacency over these issues will become an issue of national security. If we want our children to stay at home when other nations fight for oil, and avoid leukaemia clusters around nuclear plants – this sort of industry wide initiative may be a constructive way forward. ❖

www.zedstandards.com

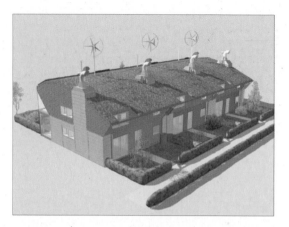

From A to ZED book review
Realising Zero (fossil) Energy Developments

In response to the thousands of people who have been to see BedZED or contacted him for more information, Bill Dunster has brought out the book of the buildings, a sign of a really successful development! This is bottom up architecture! Here the man on the street, student in the studio or architect in his practice – is asking the questions and Bill, has produced this book to answer them. It is very unlike the glossy, people free monographs, produced by the 'great architects' to set their own creations off in works of art like images, where descriptions of how the building works are limited to the captions of images.

This book is a practical guide to the principals, theories and operation of the BedZED development and is full of useful information. Most architects will know of the Beddington Zero (Fossil) Energy Development (BedZED) in South London initiated by Bioregional Development Group and Bill Dunster Architects. BedZED was developed by London's largest housing association, the Peabody Trust, as a mixed-use development with 82 homes and 3,000m² of commercial or live/work space. The first units were complete in March 2002 with total completion and occupation in September 2002. From A to Zed is a practical guide on how to realise a ZED - with sets of Housing Corporation accredited standard house types, an inventory of the ZEDproducts used to build them, and exemplar case studies applying the principles to real sites.

The book describes the 'tools' to make the process quicker and easier, such as ZEDestimator which predicts the likely cost of a development and defines how much to pay for a site to achieve a target profit return. The principles behind ZED's are also described, by means of a journey through the three main phases of a typical medium to large-scale project - feasibility; the planning process and detailed design; and the construction process, with a good section on the selection of materials.

What would also have been interesting is a review of the strengths and weakness of the development, of how the units actually work, not 'were designed to work', in terms of build costs, energy consumption, air-pressure testing, mixed-use ideas, heating systems, electric cars provisions and comfort. I do know that many of the residents love the 'passive solar' feel of the houses and the airiness and lightness and winter warmth. I have not heard yet how they perform in months like August 2003? Ultimately if we are to have really sustainable developments we need to understand how they actually work, in relation to each other, and with all the studies done on BedZed, this development has been researched more than most!

This book is just as interesting to architects, developers, councils and building owners, and provides an important prototype for the sort of new building paradigms we will need soon enough if the energy prices keep climbing as they are, and we are to attempt to control the greenhouse gas emissions that are driving climate change!

Reviewed by Sue Roaf

Published by Bill Dunster Architects.
ISBN: 0 9545050 0 5

Available from the Green Building Press website:
www.newbuilder.co.uk/books/ *£38.50*

The thought of living in a home full of light, smelling of springtime and awash with the colours of nature cannot fail to tempt. A carefree and safe environment where the indoors reflects, rather than abandons its links with the outdoors. A place where you can be confident your children can play and relax among natural, yet practical surroundings. Why aren't all houses already built like this? **Keith Hall** muses ...

So you want an ecohome!

Eco-apartments for sale at Greenwich Millennium Village, London

The answer could be quite simple really. We have probably been brainwashed with the wrong values and aspirations. Our lives are dictated by consumerism and materialism force-fed to us by multinational corporations. This encourages a copycat mentality, thus ensuring that they have an unlimited supply of punters to buy their wares.

What has this to do with ecohomes you ask? Well, an ecohome can be the antidote we all need, Its start point is minimalist. A true ecohome need not stand out from the crowd but blend in with the environment. Everything in this home would be functional and aesthetically pleasing but need not be showy. Its most endearing assets will be out of sight but always purposeful.

An ecohome would not make you buzz but help you to feel relaxed and calm. It would, by its very design, enhance your interest in the surroundings and increase your enjoyment of nature that in abundance will surround it.

Most housebuilders have not yet caught on that there are a growing number of people that have interests beyond the flashy kitchen, bathroom and latest gadgets and gizmos. Their market research tells them that it's just the 'In-your-face' buildings that get attention and make quick sales. They also assume that simple boxes, near to good commuter links, sell quickly with the highest profit.

Most house buyers tend to accept we are limited to buying what we are offered and not what we may actually want.

Defining the standard

There are a number of organisations currently pursuing the ideal green home standards but these vary as there is currently little common consensus between them regarding the ideal standards to adopt and perhaps we should therefore conclude that there is no one answer. However, some of these are discussed elsewhere in this book.

One million sustainable homes?

In 2002 WWF (the Worldwide Fund for Nature) launched its One Million Sustainable Homes campaign to bring sustainable homes from the fringes of the housing sector to the mainstream. Not much has happened to date but in this ambitious project, WWF is endeavouring to work with the government, industry and consumers to ensure that one million sustainable homes (refur-

bishments and new build) are developed across the UK by 2012. WWF, CABE (Commission for Architecture and the Built Environment) and others undertook research into consumer attitudes to the built environment. The results (visit **www.wwf.org.uk/sustainablehomes**) demonstrated an overwhelming interest in sustainable homes with 87% of respondents saying they were interested in knowing the environmental rating of the home they were considering buying which would help them make an informed decision. 84% said they were willing to pay around 2% more on the purchase price for a sustainable home.

Finding your eco home

Here is a list of contacts for developers offering new houses that they claim are sustainable. If you are looking to rent then many housing associations are incorporating serious sustainability measures into their new and refurbishment projects, there are also many tenant led schemes across the UK.

The following list is not exhaustive and is offered as much as a lead to spark ideas for your own research as anything else.

CABE (with the help of WWF) has produced a guide and website for potential homeowners at **www.thehomebuyersguide.org** ❖

Douch Partners Ltd
New development in Forest Row, East Sussex: one block consisting of two, three bedroom maisonettes and two, one bedroom flats. A detached, two bedroom studio house. The development will incorporate solar heating, extensive insulation, and use of environmentally friendly materials. 01342 825766
www.douchpartners.co.uk

Eco-Village Ltd
Building plots in Moray, Scotland, possible houses 01309 690154 **www.ecovillagefindorn.com**

Greener Living Homes
New homes near Lewis that achieve 'Very Good rating in the EcoHomes standard. **www.greenerlivinghomes.co.uk**

Greenwich Millennium Village
186 one two and three bedroomed apartments in this waterside development in London's dockland that have achieved an 'Excellent" rating in the BRE's Ecohomes standard. 020 8293 6900

Housing Associations
Many housing associations around the country are building homes with sustainable aspects but they usually have restrictions on who may rent or in some cases buy them. For example they may have a bias towards people with local links or those who are needy.

Housing Corporation - 020 7393 2000

Sustainable Homes
Hastoe Housing Association run Sustainable Homes on behalf of the Housing Corporation. It is a project which has had great success in encouraging many players in the social housing sector to improve environmental aspects of their buildings. Call them for details on greener social housing schemes in your district. 020 8973 0429

Peabody Trust
Charitable organisation building homes for sale and rent. Notable for the development of the Beddington Zero Energy Development. (BEDZED) 020 7928 7811

Sherwood Energy Village (SEV)
SEV have now gained planning permission for an innovative housing scheme of about 185 dwellings which will be built to high energy efficiency standards and Includes a wide range of house styles. Sherwood Energy Village is probably the largest development in the UK to date that is founded on totally green principles. These principles are also attracting a lot of sustainably led businesses to relocate to the area creating many new jobs. One such company is Center Parcs who have recently built their new headquarters at SEV 01623 860222 **info@sev.org.uk**

Somerset Trust for Sustainable Development
Building first 12 ecohouses this year. 01458 259400 **www.sustainablehousing.org.uk**

Sustainable Property Group
New build/ barn conversions and renovations always underway. 01296 747157

Urbane
Has completed a number of award winning ecohomes in Bristol in recent years. Soon embarking on larger developments in the region. Also able to assist selfbuilders. 0117 955 7224 **urban.e@btopenworld.com**

Walter Segal Self Build Trust
Provides basic information on ecobuilding and more detailed support for community led projects for self build using the Segal timber frame method. Runs regular training courses. Over 24 supported projects completed ranging in size from 3-24 houses. Also support for community building. 01668 213544 **www.segalselfbuild.co.uk**

This list is by no way exhaustive. It is also recommended that you check out the professional listings at the back of this book.

Facing page: the UK's first two storey, straw bale house under construction at St Dogmael's, Cardigan. Full story in Building for a Future, Vol 14, No 3, **www.newbuilder.co.uk**

Case study

Eco flagship housing

Eco-homes may take many forms. What is clear is that the last thing any of us want to see is a standardised, homogenised monocultural home. We are a long way from having all the answers but new housing probably has the greatest opportunities to take advantage of the latest technology and to incorporate the highest insulation standard. **Damian Bree** reports on the design and creation of a whole new breed of eco-housing from the ground up...

Our first live sustainable project was for the construction of a demonstration house at the Building Research Establishment (BRE) at Garston in 1996. Knowledge on environmental issues and solutions were well documented but practical examples were few. We wanted to also consider the environmental aspects of how we build our homes, from both the energy in day-to-day use through to benefit in the method of construction.

I recently saw an excellent analogy of the aviation versus construction industry, from the Wright brothers first flight 100 years ago in 1904, then commercial flight, helicopters through to the Space Shuttle. 100 years ago the Victorians hand-built their houses brick-by-brick on site. Now, as we head towards the future, we read about private individuals building their own spaceship and flying towards the very edge of space, while back on the ground we are still building our houses brick-by-brick on damp windy sites.

We asked ourselves why is it that the aviation industry, motor industry and even the relatively

new computer industry have all made huge advances in the past few decades, but the construction industry still builds as we have done for 150 years.

We decided that our demonstration house should be designed to unite four interrelated innovation strategies:

1. Design - more space, improved safety, comfort and control
2. Intelligent systems - home management, communications, entertainment, security
3. Environmental performance - application of green technologies to minimise greenhouse gas emissions, water usage, waste reduction, sustainable use of materials
4. Building construction – prefabrication, process monitoring

Improving the way we construct also has a significant effect in the way we can build responsibly. But it can also have other practical benefits such as a shorter on-site construction programme, resulting in earlier handover and therefore less interest payments on loans. Prefabrication can provide better workmanship and allows alternative methods of construction to be considered and economies of scale.

The demonstration house incorporated as many features and systems as we could obtain. We had no funds for materials or construction, but with the backing of the BBC we obtained sponsorship and support from over 150 partners, designed the house in 6 weeks and built it in 13.

The experience and lessons learned from the BRE demonstration house, built under the Integer banner, led to the first pilot project for 2 dwellings at Cherhill in Wiltshire for a local housing association on the edge of an AONB (Area of Outstanding Natural Beauty). This project incorporated all of the 4 innovation strategies previously referred to, and was occupied by local families.

With a UK average score of 55% in the DETR Housing Quality Indicators (HQI) assessment, these 2 dwellings achieved a remarkable 77%.

After Cherhill, we were appointed to design a scheme of 27 houses and flats at Maidenhead in Berkshire by the MDHA.

The period saw many new companies and new products appearing on the market and existing products being refined and improved, mainly due to advances in technology and a wider choice of materials founded on solid research. With each subsequent development we were able to refine the design by incorporating these advances, whilst improving on our basic design.

The site for the Maidenhead project was brownfield, (133 concrete garages were on the site, which were crushed and recycled), located close to the town centre and public transport network, which enabled the local authority to reduce its normal car parking standards.

The particular features of this project were:

- a site layout that enabled all units to take maximum advantage of passive solar design principles
- increased levels of Insulation (cellulose)
- grey water
- passive stack
- solar thermal
- photovoltaics
- prefabricated timber construction and PODs (off site manufactured units)
- sedum roof
- services accessibility
- internal flexibility etc.

The chosen method of construction was to prefabricate as much as possible. Timber frame wall panels and floor cassettes formed the shell and incorporated combined bathroom and kitchen PODs.

Using engineered timber 'I' beams we were able to fill the cavity with 170mm of Warmcel cellulose insulation, giving a U=Value of 0.19 W/m^2, compared to the requirement at the time of 0.45 W/m^2.

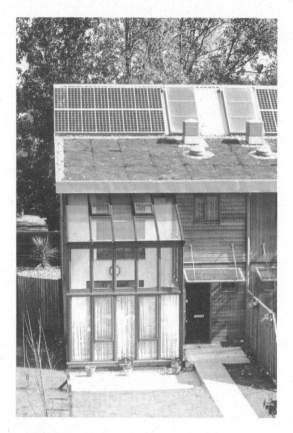

Both grey water recycling and surface water Harvesting technologies were built into the development, as interest in water conservation was fresh in the local population's mind. The previous winter saw the Thames bursting its banks locally and flooding many acres of nearby land, although not this site. However, to compliment the water saving strategies a green roof was built to help retain rainwater during the initial stages of a downpour. It prevents a surge on the local drainage system whilst providing a habitat for wildlife and plants and prolongs the lifespan of the waterproofing membrane.

Durability is of concern to all clients, and more so to those who have an invested long term interest such as housing associations. Untreated western red cedar clad the exterior walls, with vertical and horizontal cladding helping the tenants to differentiate their homes and providing them with a sense of defined ownership. Advice from the timber supplier resulted in a different profile for the vertical cladding to the horizontal, to ensure optimum weathering.

Internally, future maintenance and tenant upgrading of facilities (burglar alarm, sound system etc) was facilitated via accessible ducts behind the skirting boards and at high level coving, with a main vertical service duct in the core. These ducts allowed access to practically every part of the internal structure for adding any new services without the need for redecoration. This benefited the housing association by preventing major disruption to tenants should they ever need to install new services.

This philosophy was also taken to the extents of the site, by providing separate underground ducts for cable, BT and other utilities from the site boundary into a central plant room for the whole development, where the services were then re-directed into each home, and insisting that all utility companies used these ducts.

Other technological benefits included remote monitoring of heat meters, water and gas meters and the electricity supply, as well as diagnostic monitoring of the communal boilers and water

Don't build your dream on someone else's nightmare.

Help prevent habitat destruction—ask for FSC certified wood. Learn more at www.fsc-uk.org

FSC

sump overflow. A single aerial point features 1 satellite dish, 1 analogue TV, 1 FM radio and 1 digital radio aerial on a single pole servicing all 27 dwellings. This, along with the telecoms service duct, considerably reduced the visual clutter that can occur on new developments by controlling where services were brought into the site and how they were distributed throughout the scheme.

The design of the dwellings incorporated a solar upstand to the rear of the mono-pitch roof. It was intended that the upstand would feature PV as well as solar water panels, but costs initially precluded their use. However, during construction we successfully obtained funding under the DTI field trial for 15 installations and these were fixed by Solar Century alongside the solar hot water panel collectors. 20 kW of electricity can be generated with surplus being sold back to the grid.

Since completing the development in 2002 tenant feedback has been extremely positive. Practically all the tenants have taken ownership of their unique environment and contribute to its upkeep by ensuring it is well maintained, not in any planned sense but by keeping it clean, adding their own unique personal touches. MDHA has reported that tenant satisfaction is high with only one tenant moving out (moved to another part of the country).

All of these early projects had been for housing associations but we had always seen the challenge to use these ideas and principles on mainstream, privately funded, residential developments for the open market.

The opportunity came when we entered and won an open competition run by Basingstoke and Deane Borough Council in Hampshire. The scheme was for a mix of houses and flats on a south facing sloping site.

Having received planning approval early 2004 work started on site in 2005. This will be one of the first sustainable residential developments in the UK offered for private sale, with 50 of the 75 dwellings being offered to the public.

We predict that the completion of this development will be the starting point for many other national housebuilders offering buyers environmental houses. ❖

Photos: by Bree Day Partnership, show the 27 house scheme in Maidenhead, Berkshire.

Smoothing the planning process

For many, achieving planning consent is one of the most stressful parts of the building process. **Gideon Richards** suggests steps you can take that should help the process...

Firstly, it's important to remember that planners are not building regulation officers and there may be little communication between the two offices. Planners also have constraints that can appear barmy to the layperson, however, the rules have come from somewhere and the planners job is to interpret them. After saying planners have constraints, they also have a great deal of flexibility in interpreting the rules and guidelines.

The level of understanding about renewable energy and environmental issues and products varies widely among planners.

Planners, like all of us, have very different backgrounds and interests. What is important to you may not be a key driver to them! It isn't always about logic, unfortunately!

Here are a few simple guidelines. They may appear obvious and straightforward, however, planning departments often feel they are missing in many applications submitted.

First and foremost you should understand the issues and problems you are going to face with an application. Good communication and relationships with the planners can be essential.

Understanding the system

A bit of research, early on, will save you a lot of stress later. Find out what the local strategy for planning is based on. A good starting point is the Unitary Development Plan (UDP) and Local Planning Policies (LPP). These are usually published on the internet or can be provided by the local council. Attempting to get a consent that conflicts with these policies will immediately put your application at a disadvantage and probably set you up to fail.

Prior to completing your application form consider the information you think will benefit your application and TALK to the planners. This simple act will give you an immediate understanding of the planning officers' and the authorities' standpoint and the issues that your proposal faces and has to meet. More information, when laid out well, is better than less if it allows for better understanding of your intentions but please keep in mind that lots of information is no guarantee of overcoming the occasional immovable obstacles that can hinder some applications. There is no doubt that well constructed information that allows the planners to tick their appropriate boxes against relevant criteria can help things along.

The site

Do your homework. A good site appraisal will show more than where your boundaries and utilities are. It will also demonstrate that you have considered any potential impacts on the site, local community and the environment.

The planners always seek comment from other parties including neighbours, highways, parks authorities (in National Parks) and local or parish councils. There is no real order of importance in the interested parties but suffice to say that any single one of them can be highly influential in the outcome of your application. Strategic site access and services requirements will almost certainly need to be met or addressed. Ensure that the application takes these into consideration. For instance vehicular access to the site could be a hazard to pedestrians and other motorists. Choose your site access proposal carefully. It may be that you don't want or cannot get vehicular access. This could be a stumbling block but some very green minded people have successfully argued for and gained planning permission for houses where vehicles cannot

access.

The neighbours

Just remember it isn't only about planning officers approving the plan. There are many cases where planning officers have recommended approval but it has been overridden and rejected by the planning committee (elected representatives from the local council). The elected representatives have the final say, (except in an appeal against their decision which is decided by a representative of the Home Secretary). Why might the planning committee go against the recommendations of the planning officer? Usually this happens if they have been influenced by strong local protest against the proposal. The public, especially neighbours, can be powerful allies or enemies in a planning application. Do your utmost to get them on board with your ideas at an early stage. They have the right to inspect all applications and make observations. If they can understand what you are looking to achieve and the efforts that have been made to reduce the impact on others there should be less resistance. If there is strong local and neighbourly resistance to your application then treat it seriously. Try to negotiate acceptable modifications with neighbours before you make your application.

Strategic complications

Be prepared to accept that in some circumstances rigorous restrictions may be imposed on the development. There are many national, regional and local designations that can be put on land. For instance there is Green Belt (PPG2), Green Field / Brown Field (PPS3), Landscape Designation (Locally Assigned – PPS7), Green Corridors (Predominantly Rural, Ecology routes), listed-building, conservation areas, to name but a few. The restrictions and requirements that ascertain to all of these can easily be researched on the internet.

If your project is in a restricted area such as a National Park, Area of National Outstanding Beauty (AONB), Conservation area etc. then you will need to prove exceptional circumstances for your propsal. Having established early on what the designation of the area is or what the building's status is, a decision can be taken as to

whether you give up and find somewhere else or struggle on. If you do carry on then building that relationship with the appropriate authorities is going to be critical.

Be prepared to negotiate and adapt your proposal. If possible have the alternatives up your sleeve prior to any meeting. As a minimum know what your bottom line is going to be. A win-win will get you further than a win-lose invariably, as it can come back to haunt you.

Communication and professionals

If your proposal is complicated or very specialised and you believe that you will struggle to explain it effectively, it is worth considering hiring an architect or agent who is familiar and comfortable dealing with your type of project. Try and choose someone who already has a good relationship with the local planning department and you can work with. Don't be bullied into decisions. Take your time to consider all the implications and if necessary do your research.

Remember good drawings, descriptions of schemes and support information may make the difference between 'high quality' applications and average ones, especially if you are looking to do something special or different. Be careful, however, not to over-invest in pre-approval fees. Ask for a no-approval no fee arrangement. You may be shown the door but if a professional is confident and likes the look of your project then you might get a deal.

Don't drop your own research and choose your professional carefully. For instance when selecting an architect, ask how well does he or she know the planners / development controller for your area? A good architect will have a rapport with them. A bad architect who fails to understand the local requirements/protocol can be as good as pouring money your money down the drain. Ask for references from past clients, look at locally completed projects that they have designed and ask the opinion of the planning officer.

If you do choose a professional to represent your application then consider going along to the first meeting between them and the planning officer to see how they get on. Look for any problems early on before a lot of work has been put to paper. Put yourself in the planner's shoes

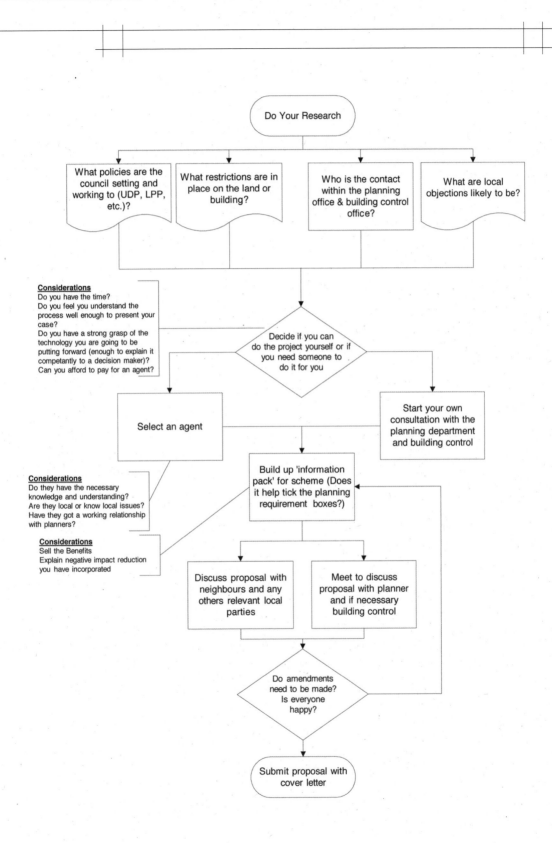

Do Your Research

What policies are the council setting and working to (UDP, LPP, etc.)?

What restrictions are in place on the land or building?

Who is the contact within the planning office & building control office?

What are local objections likely to be?

Considerations
Do you have the time?
Do you feel you understand the process well enough to present your case?
Do you have a strong grasp of the technology you are going to be putting forward (enough to explain it competantly to a decision maker)?
Can you afford to pay for an agent?

Decide if you can do the project yourself or if you need someone to do it for you

Select an agent

Start your own consultation with the planning department and building control

Considerations
Do they have the necessary knowledge and understanding?
Are they local or know local issues?
Have they got a working relationship with planners?

Build up 'information pack' for scheme (Does it help tick the planning requirement boxes?)

Considerations
Sell the Benefits
Explain negative impact reduction you have incorporated

Discuss proposal with neighbours and any others relevant local parties

Meet to discuss proposal with planner and if necessary building control

Do amendments need to be made? Is everyone happy?

Submit proposal with cover letter

and think through any possible objections and look at solutions or offer information in support of the benefits for your approach.

Explain why you have chosen the options you have. List the benefits that your project might have for the wider community. Remember in the language of planning – "cost is not a material planning consideration, however, impact on visual amenity and the environment are".

The submission

Submit a short letter outlining your proposal. This letter should help the planner tick the boxes needed to achieve the authority's objectives. Also sell the positives but don't ignore the negatives. If there are negatives face them head-on and explain the measures taken to mitigate and overcome them. If that's not possible have alternative solutions up your sleeve early on. Putting the positives in a way that meets planning needs helps them to promote the project to the planning committee. Remember to always explain the benefits of your project in a way that the planning officer can understand and buy-into.

Planners are humans. They can have good and bad days. They are not infallible and they do make mistakes and unfathomable decisions. Remember at the end of the day if you really don't agree with the decision there is an appeal's process. Hopefully by taking the above steps you'll have come to an agreement well before that.

Conclusion

The planning process can be confusing and frustrating. It is important you do your research thoroughly. Keep smiling and develop a rapport with your local planning officer.

Most planners are looking to reach a balanced, fair outcome. Most minor developments (home extensions and improvements) are generally supported by the planning system. You may find a staged approach to a development appropriate and less fraught with difficulties. However, you would need to weigh up the benefits of doing the improvements all at once or carrying out the work piecemeal.

Help them to help you achieve your planning consent by giving them adequate information, including the benefits, for them to support your

approval. Demonstrate that you have looked at all the scenarios and this is your preferred one. Explain why you consider your propsal is the best option.

Remember that there are a number of boxes (policy, local strategy and technical) that need to be ticked for your plans to be approved - providing as many of those ticks as possible could give you a positive outcome. ❖

Glossary

Unitary Development Plan – sets out a statutory framework for land-use to ensure consistent decision making. It aims to secure the most efficient and effective use of land in the public interest.

Local Planning Policy – These are also being incorporated into other framework documents, so ensure you identify what the policies are.

PPG – These are the government's Planning Policy Guidelines issued by the Office of the Deputy Prime Minister (ODPM), which give guidance to planning departments and the public on how the government's planning and development policies are interpreted. The revised equivalents to these are PPS Planning Policy Statements.

Checklist

- What local restriction are there?
  - UDP
  - LPP
  - Listed Building
  - Conservation Area
  - Green Belt
  - Green Field / Brown Field, etc.
- Who is your planning officer (PO)?
- Who is your building control officer (BCO)?
- Build a positive rapport
- How much do PO & BCO understand about renewable and sustainable buildings and energy?
- Have regular meetings to discuss your proposals
  - With PO
  - With BCO
  - With Neighbours
- Be prepared to compromise and negotiate
- If using an agent
  - Do they have knowledge and understanding of your project?
  - Are they local or have they an understanding of local planning constraints?
  - Do they have a good working relationship with the planner?
- Provide an 'information pack' to support your case
  - Explain what you have done to minimise any negative impacts
  - Demonstrate that you have ensured the planners can tick their consent requirements
- Write a cover letter that explains the project in a way that supports planning policy (i.e. This project supports the councils requirements to reduce CO_2 emissions by X through its use of Y)

THE NATURAL EVOLUTION OF INSULATION

Ochre Wool Thermal Insulation - Ochre Wool is a new type of building insulation that provides thermal and acoustic protection. Made using sheep's wool, the product is formed and thermally bonded to last a lifetime while providing superior protection.

AIR CONDITIONING - Wool fibres can remove moisture and dampness from a cold building warming the space faster. In very warm weather, this moisture is slowly released to cool the building.

ACOUSTIC INSULATION - Because of its structural durability and density, Ochre Wool Thermal Insulation also acts as an effective sound insulator with properties similar to Rockwool.

FLEXIBILITY - Ochre Wool Thermal Insulation is a durable, safe and effective insulation material. Safe to handle and fit without protection, Ochre Wool can be refitted and re-used as and when required.

For more information contact: Joulesave EMES

27 Water Lane, Sth. Witham, Grantham, NG33 5PH
Sales: (1443) 225-358 **Main:** (1572) 768-362
E: sales@joulesave.co.uk **Fax:** (1572)-767-146

www.ochre-wool.co.uk

Sustainability in forestry

Timber may be renewable but just how sustainable is our usage of this material? At the beginning of a new century the forestry industry is facing a crisis which has been building over many decades – news-broadcasts confront us with images of forest fires on a regional scale, destroying communities and hastening climate change. **Jerry Clark** summarises findings from 'The Forest Industry in the 21st Century' published by WWF

Around half of the world's original forest cover has been destroyed, largely during the latter half of the 20th Century. Unfortunately, the forest industry is heavily linked with this forest destruction, even though a large proportion of the clearance is for other purposes, including subsistence agriculture and beef ranching.

Globally, around 1.6 billion cubic metres of timber are currently harvested annually, and realistic estimates expect this to rise to 2.5 billion cubic metres by 2050. Can this level of extraction be sustained? Well, perhaps surprisingly, current research suggests that with responsible forest management a major crisis can be averted.

Current usage

Of the 1.6 billion cubic metres of wood currently harvested, well over a quarter of this is used by the USA. This may sound extravagant, and it probably is, but the USA is also the largest timber producer, making them almost self-sufficient in timber from their own forests (more than can be said for the UK). Unfortunately a proportion of this is still extracted from old growth forests near the west-coast. On a per-capita basis, the rest of the world has a timber consumption far less than the average American – for example, an American uses 15 times more than a Chinaman.

When we think of forests in crisis it is often in response to problems of extraction from tropical regions. Surprisingly, the harvest from Brazil is less than a quarter of that from the USA. Indonesia and Malaya together harvest about as much as Brazil. The difference is that a large proportion of North-American production is now from plantations – forests in the USA were massively replanted at the end of the 19th Century when they realised how little they had left after their initial colonisation of the country. Added to this, the area under forest in North-America and Europe is currently on the increase, whereas tropical forests are still declining.

Results of an analysis undertaken for the Worldwide Fund for Nature (WWF) shows that our current timber usage amounts to the productivity of just 20% of the world's forests. In simple terms this suggests that 80% of the world's forest cover could remain untouched. This is of course assuming that the current area of forest cover can be maintained. In theory, even the increased supply required by 2050 could be sustainably extracted from around a quarter of the world's forests, perhaps allowing us some cause for hope in the future.

Present threats

Unfortunately deforestation continues – of a world forest cover of 600 million hectares, some 9 million hectares are lost each year. The decline is actually greater than this in tropical forests, but losses are partly offset by planting in the northern-hemisphere. As regulations tighten, illegal logging is becoming the new challenge. Forest fires too are having an enormous impact, destroying tens of millions of hectares in the late 1990's. In Indonesia alone, 14 million hectares of forest and scrub were lost in 1997/98, leading to serious economic and health costs to around 70 million people. This burning is mostly deliberate, the main objective being a massive spread of oil palm plantations, implicating the greed of the processed food industry. Fires are not restricted to Southeast Asia; around 2.7 million hectares of forest were lost to fire in the USA in 2000.

Forest management

In general it is not currently known how well the world's forests are managed. We do know that many forests in developed countries are very well managed, delivering multiple economic and environmental benefits. We also know that illegal logging is widespread, and forest conversion to other uses contributes considerably to timber supply in many regions, but this can hardly be described as forest management. Many developing countries are managing to improve their forestry practises, often having the protective legislation in place, but perhaps falling a little short on enforcement. All this suggests that a significant proportion of global timber harvests come from 'managed' sources, although the quality of management can be highly variable. But, at least we can say that a significant proportion of production is from forests which are within reach of the ideal standard for responsible forestry. If the necessary improvements can be made to achieve sound management in these areas, then perhaps bad forestry can be squeezed out of the system as consumers and investors demand increased environmental performance, simultaneously making life harder for illegal operators.

Improving efficiency

The proportion of timber production coming from fast growing plantations (planting to harvesting less than 50 years) is rapidly increasing, currently producing 20% of requirements from 50 million hectares of plantation (only 0.33% of the world's land area). These plantations produce timber 5 to 10 times higher than the average forest yield. It is expected that this type of plantation will be supplying around half of the worldwide wood demand within the next 30 years, and the proportion will still be on the increase. Many of the older plantations are poorly established and have replaced natural forest, with all that implies for loss of biodiversity, but we are now seeing plantation establishment to new and higher standards, contributing considerably to future timber and fibre demands, while minimising environmental impact.

Improved silviculture in existing forests is also improving forestry efficiency, with 'low impact' logging making its way into many forests in the tropics and elsewhere. Better mapping and planning pre-harvest, and less wasteful post-harvest treatments are all helping. These improved practises have demonstrated their worth, with damage to the remaining forest reduced by half, and productivity increased by 20% leading to increased profitability.

More efficient wood conversion also helps to reduce impact on forests. Sawmills in the US and Europe can produce 70% of saleable wood from each log, and residual chips are used for particleboard. By contrast, the current figure in developing countries is nearer to 30%, with very little use of chips. If by transfer of technology we can double this efficiency figure, then only half the number of logs need be extracted or at least it will help keep up with demand.

The paper industry has also improved its efficiency, producing more paper from less wood.

Independent certification

WWF and many others believe independent certification is the answer to recognising good forest management and extending good practises to a greater area of forest. For this purpose they were instrumental in setting up the Forest Stewardship Council (FSC), providing a framework for standard setting and auditing to be applied worldwide. Most operators who have had to modify forest practises to achieve certification have since reaped social and economic benefits.

Studies show that the scale of the challenge of extending certification is manageable given appropriate leadership from industry and the green movement. The biggest producers and users have been identified, and many of these are already making moves in the right direction. There are now around 700 companies in the Global Forest and Trade Network committed to producing, trading or purchasing forest products certified as sustainably produced. This applies pressure to the remaining slightly more reticent companies to clean up their act or lose out as consumers spend elsewhere. If a proportion of the largest companies are brought on board, either producing or using only certified timber, then a critical mass will be created for the uptake of certification.

The basic expectations for a credible forest certification system

Certification is a process by which an independent third party gives written assurances that a product, process or service conforms to specified requirements. To be effective, forest certification must be based on:

- objective, comprehensive, independent and measurable performance-based standards - both environmental and social
- equal and balanced participation of a broad range of stake holders
- a labelling system that includes a credible chain of custody
- reliable and independent third party assessments and include annual field audits
- full transparency - to the parties involved and the public

It must also:

- take place at the forest management unit level (and not at country or regional level)
- be cost effective and voluntary
- positively demonstrate commitment from the forest owner/manager towards improving forest management
- be applicable globally and to all sorts of tenure systems, to avoid discrimination and distortion in the market place

Who to believe?

The Forests & European Resource Network (Fern) concludes that only the FSC delivers on every important component of a credible forest management certification system. Consequently, Fern consider the FSC to be the only available framework that meets the basic expectations outlined above. The FSC is therefore the only credible forest certification system that can be recommended to consumers or promoted among forest managers, policy makers and the public. ❖

Acknowledgements

This article is largely based on research commissioned by the WWF and published in a booklet entitled 'The Forest Industry in the 21st Century' as part of their Forests for Life campaign and they have recently launched an updated report entitle 'One Million Sustainable Homes' www.wwf.org.uk

Some of the above information is extracted from 'Behind the Logo'. The full report is availabe at www.fern.org *(follow links from campaigns/FSC)*

Sourcing and using timber

Timber is not without its environmental problems. Thanks to campaign groups such as Friends of the Earth and Greenpeace we are all aware of the deforestation and unsustainable logging practices that still exist in many parts of the world. **Keith Hall** offers a few suggestions on what timber to buy and how to avoid unnecessary treatments.

The tropical timber problems are perhaps the best known of the environmental concerns surrounding tiimber. Consequently use of unsustainably produced tropical timber has reduced in the UK. However, fewer people realise that unsustainable logging practices also exist in Northern industrialised countries. The solution is not to avoid using timber but to insist on timber and wood products that have come from certified, well managed forests. Yet how can we ensure that the timber we use does come from sustainable sources?

The **Forest Stewardship Council** (FSC) (tel 01686 413916 **www.fsc-uk.org**) set up by representatives from environmental groups and the timber industry was formed to provide an independent, international and credible labelling scheme for timber and timber products. This scheme takes into account how forests should be managed in a way which is environmentally appropriate and respects the interests of local and indigenous people but at the same time is economically viable. The actual inspection and evaluation of the forests is carried out by independent certification bodies such as the *Soil Association*. Once approved all wood and wood products from that forest are endorsed by the FSC and can bear its logo. Certified forests now exist in a growing number of countries, includ-

ing the UK. To be successful the scheme needs support. You can help by asking for timber and wood products that bear the FSC logo. Most wood supplied by builders and timber merchants has been imported into Britain from elsewhere. Under 15% of the total wood and wood products consumed in Britain each year come from British woodland. Most of this goes into agriculture and fencing yet much of it is highly suitable for use in buildings but is simply over-looked by merchants because supplies can be erratic and involve more legwork on their part to ensure throughput. If you are interested in purchasing timber in the round from local woodlands contact **Beacon Forestry** (01721 724788 **www.ecolots.co.uk www.certifiedtimber.co.uk**) who can provide contacts for FSC timber and locally grown timber throughout the UK.

Choose species carefully

Carefully select a timber species to suit its intended purpose. The **Timber Research and Development Agency** (TRADA) can give advice on this subject (01494 569600 **www.trada. co.uk**).

Avoid preservatives

Over the last 40 years we have witnessed the mass production of cheap synthetic insecticides, fungicides and organic solvents. Many have come (lindane, pentachlorophenol, tributaltinoxide) and gone due to their extreme toxicity. Unfortunately it seems that the homeowner and buildings are likely to be the guinea pigs that ascertain the true toxicity of the chemical cocktails that have been used over the years. Many toxic chemicals are only banned after the damage is done.

For many years now there has been an emphasis on treating internal timber, more often than not as a precautionary measure rather than an identified need. Many building societies (but thankfully not all now) still insist on treatment as a condition of a loan (usually based on a surveyor's report). Every year thousands of preservation companies place around 100 tons of toxic chemicals in buildings, endangering their own workers and the building occupiers, often with little justifiable reason.

By their very nature timber treatment systems have to be toxic in order to destroy fungi and insects. They cannot therefore be guaranteed safe. Many of the chemicals still approved for use in the UK by the Health and Safety Executive are banned or restricted in other countries. The toxic effects of these various chemicals are becoming well documented and can make frightening reading.

Practical avoidance

For new or replacement work, carefully select the most appropriate timber species and follow good design and building practice. This will help eliminate the need for chemical treatment. Roof tile battens and fascia boards may require treatment but use boron which is a natural mineral. For windows and doors most common softwood species may need treatment to meet the building regulations (but not those categorised as durable). You should note that current UK building regulations **DO NOT** require timber of any species to be treated when used for internal carpentry or joinery except bathroom and kitchen floors that are made of chipboard. This can be overcome by using solid timber instead.

Renovation work in old buildings frequently uncovers some degree of fungal or insect attack to existing timbers. In these cases the cause of the attack (symptoms) should first be established and rectified (finding and sorting leaks and sources of damp; adjusting temperature, ventilation etc). In many instances environmental control will solve the problem but do bear in mind that, for example, the life cycle of woodworm is three years so results may not be instant. There are companies that specialise in environmental controls. In some cases badly infested timber may need to be carefully cut out and replaced with sound timber. Only replace timber when absolutely necessary and then try to use reclaimed timber of a similar age and species. Where treatment is unavoidable use a boron-based treatment. Inorganic borate has low mammalian toxicity, is a naturally occurring mineral and has a long history of use.
If you must treat timber, then always:
● get at least three quotations
● ensure that all health risks are fully considered prior to finalising a contract
● insist on boron based systems only. ❖

Have confidence in wood windows

There is growing public awareness that timber must be sourced carefully to preserve this natural resource. Manufacturers have been rethinking sourcing and other environmental issues as a result. **Peter Kaczmar**, discusses the pros and cons of environmentally friendly finishes for windows...

Concerned about sustainability, today's consumer might be forgiven for thinking twice before choosing timber windows. They might also have concerns that timber windows need intensive maintenance regimes that could carry hidden costs. However, with modern production and finishing techniques, nothing could be further from the truth: manufacturers have worked with political, economic and legislative factors to change things for the better for the consumer.

Drivers such as the Environmental Protection (Prescribed Processes and Substances) Regulations of 1991 have led to a shift by the joinery industry to using 'safer', alternative preservatives with much lower toxicity. Manufacturers have also paid heed to performance expectations, adopting an 'holistic' approach to the specification of all materials used, and giving due attention to better component design.

Today, a joinery manufacturer will build into his design instructions a very wide range of factors. For instance, which timber species should be used, chosen on the basis of its durability, dimensional stability and above all its sustainability and environmental impact. The design specification of the window would provide instructions regarding appropriate water shedding and anti-capillary details. It would incorporate end grain priming of components prior to assembly as standard practice - and include instructions on the most appropriate adhesives, glazing system and coating as necessary.

The wood coatings sector has also responded to environmental demands by reducing solvent content and developing high-solids coatings and improved water-borne formulations with lower dirt retention characteristics.

However, the expectation of higher performance and sustainability carries with it its own demands. Prefinishing of external joinery has many advantages which offer the end user a very high quality product. But in order for the end user to benefit from that quality, there needs to be a parallel responsibility by the construction industry to handle and use pre-finished joinery in a manner which reflects this value. Sadly, it is all too common to see pre-finished windows thrown around on site at the hands of ill-informed site labour.

There are ways of ensuring that the products (windows and doors) are given adequate protection until the point of hand-over. This may require the adoption of such practice as installing windows into openings built around pre-fabricated plastic or wooden formers.

The joinery and wood coatings industries have shown that they can both respond positively to change through a process of integration and closer co-operation. It is only by further extending this approach, working with the installers, going beyond the manufacturing operation into the building process and above all meeting and addressing the requirements and concerns of the consumer, that these industries will secure their rightful place on the evolutionary ladder of success. ❖

The Timber Research and Development Association (TRADA) can advise on timber species choice, finishing and installation issues - all visitors to the TRADA website may register free of charge to gain access to the core technical information on the askTRADA website.

TRADA 01494 569600 **www.trada.co.uk**

Sustainable roofing

In these days of greater concern about climate change, and the use of energy which leads to it, some people will be surprised to learn that 50% of all energy use is caused directly by buildings. This means that addressing the issue of energy efficiency in buildings is now of paramount importance. **Jerry Clark** summarises a report carried out for Lafarge ...

Of the energy consumed in buildings, 90% is used by the building and its occupants and 10% is the embodied energy, i.e. the energy used to manufacture or extract the raw materials for the building components of which the building itself is built.

It is, however, widely recognised that vast improvements can be made in building structures and insulation levels, which could easily reduce in-use energy by 75%. This would make the energy embodied in the fabric of the building of far greater significance.

The following is a brief list of the functions a roofing system can or could perform:

- shelter from the rain and possible rainwater collection
- shade from the sun and UV protection
- skylights for daylighting deep within buildings
- surface for energy collection, solar hot water and photovoltaics
- roof form designed to minimise wind turbulence
- wind driven stack ventilation
- thermal and environmental barrier
- space for insulation
- green roof for wildlife or recreation

Getting the design of the roof and the rest of the building envelope right will give the greatest benefits in terms of reduced energy use. But which roofing materials carry the least embodied energy? Which are better in terms of other pollution emissions and which are more likely to be recycled / reclaimed at the end of the life of the building?

Roofing materials

First a little about the manufacturing processes of the various roof cladding materials.

Clay tiles are manufactured from kaolinite clay with various additives. The minerals are vitrified to bind the tiles at a high firing temperature in excess of 1100°C, apparently the higher the temperature the longer the life of the tile. However, the high temperatures involved lead to a high embodied energy.

Concrete tiles are made in the proportions of 1:4 Portland cement and aggregate. Mixing and chemical curing take place in temperature controlled conditions.

Natural slate was formed within the Earth's crust many millions of years ago when mudstones were subjected to colossal heat and pressure, causing partial recrystalisation of the minerals during a process known as metamorphosis. These rocks are split along natural seams to produce the roofing slates.

Steel is produced from mined iron ore, coke and limestone melted together in a high temperature furnace. The coke turns to carbon monoxide reducing the iron oxide to iron. Approximately 25% scrap material is used in the final steel making process.

Aluminium is extracted from its bauxite ore by a highly energy intensive process, but outside the UK this process is often powered by hydro-electricity. Within the UK a large proportion of aluminium is from recycled feedstock, which gives the product a much lower embodied energy (see table).

Bitumen is the residual material produced after removal of all the volatile products from crude oil, such as petrol and diesel.

Asphalt is manufactured from bitumen blended with limestone powder and fine limestone aggregate. Another source is lake asphalt, a naturally occurring material mainly imported from Trinidad. Asphalt tiles make up 75% of the US roofing market, but unfortunately these products have low durability.

Timber shingles are riven or sawn from suitable timber such as oak or western red cedar.

In the table (next page), the figures in the first two columns refer to a square metre of roof cladding material, making it easy to compare various materials.

Embodied pollution

Another important aspect of sustainability which is difficult to encapsulate in the above table is that of the pollution caused during manufac-ture and supply of the various materials. The Embodied Energy column in the table gives a good indication of the relative quantities of carbon dioxide produced during manufacture, but says nothing of all the other more toxic pollutants. It is recommended that materials should be selected to perform the set task while minimising all impacts, including pollution.

Direct comparisons of the various pollution risks are difficult to make, but the following gives a rough indication of the kinds of pollutants involved.

Though the embodied energy is high, there are few toxicity issues involved in the manufacture of clay tiles. Concrete has a lower embodied energy, but greater toxicity in its emissions. The main pollution issues with steel roofing are the dioxins produced during smelting, and the pollutants produced in the manufacture of the

Environmental Criteria for Selection of Roofing Materials

	Embodied Energy (1) (MJ/m²)	Weight(kg/m²)	Life(years)	Material Resources	Recyclability
Clay tiles	270 – 430	40 – 60	30 – 100	Abundant	Good
Concrete tiles	40 – 90	40 – 90	30 – 100	Abundant	Good
Natural slates	130 – 290	20 – 30	100+	150 (Welsh)	Very good
Coated steel	180 – 160	7	30	300	Fair
Aluminium (virgin)	550 – 920	<10	100+	230	Good
Aluminium (recycled)	30 – 90	<10	100+	260	Good
Asphalt shingles	285	low	20 – 30	75	Poor
Timber shingles	very low	low	50	renewable	Fair
Membrane structures	high	very low	15 – 25	75	Poor

usual PVC (Plastisol) coating. PVC manufacture involves considerable amounts of chlorine (a nerve gas) and results in the release of further dioxins when the steel is recycled. The main problems with aluminium (although it can have a high recycled content) are the very high energy costs when using virgin material, and the unnecessary use of polyester powder coatings to colour the sheets. Lead and copper both have a high degree of corrosion resistance, but their use for large areas of roofing can lead to a degree of contamination in the rainwater runoff. Copper is extracted from sulphide ores and the mining process is associated with pollution of waterways by heavy metals.

Bitumen and asphalt systems are renowned for their short product life. Due to their being very difficult to recycle, this leads to further use of precious oil reserves, unless an alternative replacement material is used. Both slate and shingles have no pollution implications apart from that involved in extraction and transport.

Conclusions

From the above it can be seen that the most sustainable options for roof cladding are timber shingles, closely followed by natural slate, as long as these materials are obtained from a local source (or at least within the same country).

After this, selection can be made on the basis of embodied energy, pollution and length of life. Consideration can also be given to recyclability, and it is likely that slates, concrete and clay tiles will be available second hand somewhere quite local. ❖

References

Woolley, Kimmins, Harrison and Harrison, Green Building Handbook, E&FN Spon, 1997, available from The Green Shop, **www.greenshop.co.uk** 01452 770629

Acknowledgements

Most of the information in this article is based on 'A Guide to Sustainable Roofing' published by Redland Roofing Systems (now Lafarge Roofing).

The report was carried out by XCO2.
A downloadable version of the report is available from the XCO2 website - **www.xco2.com**

Who goes on green building courses?

Green building is having an uncanny attraction to people from very diverse backgrounds. The more the merrier we say. Just to encourage you to think of getting your hands dirty we sent **Barbara Tremain** along to mingle with the trainees at an eco-construction and design course at the Centre for Alternative Technology. Her mission... to find what had attracted them to the course and what they intend to do with their new-found knowledge afterwards ...

Occupations of the attendees were diverse - architects, TV programme makers, university lecturers, ecologists, eco self-builders, mainstream builders, Phd students, garden designers, commercial & private projecteers, (self builders working on their own projects) eco-warriors, (yes they still exist) local authority employees, eco-village designers, artists, permaculturists, career changers, downshifters and the generally curious.

Among the course tutors were the UK's best loved green building double act - architect, **Pat Borer**, who designed most of the buildings at CAT, and builder **Cindy Harris**, who built most of them. They were ably assisted by Blanche Cameron, Judith Thornton, Ian Taylor and Rob Gwillim.

With this line up we were certain to have lots of very educational fun over the next few days. Subjects on the menu included 'design strategies for sustainable buildings', 'the healthy house', 'legislation and standards' as well as touching on transport issues, sustainable cities, economic, social and political issues.

Even with my cover broken, we all quickly shared a great rapport, laughing, networking, sharing new ideas, and forming friendships. The lecturers were enjoying themselves too, delivering their subjects in an informative, engaging and often amusing way. They must really like what they do.

Help and advice abounded, an experienced architect was even spotted supporting a trainee architect, who had been encouraged by a client to go on the course (message there).

As expected, 'After hours' people socialised mainly in the local pubs but some went walking together, enjoying the beautiful setting, they said, despite the challenging weather conditions of North Wales.

C.A.T is a great place to see practical examples of what we were being taught. Probably unique in this respect but not for long if some of the students I talked to have their way. They say copying is the best form of flattery.

This place is great because it has been developed by trial and error. This is what real learning is all about and by pioneers who started almost thirty years ago (some of our tutors were there at the start), and they display no arrogance but have a continued willingness to keep learning and to accept constructive criticism. The absolute absence of 'wooliness' was refreshing.

There was a clear encouragement from the lecturers for us, after the course, to become more involved publicly with legislation, planning and lobbying; to join or form groups to further sustainability in whichever way is appropriate for the individual.

I took the opportunity to take a few of the participants to one side and wheedle out of them their action plans for post course:

Adrian Davis works as a Director of 'Wildoutdoors', an organisation focusing on ecology, running & cycling holidays. He has over 20 year's experience in the environmental field, including work as an Ecological Consultant and as an Area Officer with Scottish Natural Heritage.

Adrian said that the Eco-Construction &

Design Course at C.A.T was just what he really needed, although he would have appreciated a few more examples.

He felt over all it was very good, and especially enjoyed learning from Rob Gwillim about building integrated renewable energy systems.

Adrian came on the course because he is hoping to develop an eco-building environmental holiday centre in Scotland. He created a rough design during the last day and will be seeking the right architect to join the project.

This would be a natural continuation of the ecology and wildlife theme; Wildoutdoors, in partnership with the Natural Trust of Scotland is planning to develop a suitable site to demonstrate sustainable building and ways of living. The Centre and the activities there exemplifying the green concept of minimising the impact of lifestyles upon the planet and the body by taking responsibility for self and the environment, creating health, fitness, balance and wellbeing.

When the present issues of site location and planning permission are overcome, Adrian and his team intend to self-build the Centre, and are looking for experienced craftsmen, including a joiner working with green timber, to help complete the project.

Lorely Lloyd is studying Spatial Design at Falmouth College of Art. She is currently working with the Falmouth Green Centre, and is an Independently elected member of Falmouth Town Council. Lorely recognizes a need for a cohesive network in Cornwall for those involved in and wishing to learn about sustainability, green living and eco pro-activism.

Lorely first visited C.A.T about 15 years ago and enjoyed revisiting to do the course. The Centre represents to her a model of setting up sustainable businesses and she sees it as a great information resource.

The course helped her gain a whole picture of design principles, which are in keeping with the high sustainability focus maintained at Falmouth College, and in her own life.

Lorely's studies include interior landscape, and community building, featuring capacity building where people are fully involved in creating and working with their own particular communities.

She is also interested in creating eco-villages in Britain, and co-housing projects.

She was inspired by Blanche Cameron's positive attitude towards the wonderful sense of community in tenement built areas with neighbourliness, shared outdoor spaces and the actual sustainability of terraced houses.

The diverse cross section of course attendees surprised and encouraged Lorely.

She commented on how the high level of practical information available at C.A.T was gained entirely from experience and how progress is being made through considered compromise based on sustainable ethical principles - a holistic methodology constantly evolving and responding to changing times.

Lorely is continuously developing her own ideas, integrating the information she gained from the course. She uses these principles all the time at college and is benefiting from the way that C.A.T has helped her consolidate her own ideas. The information she has in her folder from the course is a source of inspiration for the other students and lecturers at college.

Helen Sanders is a Chartered Building Surveyor working for Leeds City Council Housing Department. At her persuasion her employers kindly covered the cost of her attending the course.

She plans to apply what she learnt to the large scale refurbishment of council housing, upgrading housing and eco-interpreting the building regulations (which is very possible).

The subject of better Insulation is her particular interest. She sees this as the No.1 social benefit that the residents will appreciate most, helping them to use less fuel, reduce their bills and help the environment at the same time. Poverty is a serious issue in Leeds Helen says.

Helen will be taking back information from the course about external insulation, and applying it to existing concrete tenement blocks. External insulation involves the cladding of the outside of the building with insulation, then adding a scrim and render finish or a proprietary rainscreen which could be any variety of materials depending on budget. External insulation is not the cheapest option but it is the best.

Helen felt that her work posed different problems from many of the other course attendees.

She found it interesting that the lecturers favoured mains electricity, water, and effluent disposal in most cases. It just needs to be 'greened' up. She has visions of putting solar panels across the rooftops of council houses in Leeds. I'll be looking for them next time I pass through.

She would like to install wood frame double glazed windows instead of UPVC, but says that a she cannot find a supplier in the UK or Europe who can meet the very large order quantities, (*sounds odd. ed*). "Leeds has a UPVC manufacturing unit that employs disabled people, and if that should close it would cause further social problems". Helen's personal thoughts are that corporations are slow to change, and she hopes that small progression will eventually lead to large scale positive influences.

John Packer is a sculptor. He is working mainly in metal, creating freestanding artworks, railings and grills with an artistic function. Recent works include a bridge for Surestart in Minehead, sculptures for the Celtic Otherworld Garden designed by Mira Engler at Westonbirt, and artworks for public community regeneration projects at Capricorn Quay and Georges Square in Bristol.

He went on the course at C.A.T because of his involvement with a South West based Eco-Village project. Though this is still in its inception stages. He is inspired by the many eco-building influences on architectural design, and wants to develop his own work following these influences. Professionally John wants to be more aware of the environmental impact that his choice of materials have. Currently he uses mostly steel.

John is trying to reassess his whole career from the perspective of what he describes as the unfolding nightmare of global warming.

He asked "How can sculpture have a positive effect environmentally speaking?" "Is there a way I can influence people by direct, indirect or artistic means with my work and skills?".

Leroy Pierre was a larger than life, charismatic, liquorice stick chewing, young eco warrior. He is enthusiastic about alternative lifestyles and seeking experiences. He is a radical broad minded thinker, constantly pursuing new ideas and concepts.

Congenial and easy going, Leroy was fun, entertaining and good company during mealtimes and the social side of the group's activities. We enjoyed listening to his unusual adventures, dreams, and stories of festivals, communities and mixing with other 'on the edge' people. Leroy was one of the many who asked stimulating questions, eliciting responses that educated all present. Not sure what his plans were after the course though.

Andre Tulder has a degree in Recreation and Ecology (NZ) and has worked in Washington State USA with the US Forest Service on a trail crew during an internment programme in the Cascade Mountains.

Currently Andre is involved in renovating and reconstructing mainly stone walled houses in Las Alpujarras in S.E Spain. He arrived in that area as a WWOOFer (Willing Worker on Organic Farms) . There are a growing number of alternative thinkers living in that area, and this appeals to him.

Andre travelled to the course at C.A.T seeing it as an opportunity for gaining new ideas and knowledge - greater than he can learn from books alone. He was keen to learn first hand knowledge from practical leaders and inspired pioneers of 'eco-ness'. He also wanted to meet others who are doing similar things working in associated fields, consequently gaining varied perspectives that are not normally found, along with new ideas and fresh perspectives. Also he looked forward to having a good laugh!

He gained much more from the course than he expected. More than just the practical elements of building, he learnt about the design and product philosophies, and a working overview of issues relating to eco-building and eco-houses.

Andre was surprised at the great diversity of the working backgrounds of the people on the course. It has been a fabulous resource for him, far greater than he imagined. He found it very enriching to see and hear other perspectives.

He has the opportunity to be the builder in charge of a pioneering 'eco-conscious' new build near Orgiva. To his

knowledge this will be the first attempt at this kind of project in that region. The main problem is that none of the sustainable materials required are available there. ❖

New training Centre underway

Plans for the development of C.A.T include The Wales Institute for Sustainable Education (W.I.S.E). State of the art educational facilities at the cutting edge of sustainable building are being designed for the on-site project.

CAT has a wide range of green building courses including:

Eco Footprinting

Heating your home with Wood

The Whole House

Wind Power

Solar Electric Systems

Solar Water Heating

Working with Willow

Alternative Sewage Systems

Call CAT on 01654 705981
courses@cat.org.uk

Other course venues can be found in the resource section at the back of this book.

To renovate or re-develop

It is important to identify the causes of obsolescence at the outset to ensure that the renovated building does not perpetuate the original shortcomings. If a building is to be retained and renovated it may be necessary to look at a change of use as the only way to overcome obsolescence.
Adrian Birch reports...

Buildings become obsolete for a variety of reasons:

* Physically	- physical deterioration of the structure and fabric
* Functionally	- the original purpose no longer exists
* Technologically	- does not perform as well as modern alternatives
* Geographically	- often as a result of infrastructure changes
* Economically	- when occupation is not the cheapest alternative
* Socially and legally	-as a result of changes in legislation

Levels of renovation

There are several levels of renovation. These are shown in order of complexity:-

1. Fabric repairs and consequential making good.
2. Upgrading of common parts - toilets, lift, reception.
3. Upgrading of vacant floors- might include provision of suspended ceilings, data cabling, carpets, packaged air-conditioning systems, redecoration.
4. A combination of any or all of the above. All can be undertaken whilst tenants remain in occupation.
5. Fabric repairs and comprehensive renovation to include:
   * refurbishment / renewal of lift(s).
   * refurbishment / renewal of mains services installations.
   * provision of access floors/ screed trunking for data and power supplies.
   * provision of new ventilation/cooling/ heating/lighting.
   * new ceilings, decoration, carpets, toilets, kitchens.
   * internal re-planning to increase lettable area.
   * upgrading to meet current legislation, where necessary.
6. Reconstruction - this would include most of the items at 5 above plus:
   * over-cladding or stripping back to the frame and re-cladding following any strengthening works
   * modifications to the structure to significantly increase lettable areas.
   * extensions; provision of a unique selling point - conservatory, atrium, entrance, roof garden.

Advantages and disadvantages of renovation

A renovated office building has a number of advantages over a new- build.

* The initial embodied energy expended in construction is largely retained.
* Less waste generated, normally less energy is consumed in the process.
* Normally generates less environmental pollution than new-build.
* The process is normally quicker than redevelopment, reducing site overhead costs and interest charges and permitting earlier occupation and income flow.
* Planning permission and listed building Consent may not be necessary.
* Where permission is required, the planners may be more sympathetic towards extension.
* Planning policies may be more restrictive for new-build, which would need to conform to current policies on plot ratio, parking provision, height etc.
* Where the building is occupied, certain works can be done with tenants remaining in place. Disruption to tenants may be minimised if the work is properly planned, with noisy operations outside working hours. Overall, this can be cost-effective for both owner and occupier.

However there are disadvantages.

* The building may require major repairs, underpinning etc.
* The building may contain asbestos or other 'deleterious materials'.
* Existing mains services are likely to be inadequate.
* Existing drainage systems may be inadequate.
* Rent and yield are unlikely to be as competitive as for a new-build.
* The orientation of the building may not maximise passive solar design.
* Overshadowing by other buildings may limit daylight and passive solar benefits.
* Inner-city pollution may necessitate a sealed air-conditioned building.
* The internal layout may be inefficient by current standards.
* The building structure may require strengthening and/or repair.

* The wall-to-wall depth may be too great for cross-ventilation.
* The floor to ceiling height may be too low to permit raised access floors.
* Concrete downstand beams may inhibit service runs and duct provision.
* There are likely to be inaccuracies and shortcomings in the construction.
* Daylight provision may be poor, conversely,
* Extensive glazing may lead to glare and excessive heat gains/losses.
* Extensive alterations may be necessary to meet current health & safety and disability access legislation.

The need for a feasibility study

Before financial commitment is entered into, a feasibility study should be prepared by a suitably experienced person or organisation and should ideally encompass all or most of the following, where time and funds permit.

* A detailed report on the structure, fabric, components and services.
* An environmental assessment report, asbestos report, mining reports etc.
* A desk study to identify the planning history, extracts from the local plan and any comments raised by the planners following an initial meeting.
* A report to identify capacity and location of underground services, drains.
* Measured survey drawings of the site and building(s).
* A series of initial sketch schemes identifying alternative layouts/uses.
* Initial cost estimates based on sketch schemes and likely specification.
* A residual valuation of each alternative, with a sensitivity analysis of each.
* A property market report indicating supply and demand patterns for the use being proposed.

Only when this and other financial information has been collated can risk be assessed. Further detailed investigation of the structure and fabric may be necessary. The feasibility study should attempt to demonstrate a comparative analysis of the renovation/redevelopment options, when time and other factors are included. >>>

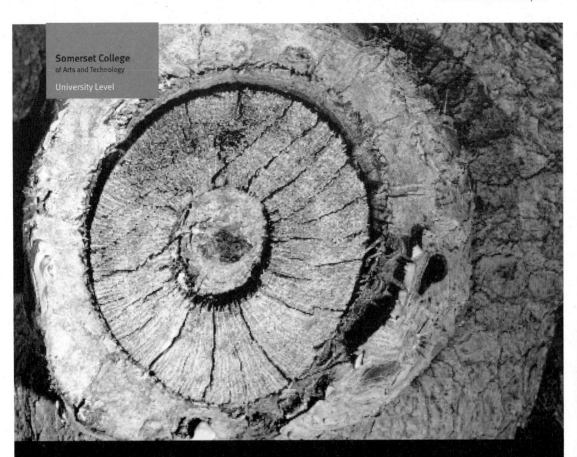

Somerset College
of Arts and Technology

University Level

Foundation Degree
Sustainable Development: Construction

This unique qualification takes a solid grounding in good construction methods, combined with a study of sustainable techniques and issues to provide you with the knowledge required for a successful career at the cutting edge of the construction industry.

This is an industry led vocational qualification that has been devised with the direct involvement of leading professionals and employers who have identified the skills and knowledge they want from the graduates they employ.

On completion you can study for a full honours degree by undertaking a third, final year at the University of Plymouth.

Available full-time (3 days per week over 2 years) or part-time (1 day and 1 evening per week over 3 years). This course includes 4 week long residentials and a work placement module. A Higher National Certificate qualification is also available.

To find out more, call Kirstie Slocombe on **01823 366 344** or email **construction@somerset.ac.uk**

Genesis, the sustainable construction centre for the South West is under construction at the College during 2005. Keep an eye on the Genesis website **www.genesisproject.com** for details and news.

UNIVERSITY
OF PLYMOUTH·COLLEGES
SOMERSET

Wellington Road Taunton Somerset TA1 5AX
T 01823 366 366   www.somerset.ac.uk

Change of use

30 years ago there was a trend to convert elegant townhouses to office use. Today the trend is reversed. With the ongoing demand for new housing, offices in secondary locations may be more valuable if converted to residential use. The corresponding growth in higher education has also created a demand for student housing and it is no coincidence that in many university cities, redundant offices have been converted to student accommodation. Increased inward tourism has also generated demand for budget hotels in many cities. Again redundant offices may be suitable for such a change of use, where strong demand exists.

The local planners should be consulted early in the process to determine their views on a change of use before following this route. There are particular issues regarding fire resistance, compartmentation and means of escape in case of fire that must be addressed, as well as matters such as car parking, amenity space, availability of food shops etc.

When assessing offices for renovation or redevelopment the change of use option must not be ignored.

Design constraints

Apart from major defects to the structure or fabric, one of the main constraints upon renovating existing office buildings is the floor to ceiling height. In 60s and 70s buildings the height was usually less than 3 metres, with concrete downstand beams reducing the effective height to no more than 2.7 metres. It is virtually impossible to fit traditional ducted ventilation and air conditioning systems at ceiling level and provide an adequate raised access floor, whilst maintaining a floor to ceiling height of 2.6 metres in the occupied zone.

Some renovation schemes incorporate ducts externally or have extended floors outwards to permit ducts to be incorporated at the building's perimeter. Alternatively, localised heat pumps or fan-coil systems (fan assisted heat exchangers) can be used, relying on heated and chilled water to serve ceiling or wall-mounted cassettes to temper and recirculate the air in a space. An alternative is to use the raised access floor as a huge duct or plenum, with floor-mounted fan coils.

All these traditional approaches require heavy investment in fans, ducts and chiller plant. Where buildings can be naturally ventilated, this has to be the best option. Many renovated buildings are 'mixed mode' buildings where mechanical ventilation is used to assist the natural ventilation as required. This is cost-effective in winter if heat reclaim systems are incorporated. These do not have to be complex and many 'through the wall' fans can incorporate heat reclaim devices. Summer cooling can be a problem, but 'packaged' air conditioning systems should be avoided as they consume excessive amounts of electricity. They may be acceptable where there are isolated areas of internal heat gain, such as office equipment spaces.

Environmental assessment tools

An initial comparative analysis can be undertaken using software produced by the BRE (**www.bre.co.uk**). This is free to use and provides ecopoints for each strategy adopted. It is relatively simple to use and will give a relatively simple printout.

The BRE Environmental Assessment Method, (BREEAM) has been in use for 14 years and provides a more sophisticated approach. This applies to new and renovated buildings as well as empty offices and is divided into two main sections: Design and Procurement, and Management and Operation (**www.breeam.org**). This provides designers with a more detailed checklist. The design will be externally assessed, and if receiving an 'excellent' rating, a renovated building may compete more favourably with a new building.

It is difficult to obtain accurate information on how many projects are assessed in this way. It was designed by BRE to help market energy efficient buildings but has yet to be universally adopted by developers and owner-occupiers. All government projects are assessed, and it may be that all non-domestic buildings exceeding 1000m^2 will require such assessment as part of the new EC Directive.

BRE have also produced a more detailed software package which is used by BREEAM assessors and others to obtain more accurate predictions of energy consumption and CO_2 generation. ❖

A strategic approach to eco-office renovation

For environmental design a holistic approach is essential, whether for a new-build or renovation. The external fabric of the building acts as a climatic filter, allowing light, air and solar gain in, and allowing polluted air out. Openings such as windows and vents provide fine control of the airflow. When assessing an existing building, various strategies need to be considered both individually and collectively in order to reach an optimum environmental solution. This then, says **Adrian Birch**, has to be tested alongside other criteria such as initial and lifecycle costs, time, buildability, risk etc.

Fabric Strategy

Insulation

In the UK climate, the type and location of insulation can have a major effect on the demand for energy and the performance of the building.

External insulation utilises the thermal storage capacity of the structure and fabric, but needs to be protected from the weather and from impact damage. Only certain types of insulation are suitable for external application, and most organically derived insulants may be unsuitable if wetted. Openings require attention to detail.

Internal insulation is less costly to fit but can cause disruption and will reduce room sizes. It can also cause 'interstitial' condensation affecting the performance of the external fabric, which will remain cold in the winter months.

Cavity insulation is often seen as the best of both worlds, particularly if retro-fitted to existing claddings such as cavity brickwork. However, problems can occur if water subsequently penetrates to the inner skin of the wall. It should only be undertaken where the site is relatively sheltered and the building is low to medium rise. The quality of the external skin should be assessed as it will be subject to greater fluctuations of temperature than before, and if porous could suffer from frost damage.

Over-cladding and re-cladding

Many older buildings leak - most often from defects to flat roofs, at junctions with windows, or if constructed of prefabricated cladding panels, around panel joints. Wall and roof junctions are particularly vulnerable. There are several possible repair options depending upon the form of construction. One way to deal with this is to remove the cladding (if possible) and start again. This is usually quite costly and usually requires the building to be empty. An alternative is over-cladding, where a lightweight rainscreen cladding system of steel, aluminium, or fibre cement is fitted to a metal sub-frame over the existing cladding. These systems are designed to shed the water either by 'drainage and back ventilation' or by 'pressure equalisation'. Cavity insulation is normally incorporated between new and existing claddings. It has the added advantage of being capable of being fitted whilst tenants remain in occupation. The disadvantage is that it will increase the load on the structure and foundations and if fitted to a prefabricated panel system will increase the load on the original panel fixings. If the original cladding is concrete, tests of the concrete are necessary to ensure it has not 'carbonated' to an extent where it could fail within the lifetime of the over-cladding system. Fire stopping is also required to the cavity.

Openings

If windows and other components are poorly fitted in openings then heat losses will occur due to cold bridging or air leakage. The more complex the construction, the greater the probability of leakage. Building Regulations L2 give guidance on what is required.

Lighting strategy

By increasing the availability of natural lighting it should be possible to minimise demand for artificial lighting and its associated heat gains. The difficulty of course is that natural light is variable and sunlight is directional, and problems can arise with glare when the sun is at a low altitude. The orientation of the building is critical. A lighting strategy must take all these elements into account. Sensors and switching should be designed to provide close control of artificial lighting components if energy is to be saved and heat gain minimised.

Glare can normally be controlled by specialist glass or Venetian blinds. Electrically operated internal and external blinds have a poor track record and can cause maintenance problems. Certain inter-pane blinds are to be avoided as they reduce the amount of natural light. Manually operated systems are the least troublesome but tend to be less liked by occupiers, who have to get up from their desk and operate them! There can be problems with poorly selected windows fouling blind systems. Cleaning can also be a problem.

Solar heat gain can be controlled by specialist glass or externally located shades or blinds above windows. Solar reflective glass can present problems, as there is a loss of daylight, resulting in the need for artificial lighting and consequen-

tial internal heat gains. Specialist films can be applied to existing windows, but are prone to delamination if incorrectly applied.

Ventilation strategy

The occupational density of offices can vary considerably depending upon the nature of the activity taking place. Meeting rooms and call centres with 24-hour occupancy have different environmental and ventilation requirements from an executive's office that is partially occupied. Where occupational density is high there may be a requirement for mechanical ventilation and cooling, for all others natural ventilation may be possible and for health reasons, desirable.

Air flows from high pressure to low pressure and for buildings this normally means from windward to leeward (to borrow a nautical expression!). The greater the pressure drop the greater the potential air speed. As a rule of thumb single-sided ventilation (i.e. to cellular offices), works optimally where the depth does not exceed 2.5 times the clear height. For cross-ventilation (to open plan offices) the rule of thumb is 5 times the clear height. As floor to ceiling heights in many older office buildings are in the region of 3 metres the maximum window-to-window distance across the building should not exceed 15 metres for natural ventilation to operate. Luckily many 60s buildings are quite narrow and would be suitable for cross ventilation, all things being equal. In many city locations air and noise pollution may prevent effective natural ventilation unless the building is 20 metres or so from the roadway or shielded from traffic by other buildings or trees.

One particular benefit is night ventilation. If windows remain open overnight in summer the cooler night air will cool the building down, particularly if the concrete ceilings are exposed and act as heat exchangers. The building can be pre-cooled for the following day using sensors and meteorological data. There are obviously security considerations together with motorised control of night vents to be considered in the design of such a window system. Low velocity extract fans are normally incorporated so as to purge the building of stale warm air.

Another way of benefiting from natural ventilation is by harnessing the natural buoyancy of heated air (the stack effect) by the creation of vertical ducts within the building drawing warmed polluted air up and out, to be replaced by cooler fresher air at lower levels. Atria fulfil this function. With existing buildings the scope for providing a glazed atrium may be limited, nevertheless there are several proprietary stack ventilation systems that can be retro-fitted into existing buildings, incorporating fans if necessary and/or 'light pipes' to duct natural light to dark interiors.

One of the simplest forms of natural ventilation is the provision of trickle vents to windows. These are manually controlled or can be motorised in more sophisticated systems. Alternatively 'through the wall' vents can be retrofitted, with sensor-controlled or fan assisted variants available, as well as a heat reclaim capability.

Mechanical ventilation and cooling strategy

One of the main problems in recent years with both new and renovated offices has been internal heat gain generated by people, lights, computers and other business equipment. This has been resolved to some extent by developments in technology, with new generations of lighting and computers giving off far less heat. Servers and other office equipment will require cooling and these can usually be located away from the occupied zone and can be locally air-conditioned, if necessary.

Fans, chiller plant and the like consume large amounts of electrical energy and if a building has been properly designed their use should be minimised. Nevertheless, with existing buildings such decisions are often dictated by the location and form of the building and the client's desire to compete with new buildings nearby.

The problems of retrofitting air conditioning have been discussed above. The optimum approach is to minimise internal and external heat gains, to naturally ventilate occupied spaces and to provide extract ventilation and cooling if necessary to equipment rooms. Air quality is an important matter, particularly in equipment rooms, and filtration must be adequately maintained whichever mechanical ventilation systems are fitted.

Operational strategy

Underlying all the above strategies is how the user engages with the building and its systems. Complex systems are unlikely to be understood by most users unless facilities management staff initiates a proper induction process. Building management systems have their place but often produce disappointing outcomes, particularly if building users have no personal control over their internal environment or little faith in the management system adopted. ❖

Dyfi Business Park near Mychhunthleth is a fine example of creative use of brownfield land for new business and industrial units.

Creative re-use of buildings

If you have the task of deciding what to do with an existing building then read this two volume set from Donhead first. Volume 1 explains how to identify appropriate uses for buildings using numerous examples and case studies. It discusses the choices between design intervention, repair and replication and when to use new techniques or traditional skills. Volume 2 offers an extensive collection of illustrated examples from different parts of the UK showing buildings of every shape, size and type including country houses, churches and industrial buildings.

£45 each or both for £80. Published by Donhead and available from The Green Shop www.greenshop.co.uk 01452 770629

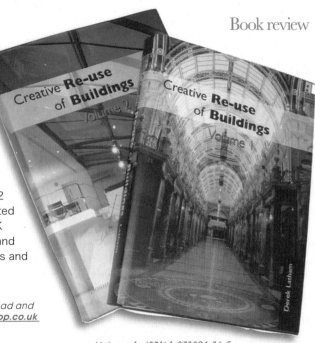

Volume 1 - ISBN 1-873394-36-5

Volume 2 - ISBN 1-873394-37-3

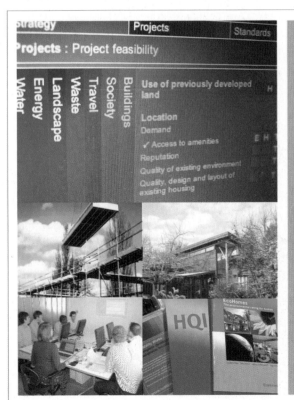

Renovating commercial property

Before looking in detail at renovation strategies it may be helpful to consider the market for new and renovated commercial and industrial buildings and the context in which decisions are made. **Adrian Birch** explores the concept...

The last 30 years has seen the ongoing decline of manufacturing and a move to service industries, with the workforce becoming more office-bound. Coupled with this has been the IT revolution, the desktop computer at every workspace, and the consequential development of the out of town business park near to motorway connections. The growth of car ownership, lack of investment in infrastructure and public transport and inner-city congestion has fuelled this migration of offices from the traditional business districts to the suburbs. This has left a residue of unloved crumbling concrete monuments to the first post-war office boom becoming hard-to-let and neglected, and thus offering potential for those developers and others with the requisite nerve and funds to renovate or redevelop.

Because of the buoyancy of the housing market many obsolescent city-centre office buildings have been converted to residential use, student accommodation or budget hotel use. Local authorities have generally welcomed this as it can serve to revitalise city centres, which in turn increases demand for leisure and other facilities, gyms, restaurants etc.

Many industrial estates established in the post–war period are in inner city and inner suburban areas. Most buildings are of steel or concrete portal-frame construction and many are clad with asbestos cement or steel profiled sheet claddings, with minimal insulation. There was little provision made for offices, car parks and landscaping and many estates are looking run-down by comparison with more recent developments nearer to motorway junctions.

Industrial buildings are less reliant on location than offices but easy access to the motorway network and to the available labour force is desirable. Inner city industrial sites may be incompatible with the residential use surrounding them. Because industrial buildings were often constructed as short-life buildings there is less incentive to renovate them, and redevelopment may be more attractive. Planners have to strike a balance between retaining manufacturing employment and improvement of the environment.

There has been growth in demand for taller and wider buildings to maximise use of storage racking and more sophisticated loading and unloading facilities. Demand for small nursery or start-up units has also risen. Medium-sized buildings may be more likely to be obsolescent, unless they can be extended or converted to a number of smaller self-contained nursery units.

The participants

The commercial property market in the UK is one of the most sophisticated in the developed world with battalions of pinstripe-suited property professionals offering a wide range of property investment advice to the unwary, for a fee. Commercial and industrial property, more than any other, is treated as a commodity to be traded in a market where the property agent sets the ground rules.

Due to fiscal and other reasons, the number of owner-occupiers is declining as 'footloose' organisations dispose of property assets to concentrate on core business.

Major commercial and industrial developments are normally owned by pension funds and other financial institutions, which expect property they invest in to meet certain 'institutionally-acceptable' criteria. These organisations are generally risk-averse and will normally only purchase a completed development from a developer when it is fully-tenanted and is providing a regular flow of income in the form of rents and service charges.

The 'risk' is taken by the property development companies who purchase sites for redevelopment in locations they think will maximise their returns in the relatively short term. They will normally manage the development process from inception through to the final sale to the financial institution, and may engage external project managers, architects, surveyors and engineers to provide advice and to share the design risk.

The commercial and industrial agent is the professional go-between providing market sector advice to developers and investors and procuring tenants for projected or completed developments. Developers will try and manage their risk by ensuring that a suitable tenant or tenants are signed up in a 'pre-let' and the pension fund or other institution is willing to take on the completed development before the developer commits funds to the development.

In order to appeal to the widest range of tenants the property has to be 'lettable'. Most office agents will say that for the building to be lettable it needs to be sufficiently flexible to accommodate different space-plan configurations, and air-conditioned to accommodate variable occupational densities. They can also charge a higher rent if the building is air-conditioned as this 'adds value' in their terms. This of course 'adds value' to their fees, which are based on the rent achieved. They don't add that air-conditioning adds significantly to operating and maintenance costs, as well as consuming substantial amounts of electricity, and if poorly maintained can lead to humidifier fever and other respiratory infections such as legionella.

Tenants will normally base their property decisions on a number of different criteria, with location, parking provision and space flexibility being high on their list. Operating and maintenance costs are of less consequence, as they will argue that these form a minimal part of their overhead, maybe as little as 5%, and any reduction will have minimal effect on the bottom line. It is perhaps not surprising therefore that there is little incentive for tenants to save energy, and property agents will argue that the market is tenant-driven.

The government has set an ambitious energy-reduction target and has introduced the Climate Change Levy in an attempt to raise awareness of the issues by hitting the bottom line. Responses to this have been mixed. Forthcoming EC legislation will require commercial buildings offered for sale or lease to have an 'energy label' to inform prospective tenants of the building's energy consumption, in an attempt to encourage developers and agents to improve energy efficiency.

Is there a market for green buildings?

In the light of the difficulties of oversupply in the early 1990s and the bankruptcies and redundancies that followed, developers, fund managers and commercial agents in the U.K. are risk-averse. Whilst many will appear to be supportive of energy efficiency measures, they will only do so if it has no effect on the initial costs and can be seen to be as simple and predictable to install and operate as air conditioning.

There have been a number of post occupancy evaluations of 'green' office buildings constructed within the last 5 years (See the PROBE reports at www.usablebuildings.co.uk). These have identified a number of successful buildings as well as a few problem areas. Most of the buildings assessed were owner-occupied, where the client was supportive of energy efficiency measures as they had control over both initial and operating costs. Nevertheless it was apparent that even in these buildings, unless the designers' intentions had been properly conveyed to the occupiers, there was a risk of the buildings underperforming. This was mainly due to lack of awareness by facility managers and others, complex building management systems and inadequate commissioning.

There have been very few speculative 'green' office developments, as developers are worried about lettability, and the perceived lack of commitment by an unknown tenant to engage with the building and share the objectives of the original design team.

It is reported that when the Ionica Building,

an owner-occupied office building with a number of green innovations, came onto the market, the commercial agents were so concerned about lettability that air-conditioning was retro-fitted. Previously, it had performed well as a mixed-mode building.

Clearly there needs to be a greater understanding of technical innovation and green design by office agents and facility managers acting for tenants for green buildings to make an impact on the commercial market.

Is there a market for renovated buildings?

Renovated office buildings have to compete with new buildings. If they have 'character' or a Unique Selling Point (USP) and are in a location regarded as desirable then they are likely to be attractive to a range of smaller organisations. They have to meet normal expectations regarding comfort and service provision. It is not surprising that some of the most desirable offices are renovated Georgian townhouses full of period features, which have been skilfully kitted-out with new technology.

But what about the 60s concrete-framed office building clad with spalling concrete panels, rusting metal windows and the dodgy roof? It will almost certainly need structural repairs and a facelift to be attractive to prospective tenants. It is no wonder that many such buildings have been converted to other uses, particularly residential.

But is there a market for green renovated buildings?

Like any form of development it comes down to the character of the building and the character of the location. A new or renovated office building in the wrong location is unlikely to attract tenants no matter how good its green credentials might be. A green building may act as a disincentive to certain tenants who may not wish to engage with such buildings. Green features should not be seen as bolt-on tokens to help 'sell' the building but more as the result of a series of co-ordinated strategies to produce a building that is both attractive and timeless, energy efficient and healthy. ❖

Where can you get the UK's biggest choice of ECO-building products?

GreenPro is an online internet library and archive of eco-building products, case studies and research specifically selected for their environmental credentials. It is an economical and invaluable resource tool for everyone involved in building construction and use. All of the selected products are qualified and supported by ample information which provides the user with ample guidance throughout the selection process. GreenPro has a proven track record for the provision of independently researched building products and methods. It has been unrivalled for almost 14 years.

Access to GreenPro is free for life but there is a one-off registration fee of just £11.75 (incl VAT) to cover the setting up your access login and password.

Unrivalled for the presentation of appropriate environmental information.

Don't waste precious time sifting through thousands of irrelevant entries on all the other building product search engines. GreenPro ensures economical and fast access to the green building information you need. GreenPro contains detailed descriptions of over 1000 products. Many listings include guide prices, images, web links as well as full contact details. All are regularly checked and updated to ensure users have direct access to the most recent information! GreenPro also has a searchable library of case studies, articles and reviews.

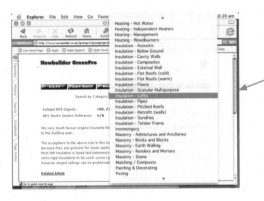

Search by logical arrangement through a vast range of product groups

Found the ideal product? See a photograph, read about its properties and compare it with similar products from other suppliers

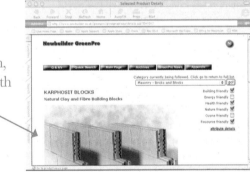

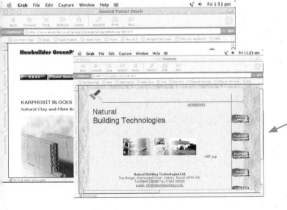

Once you are happy with your selection go to the supplier's website or give them a call to find out about further in-depth info and availability.

Register now at:

www.newbuilder.co.uk

Eco-renovation FAQ's

How can you help ensure your existing home is economical to run, better for the environment and healthier for you and your family to live in? Here **Chris Morton** has compiled a number of frequently asked questions (FAQs) and set out his responses...

Please keep in mind that every building is different, so these questions and answers should be seen as indicative not definitive. Some of the techniques discussed should not be undertaken without the benefit of either experienced help or exhaustive study by yourself. This information is offered as guidance only and should you decide to follow the advice then you do so entirely at your own risk.

Do I need planning permission?

In general most renovation projects do not need planning permission. However, if your property is 'listed' it will be subject to controls, even for internal alterations and you should obtain advice from your local planning department. For all buildings there are restrictions about projections above the roof and being too close to roads or neighbours - all explained in the booklet "Planning - A Guide for Householders" available free from your local planning department. If you are still unsure you can also usually get a free informal decision from the planning department as to whether permission is needed. You should be aware, however, that if you request the decision in writing as a 'certificate of exception' it becomes a quasi application and a fee is charged.

Do I need building regulation approval?

Building regulations are often confused with planning, but are totally different. At present building regulation approval is only required for renovation if works are of a type controlled by the regulations eg structural alterations and/or significant alterations to drainage. The regulations are being reviewed and in the draft of the 2005 regulations (free on line), on works above a threshold, it will become a legal requirement to carry out works, which the Office of the Deputy Prime Minister (ODPM) considers reasonable.

Do I need a survey?

If you are about to buy an old property it may be advisable to get a survey done by someone local, independent and prepared to report in plain English. Remember that surveys done on behalf of building societies are mainly to protect 'their' investment. Try to choose a surveyor with a good reputation and with sound knowledge of sustainable building materials and practices. Talk to some of the professionals from your area listed at the back of this book.

What is the biggest cause of damp in the home?

Rainwater leakage is the biggest cause of damp problems. Gutters, downpipes and dispersal drains must always be maintained regularly and kept in good condition. Check for anything that may stop rainwater draining cleanly off the roof and into gutters. Keep gutters clear so they do not overflow (except in extreme conditions) but discharge the rainwater properly into the hoppers (like gullies, only not trapped unless going into a combined foul/surface system). If you are going to collect rainwater, it's best to seal the bottom of the downpipe into the hopper, otherwise use a shoe that allows you to see it is all working. Mesh grids nearly always cause trouble, unless you clear them very regularly, as they block quickly with leaves etc.

Does my house need dampcoursing?

From 1875 dampcourses were obligatory and until about 1918 were made of slate possibly augmented by courses of darker harder-burnt bricks. These are usually quite good except that there is also a mixture of suspended and solid (dampish) floors with no vertical separation and often shrubs have been allowed to mound up the exterior soil above them. From about 1918 to 1965, dampcourses of reinforced bitumen were used which are not that effective.

The reasons for doing something are (a) rising damp is usually associated with deliquescent salts which make a nasty tide mark on plaster and wallpaper (b) timber built into walls is at risk of wet rot decay, not just at the obvious floor joist ends, but also skirtings, bottom of door linings and especially the timber fixing grounds built into the brick to hold them. In properties of the C18th and early C19th, these have cousins called "bonding timbers" built into the inside of walls all over the place, the worst being of elm which furniture beetle larvae (woodworm) can devour completely.

Part of the treatment is to see how much can be done to improve the humidity balance and an insulated and ventilated "dado" is much better than plaster up to the tide mark level. On walls of highly irregular stone or bricks including a proportion of hard over-burns, it is possibly all that can be done.

Do chemical dampcourses work?

They can work in brickwork of good consistency and reasonable porosity. The system where little pots are left for a week to drain in are better than quick squirt ones. Those where the holes were filled with clay sieves were clever in allowing more evaporation. If the brickwork is irregular, there are a lot of chimneys or other thicker masonry and abutting vertical garden walls and/or higher ground levels beyond your control, think some more. Rubble masonry walls are probably the least likely to be successfully remedied by injected dpc because the central section of the wall is invariably a rubble fill that will be all but impossible to fill wilth the stuff.

There was also a system of earthing a band of copper inserted into a joint. The idea is that because damp only rises (more than a few mm) because of salts and the salt solution creates an electrical potential, kill the potential and stop the rise.

There is nothing like putting in a sheet of heavy duty polythene dpc. This can be done by forming slits with a masonry saw or rebuilding brick by brick. About 900mm of brick can be left unsupported for a while and the gaps

are wedged with slate, as it is impossible to fill effectively with mortar.

What about timber treatment?

The order of greenness is (1) fresh air (ie ventilation), (2) boron derivatives and (3) commercial chemicals.

Most infestations can be solved using environmental controls and avoiding the use of any chemicals.

The odd holes on top of an architrave, around the edges of beams and/or floorboards of oak and traditional beams are ubiquitous and not worth worrying about. Make good use of fresh air and ensure adequate ventilation. This will help keep wood dry and therefore sound. Open windows as often as you can.

In a house containing elm, Stradivarius violins or antiques the situation may be more serious. Elm is favoured by beetle and the old plywoods or marquetry were made using animal glues which insects love the taste of.

Elm wallplate eaten away by woodworm

Deathwatch beetle larvae make larger holes than woodworm. They are symptomatic of long term wet timber, especially and including oak heartwood. Getting the timber dry is essential as even if the Deathwatch beetle doesn't get it, fungae could. Key areas are on roofs where the rainwater can't get away cleanly and beam ends in walls above which rainwater goods were neglected for a long period.

Wet rot merely destroys the wet timber, although it can be spectacularly destructive and softens-up timber for larvae to eat. Hack out infected areas, deal with the damp problem and don't let the new wood get wet again.

Dry rot (Merulius lacrymans) is more voracious. It not only destroys all timber dampened by the original leak, but sends scouting parties (mycelium) to find more food and then chain-gangs to wet it. If it has been allowed to fruit the spores will spread to other areas. Seek advice from a specialist.

(Editor's Note - I discovered dry rot in the corner of one of our rooms and saw how quickly the wooden floor boards were destroyed. We were determined not to use chemicals. We removed and burnt all infected timber, very carefully used a blow torch to burn off as much of the mycelia as we safely could from the stone/rubble walls. We then created plenty of ventilation and left everything to dry out for nearly a year before we replaced the floorboards with more reclaimed timber. Four years on and we have had no further evidence of the dry rot.)

Is it beyond repair?

Probably not. Almost anything can be repaired. The real question is whether or not it is worth it. Isolated disaster areas in a basically sound building are worthwhile. This bit of stonework needed rebuilding and is shown indexed so each stone can go back where it came from.

This timber framed building, with a large proportion of elm, was by normal standards beyond repair, only the Highways Agency had promised to reinstate it if moved from the M5/A417 junction. As well as normal timber splicing, the photo shows structural cast resin (Rotafix) used to repair tenons, as otherwise very few timbers could have been salvaged.

Poor quality oak from same frame repaired with mixture of traditional splices and cast resin

Compriband (available from most builder's merchants) is quite good for keeping joints air and water-tight (but do not let it get in contact with silicone).

Fig 2. Stones indexed so that the wall panel can be rebuilt with each stone back in its place

Use of Compriband to water and wind proof panel edges

If you are buying a home with walls like this (in the picture below) either insist you or your surveyor is allowed to hack off the crud to see how much, if any, timber remains, or, better, ask the conservation officer if you can over-clad it.

A timber frame in very poor poor condition where over-cladding is more likely to succeed than repair

On this one we were allowed to. It is effective, reversible and non-destructive, whereas 'repair' would degenerate into replacement and the wall leans inwards so would probably leak anyway. When overcladding, don't forget to add insulation but keep it all breathable.

We have awful mould, what can we do?

The mould is almost certainly from internal condensation rather than rain penetration. What happens is that walls of 9" brick or dense stone facing the prevailing wind are cooled by evaporation of the water absorbed during rainfall. While wet they also have zero value insulation. The mould is most common near ceiling level where warm air passes through the structure and leaves behind accumulated vapour. Breathing walls are known to be better at dealing with this problem.

Any external weather screen must be breathable, including the paint covering (limewash or mineral paints). If insulation can be added so much the better ie next to the original wall with a rainscreen outside it, which can include slate, but not too snugly laid. Rendering direct to the masonry is usually disastrous, as it cracks and then acts as a storage system without any of the benefits of a tank based one. Where absolutely unavoidable it can be done on stainless expanded metal lath fixed clear of the masonry. There are companies doing an insulated turnkey fibre-reinforced render system, but it is not cheap.

Are lime products a good thing?

They are thought to be be better because they are considered to be be vapour permeable and are 'natural'. However modern factory produced limes almost certainly lack the ad hoc local additives (cow-muck, etc.) that determined the properies of traditional limes. They therefore tend to need Pozzolans or accelerators so that they set in hours rather than weeks and my experience is that the faster the induced set, the more the resulting mortar or plaster tends to take on the undesirable rigid properties of cheaper cement equivalents. This is totally different from dealing with soft stonework, when lime putty is appropriate and essential.

Lime-wash is likewise more vapour permeable than conventional paints. Again, traditional mixes included tallow and no doubt all sorts of other substances missing from their modern equivalents.

Our bricklayer is mutinous about lime?

It does matter if you are repairing a building built of limestone or one of the softer sandstones. The best thing is that you or he should go on a day course on lime and/or masonry usage.

Briefly, the strength/porosity of mortar has to be kept in tandem with the strength/porosity of the stone or brick and as much of the extraneous salts have to be shed as practical. For the softer stones, the lime has to be 'putty' ie slaked then kept moist and of the 'non-hydraulic' family, that is without natural or artificial set accelerators. For re-pointing this is fine as it has no need to set quickly and with a little practice the procedure for overfilling the joint then skimming the

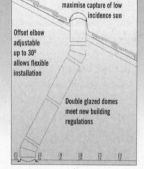

salt-laden edge and applying appropriate finish can be gained. Building is more tiresome, and this also applies to lime renders, as it takes days to stiffen. Sensible selection of 'coarse stuff' ie sand and crushed stone minimises this. Seek advice for one of the professional lime suppliers in the product section at the back of this book on mixes to suit your own particular stone/ building/ exposure etc.

For work on exposed positions, where assurance of an effective and faster set is essential, you could use 'hydraulic' or accelerated lime. My experience is that use of 1:1:6 cement/hydrated lime/coarse sand is safer cheaper and simpler. It's called hydrated because it has dried so it comes to you as powder and is available from any builders merchant. There are a few 'tricks' (a) use a 'sharp' sand, ie with up to 4mm grains, not the silt beloved of brickies (b) do not add washing up liquid, and mix it to a consistancy whereby at 18mm thick it will support a girt lump of rock without squirting out onto your feet (c) it must only be mixed in quantities that can be used within 20 minutes. After that you will see the water rising to the top and the grit falling to the bottom; dismiss any brickie that then tries to remix it after the first warning. You can also buy pre-mixed lime/sand and just add cement and water before using, but you may not get coarse enough sand for rubble stonework. Lastly don't over-stretch the good nature of this mix; if the stone is really irregular, pack the joints out with slate, tile or stone fragments so you don't get more than 18mm of mortar. ❖

Useful contacts

Rotafix www.rotafix.co.uk 01639 730481
Hutton and Rostron Environmental Investigations Ltd www.handr.co.uk 01483 203221

Further reading

Studies of the Domestic Dry Rot Fungus by Serpula Lacrymans, £24.50 ISBN 1-903570-417 published by Historic Scotland

Conservation of Timber Sash and Case Windows by Stephen Newsome £14.50 ISBN 1900-168-871 published by Historic Scotland

Timber Building in Britain; with relevance to the management of decay in buildings by R W Brunskill £25.00 ISBN 0-304-36665-X www.newbuilder.co.uk

You've Been Timber Framed by Paula Sunshine £12.99 ISBN 09545952-0-3

Tips on eco-extending your home

When you extend an existing property you have to identify its 'positive strengths' then evaluate how 'other constraints' are going to limit what you would like to do. **Chris Morton** points out the opportunities and pitfalls...

Please keep in mind that every building is different, so these questions and answers should be seen as indicative not definitive. Some of the techniques discussed should not be undertaken without the benefit of either experienced help or exhaustive study by yourself. This information is offered as guidance only and should you decide to follow the advice then you do so entirely at your own risk.

There is a spectrum of buildings in the UK, with 'Listed' buildings at one end. These are houses with character and history that are valued and planning officers have a duty to protect. This does not mean you can't extend or alter them, but you will have to prove that what you are doing is "conserving or enhancing" the property. There are buildings in 'Conservation Areas', 'Areas of Outstanding Natural Beauty' and then 'the norm' or socially acceptable, and finally your ideal eco-haunt.

Although in the same department of the local authority, building control officers are administering national and local regulations that have gone way beyond their public health origins and are, albeit clumsily, forward looking with minimum standards for insulation and fire safety.

The external volume of your extension will be scrutinised by planners. Their job is to ensure that what you want to build isn't going to 'frighten the locals'. Keep neighbours on board by explaining your ideas - much easier if you understand them yourself! There are four simple questions to ask yourself:

1. In what specific way does what you already have fail to meet your needs?
2. Is what you already have being fully utilised?
3. Are the materials used previously still available?
4. How much extra volume can you achieve and afford?

Rigid rules or common sense?

Maybe an extension will help you to get rid of an undesirable structure or layout within the existing shell. An ideal floor plan allows all spaces to be accessed from a central node without wasted space, usually the staircase. This is especially true in properties that have been extended before,

Matching up with the existing is not the only solution and many fine houses can have their character destroyed by doing so. Much of the charm of period properties and indeed whole street-scapes, comes precisely from the fact that everything does not match.

Historic street scene, Lavenham

The part of the original building that will be covered by the new extension can provide some valuable materials for the new work. For instance, taking out a gable of 9" brick can yield enough bricks to make a new wall of twice the area. But be careful, sometimes all the over-fired and bent ones were used behind the facings and you won't know until you start to remove them. If you can, hold off on ordering your new bricks until you are sure what can be salvaged and re-used. Do not take down any walls without a proper survey.

Popular traditional details may be inappropriate for new materials. Modern bricks tend to be less absorbent than old ones, (check with brick manufacturer on the performance characteristics of the bricks before building. Also our more highly insulated homes often mean that the brick outer skin is much more prone to frost attack. Cheap bricks (especially when laid frog down) can blow from frost within a couple of years. Always ensure that frogged bricks are laid with the frog upwards so the wall is solid.

Vernacular yes, but in measure

Fashion took over from vernacular a long time ago; parapets and tiny overhangs are bad news. Flat roofs even worse. If there is a single storey flat roof, build something habitable over it and consider a pitched roof instead!

Vernacular materials like cob were used in fairly limited areas where both suitable earth can be dug up and the climate is favourable. Nowadays, we have lots of high-tech materials that waterproof and insulate, but they are vapour impermeable and the thought of finding, never mind fixing, a leak is a horrid one and don't forget that any waterproof system is only as good as the person that installs it. As a rule of thumb keep away from compromised detailing and don't rely too much on techno-fixes.

Examine as many ideas as possible before settling to a strategy and be prepared to ditch an idea if it gets bogged down.

Design and designers

If designing a good, attractive and aesthetically pleasing extension was easy, then architects would have starved ages ago. So find an architect, surveyor or designer near you who can think on your wavelength. There are plenty listed at the back of this book. This is a good starting point. Extensions usually require a lot of time on site, so for practicality choose your profession-

als that are within a radius of say 30 miles. The RIBA regional office will also suggest names, but many of the more radical architects don't all belong to RIBA.

Outwitting the regulations

Watch the pitfalls in the regulations; even on insulation. South facing glass (for 'passive solar') does work despite not being recognised by some. Although it says you can't use a whole building heat loss calculation, there are enough reasonable building control officers for it to be worth asking.

2 storey conservatory style extension with 'rationed' glazing; western red cedar cladding

Conservatories don't need building control (yet), but on new homes they have to have isolating doors and no heat source (other than the

Conservatory re-using 60's sliders and no corner posts

sun!). South facing ones will almost certainly need a heat dispersal system, but allow quasi-outdoor living for several extra months of the year. Single glazing in conservatories will actually gain more heat than double glazing.

Green or pragmatic?

Most of my clients (and I) usually start green but curl at the edges like dead lettuce as the project progresses. I don't feel too guilty about pragmatism, especially on things with huge embodied energy which are going to recoup it dozens of times over, like almost all insulations.

New shell over burnt out C17th cottage using reclaimed structural timber and some green oak and elm boarding.

Tile hanging to extension above what was previously a flat roof

On extensions, especially where there is first floor space required, lightweight tends to win over heavy weight. You can rarely afford to waste a millimetre of external skin on masonry, but maybe use a floor system with insulation below it and beef up your stove chimney. Simple tile hanging can often 'balance' Hanging tiles last forever and are among the easiest materials to recycle but planners tend to dislike them unless they are in the vernacular style of the locality.

Reclaimed timber seems less good value than it used to be, but it is worth looking out for. In fact if there seems potential for using recycled materials, go to the architectural salvage yard(s) and see what is plentiful before you start your plans rather than hunting for specific items later.

On framed structures, eliminating air filtration is important. A paper-thin crack may look innocuous and not worth a showdown with the builder, but think of it like a slow puncture in your cycle tyre. Wind pressure against a building can use any crack not only to push air through, but also to take water with it. The latter is especially noticeable in those romantic oak frame buildings and their new green oak counterparts. Have the oak exposed inside, but use a complete sheathing outside.

For slightly different reasons stone is great on the inside for thermal mass as well as 'natural feel', but hopeless as an exterior skin even if you are surrounded by it as the vernacular.

And finally 'cunning'

What do you see through your glass? If it is the sky then you are getting tons of light. If it is the ground you aren't, but you are losing just as much heat, so make sure the flowers or view are worth it. And to end on good news, you won't need a larger boiler as the heat loss of the whole extension could well be (if done properly) less than it was for the bit of roof or wall where it connects to the main house. ❖

Low impact construction

One of the pleasures of most low impact constructions is that materials are safe and the processes are easy

All buildings which aim to reduce their impact on the environment could be called, at least, 'lower impact' but the term has come to mean those buildings using largely natural or organic materials. 'Low Impact Construction' serves to describe a body of work which takes in most of the more radical attempts to produce 'deep green' buildings with a quite different approach to construction and the creation of comfort. **Chris Morgan** explains...

Although the term describes a wide range of techniques, many of the principles, or characteristics of these buildings are shared and are distinct from much mainstream construction.

Small scale and rural

One characteristic of almost all low impact construction is that it remains small scale and usually rural. This often diminishes its perceived value and relevance so it is worth stressing that there are few technical reasons why most of the construction types discussed could not be employed on both a large scale, and in urban situations.

It is likely that the small scale and rural aspect to most low impact buildings is one reason why clients and builders feel able to experiment. As a result many of the most valuable innovations and developments, which will pervade more mainstream construction in the future, are probably being tried out even now in sheds, extensions and small homes up and down the country!

Very low embodied energy

Low impact buildings are almost always buildings with low embodied energy in their fabric, where the use of natural materials is often the starting point for clients and designers alike. Such buildings tend to be energy efficient as well, but this is often secondary.

Local, unconventional materials

Sourcing materials can be problematic. Simply finding the material(s) can be difficult, particularly in urban areas. In addition, materials are rarely standard, nor have any recognised performance criteria (in a conventional sense). This puts the onus onto someone involved in the construction to be sufficiently expert in the field to be confident when it comes to sourcing the right material.

In addition there is often no commonly recognised framework for cost so it can be difficult not only to budget, but to know if you are getting a good deal. And the issue of cost is complicated by transport, storage and by the seasons.

Low material costs, high labour costs

Generally speaking the material costs of low impact constructions tend to be low, but these are usually offset by higher costs associated with labour and time.

This often means that the anticipated lower costs of low impact buildings are not realised. Many self builders get involved in building in order to offset some of the labour costs associated with builders and the normal mark-ups by developers and so on. However, the costs of materials remain broadly the same, often more due to lack of trade discounts, whereas low impact construction using naturally occuring materials or resources can offer further opportunities to save money.

Passive environmental control

Most of the natural materials and coatings associated with low impact construction are hygroscopic. Clay in particular absorbs and desorbs moisture freely and as such can act as a moderator of the humidity in the air, though ventilation remains the key tool for this. This function of balancing the relative humidity in the room is particularly valuable for occupant health, since many of the health problems associated with modern buildings can be exacerbated by extremes of relative humidity.

The same is true in regard to heating, and the concept of thermal mass is well understood. With both thermal mass, and moisture mass, some

understanding of the issues is required, but it is possible to actually design the internal climate of a building so as to most benefit the health of occupants without the use of moving parts and the associated maintenance problems.

Maintenance

Maintenance has become a dirty word for some, and much talk is made of "maintenance free" construction and products. However, in cheating the natural cycles of decay, these products have invariably introduced toxins and alien materials which are environmentally damaging and in

A cob building being built up in stages. A lime and stone foundation wall has layers of a mix of earth and straw laid over. The lower parts have been 'shaved' to form a (relatively) neat surface, while the most recently added top section is 'as trodden in'.

most cases, can only prolong the inevitable for a certain time. In the process, the culture of maintenance is abandoned and when something does go wrong, even when only a small part is broken, most "maintenance free" products are removed and landfilled.

In contrast, an environmental approach – and the approach of all low impact construction – is to accept an element of maintenance and to design this into the process of co-habitation with your building. Maintenance is regular, but simple, and in the process the building and its elements are able to be kept in good order far longer – and therefore far more cheaply in the long run – than

A completed straw bale wall with the first coat of lime plaster being applied. Note the use of chicken wire over the corners to form a firmer substrate for the plaster and help protect the corners.

their maintenance-free counterparts.

Part of a wider vision

For many who undertake low impact buildings, it is part of a much wider approach to life in general. However, this is not strictly necessary, as the advantages can be appreciated on their own merits. Unfortunately, it is usually only those already disposed toward this sort of thing, and who make the leap of faith which is often required, who are able to experience the advantages.

Common materials and systems of low impact construction

Earth

Earth is still the most widespread construction material known and one third of humanity still live in earthen buildings. The material even gave its name to the entire planet – or was it the other way around - but in any event comes with significant pedigree.

Vernacular forms of earth construction survive in many parts of the world and remain instructive on the most efficient way to produce earthen buildings even today. There are a number of techniques but broadly they can be divided into three. The first involves stacking and compressing earth to form a monolithic wall – examples are 'cob' and rammed earth (using shuttering). The second uses earth pre-formed and dried into blocks or 'adobes' and then built up. Both techniques employ earth as the principal load-bearing material. The principal advantage of the latter is that it avoids most of the problems associated with shrinkage, whilst the main disadvantage is that it entails double handling.

The third alternative is to mix earth with some filler material like straw and apply it to a framework which takes the structural loads. This was more common traditionally where timber supplies were plentiful.

The common disadvantage of all

earth constructions nowadays is that it is difficult to attain the thermal insulation values required by the Building Regulations.

Light earth and hemp-lime

One way around the above problem of insulation is to increase the level of insulating filler, and usually the depth of the mix so that the overall wall complies with modern requirements for thermal performance. This can be done in a number of way, but the main techniques employed use earth / clay and straw, or in one example lime and hemp, to form a solid, non-loadbearing fairly well insulating mass wall.

Both techniques require drying out times and are still fairly labour intensive, though more mechanised, and pre-fabricated options exist.

Straw bale construction

Straw bale construction normally involves placing rectangular bales exactly as bricks are placed to form a wide, hairy wall which can be either load bearing or infill to a structural frame, and which is normally plastered on both sides with a clay or lime-based render. Straw bale construction has a number of advantages over earth and insulated earth construction types. It is a dry system and so has none of the (admittedly minor) problems associated with drying out and shrinkage. It is also a very good insulation material which, when combined with the sensible placement of thermal mass, makes a lot of sense overall in the UK.

Third, it is quite quick to construct, but possibly more involved than the other techniques to adequately finish. There is no doubt however that straw bale construction is relatively quick, cheap and easy to do, and increasingly easy to get through the legislative and financial hurdles which often bedevil low impact projects.

Other crops

A number of bio-based materials have found their way into the building material supply chain, though these are mostly imported into the UK.

This shows a gridshell roof construction which uses a very small amount of timber to form a substantial span. The gridshell is braced by the overlayers of timber boarding.

Among these are hemp, flax, and sheeps wool, all used for insulation while flax is also used in the manufacture of linoleum. Sisal, coir and jute are used in carpet manufacture, and reeds are becoming a little more common not only for traditional thatching, but bound and used as backings to plasters and renders.

Timber

So widespread it is easily overlooked that timber forms the mainstay of much conventional, very high impact construction, but has the capacity also to be an integral part of very low impact construction if used wisely.

If sourced from local (at least, not imported) and certified forests, and if used efficiently and without chemical treatment, and if detailed well so as to be durable, timber represents a low

This shows the gridshell building from the previous page but from the outside, with stone walls using both lime and clay mortars, and clay external render under a large roof overhang.

impact material choice.

The Segal method uses timber very efficiently, roundpole construction reduces the machining of timber while retaining all of its strength, and gridshell construction enables very efficient use of small amounts of timber yet creates large span structures. Using 'green' timber avoids the energy associated with kiln drying and there are a number of ways in which timber can be

A building built largely of waste tyres and tin cans, submerged into a hillside and using clay internal plasters to attempt a zero energy input construction through the use of large amounts of thermal mass.

used, such as with 'Brettstapel' construction where good use is made of a material which has little other value.

Masonry

Traditional stone and brick construction, using lime and clay mortars probably counts as a low impact strategy, depending on how the insulation required is achieved. Reclaimed elements such as tiles and slates reduce the overall impact, and it is becoming possible in some parts of England to reproduce traditional footings with stone and lime in what may be termed low impact foundations.

People are becoming more familiar with the use of lime, and increasingly, clay, for mortars and plasters. Perhaps the main advantage of these materials for mortars, unlike cement, is that the bricks or blocks can more readily be re-used at the end of their lifetime, and that is the real tragedy of cement (which acts as a type of glue).

Re-used and recycled materials

A few constructional techniques have been developed to deal directly with some of the waste arisings from industry. One of the most enduring has been the common tyre. Rammed full of earth and tied together these have become symbols, especially in the US, of ecological design through the re-use of waste (Earthships). Drinks cans and bottles, short logs and many other unlikely materials have been similarly employed to create walls, which are often however sadly little more than a matrix of cement mortar.

However, the principal of using waste materials is a sound one, and be it tyres or recycled paper insulation there is no doubt the impact of development is reduced.

Conclusion

Many of the ideas and techniques employed in these constructions appear strange or even affected, but a great deal of genuine innovation in sustainability abounds, and it is not unreasonable to imagine the lessons being learnt now in remote fields and forests becoming familiar to the mainstream construction industry. ❖

References

Berge, B The Ecology of Building Materials (Transl. Henley, Filip) Architectural Press, Oxford 2000.

Broom J & Richardson B The Self Build Book, Green Books 1991

Fairlie, S Low Impact Development: Planning and People in a Sustainable Countryside, Jon Carpenter Publishing, Charlebury 1997

Stulz, R Appropriate Building Materials A Catalogue of Potential Solutions, SKAT Swiss Centre for Appropriate Technology and Intermediate Technology Publications, St Gallen Switzerland 1983

Elizabeth L & Adams C, Alternative Construction Contemporary Natural Building Methods, John Wiley & Sons, New York 2000

Earth Construction

Houben H & Guillaud H, Earth Construction A Comprehensive Guide, Intermediate Technology Publications, London 1994

Little B & Morton T, Building with Earth in Scotland Innovative Design and Sustainability, Scottish Executive Central Research Unit Edinburgh 2001

Minke, G, Earth Construction Handbook Earth in Modern Construction, WIT Press, Southampton UK 2000

Light Earth Construction

Volhard, F. Leichtlehmbau Alter Baustoff - neue Technik (Light Earth Building – Old Building Material - New Technique), C. F. Mueller, Heidelberg 1995 (5th Edition) (In German)

Morgan, C, Light Earth Construction, DTI Research Report 2002 available from Gaia Architects, Edinburgh

Straw Bale Construction

Steen A, & Steen B, The Straw Bale House

Bainbridge D, Chelsea Green Publishing Company, Vermont 1994

Jones, B, Building With Straw Bales: A Practical Guide for the UK and Ireland, Download pdf format - www.strawbalefutures.org.uk

Myrhman M & MacDonald S, Build It With Bales

Timber

Borer P & Harris C, Out of the Woods: Ecological Designs for Timber Frame Houses, CAT Publications / Walter Segal Trust, Stungo, N The New Wood Architecture, Laurence King, 1998

Waste

Liddell H et al, Recycled Materials for Housing, Scottish Homes (now Communities Scotland) 1993.

All photos for this article were taken by the author.

Renewable insulation materials

50% of the UK's energy is used within our buildings. The Government is keen to see energy use in buildings reduced, to help meet both its climate change and fuel poverty targets, and is therefore undertaking a number of programmes to encourage increased insulation levels in buildings. In most cases, the type of insulation used is determined by its thermal properties, its costs and availability. The wider environmental impact of the insulation material is often not considered, even the energy used within manufacture and distribution. With particular insulation companies and sectors promoting their own environmental credentials, there is a dearth of credible and independent research available to specifiers and householders. **Dave Barton** summarises a market review of renewable insulation materials ...

Why choose renewable insulation?

When specifying insulation, consideration should ideally be given to the following, alongside cost, thermal properties and efficacy as a building component:

- Embodied energy (energy consumed within its processing and transport);
- Raw material extraction;
- High toxicity levels;
- Related health issues in manufacture, installation and for occupants;
- Use of ozone depleting chemicals and
- Ability to be recycled.

In other words, the type of insulation used is an important consideration alongside that of the level of insulation fitted to a building. The right specification of insulation could be a significant part of reducing the overall environmental impact of a building. The current major players in the insulation market, mineral and glass wool, do not contain any chemicals and are quite inert, but they have high embodied energy and can create dust problems during handling.

There are a number of renewable insulation materials which are on the market at the moment, such as sheep's wool, cellulose and flax. These are currently only available at a few niche outlets. Compared to the current major players in the insulation market, these materials tend to have lower embodied energy, do not involve mineral extraction and can be recycled.

Why isn't renewable insulation in widespread use?

The UK construction industry tends to be rather conservative and slow to respond to 'new' materials. Not all materials are BBA or BSI approved; without such approval they are unlikely to be taken up by the market at large. Some products are relatively new to the market and consequently there is limited experience in specification and installation, limited availability and accessibility and generally a price premium (though this is claimed to be falling). The natural benefits of the products tend to suit a breathing construction, and so their usage needs to be considered carefully and may be limited to specific applications, e.g. to lofts and internal wall insulation on existing buildings and to breathable walls and roofs in new buildings. Overall there are a number of alternatives for loft and timber framed applications but there are few suitable materials for cavity wall insulation although CAT used cork for the AtEIC building, see photo.

What types of renewable insulation are there?

There are six main types of renewable insulation, as summarised below.

Cellulose

Cellulose is currently the most common renewable insulation material available in the UK. It is made from waste or unused paper and is available in boards of various thicknesses or loose fill in bags for loft applications. It can also be wet sprayed within timber frame construction. Cellulose is particularly suited for use in ventilated or breathing constructions. Of the renewable insulation materials available, it is also the cheapest and diy is an option in some applications.

Sheep's wool

There are now a number of suppliers in the marketplace. Sheep's wool insulation is made from either new or recycled wool, some of which comes from sheep that have not been dipped in any pesticides.

The insulation comes in rolls and batts of different sizes and thicknesses. Due to its hygroscopic properties, it is ideal for use in breathable roofs and timber framed walls as it allows water vapour to move through the structure. No special tools are required in its application. It can be cut with a sharp pair of scissors or a knife.

A major benefit of sheep's wool (as with the plant products below) is its ability to absorb (and release) more than one third of its own weight in moisture without impairing the insulating properties of the fibres. This means it can control condensation in the insulated cavity and helps to cool the building in summer and warm it in winter. Wool insulation has low embodied energy and is completely biodegradable.

Flax

Flax is mainly used in the production of linseed oil but a few companies are exploiting its fibres for insulation. Flax insulation is made from the short fibres from the flax plant, currently from flax grown in Austria and Germany. Flax can be grown in the UK and is most suited to growing in Wales and the South-West of England.

Flax insulation is available in rolls or batts in a range of thicknesses and lengths. It can be used

Innovative use of cork in cavity walls for the AtEIC (autonomous environmental information centre) building at the Centre for Alternative Technology at Machynlleth. The cavity wall structure is compressed earth blocks with corkboard cavity fill insulation. Fact sheet on the whole building available from CAT 01654 705980 and a building diary featuring the project can be found at www.cat.org.uk

in pitched roofs between and over ceiling joists, in suspended floors and in timber or steel frame walls.

Hemp

Hemp is thought to have great potential as an insulation product. Hemp fibre is increasingly being used in the automotive industry as a superior product to synthetic materials, typically for interior panels. It is also used for making prestige paper, horse bedding and garden matting.

Hemp is a fibre crop well adapted for cultivation in the UK and in fact can grow in many countries throughout the world and in a range of climates. Currently the largest European producer is France.

Cork

Cork has been available for some time as an insulation product and as wall and floor tiles. However, the insulation board is still not widely available at builders merchant type outlets although it can be obtained from more specialised companies.

Cork comes from the cork oak grown mainly in Portugal as well as Northern Africa and Spain. The cork forests do not require pesticides, fertilizers or irrigation and the cork produced is both renewable and recyclable. Cork insulation comes in boards of varying thicknesses which are generally used as insulation for warm roofs (i.e. on the rafters not the joists) and in timber frames. They can be used in dormer cheeks as well.

Cotton

Cotton is not suitable for growing in the UK and all cotton used in this country is imported. Cotton grows in warm, humid climates requiring a large amount of pesticide, fertilizer and water. Using 'new' cotton for a renewable insulation does not therefore make environmental sense. However, using waste cotton and other fibres in an insulation product is a possibility. There is one organisation manufacturing insulation from waste cotton under license from a US company. It will be available in rolls or batts and can be installed without any safety precautions.

The future for renewable insulation

Whilst there are a small number of niche suppliers currently marketing renewable insulation, there is much interest in their market potential. Some suppliers are optimistic about the short-term potential, with the possibility that one of the big builders merchants will take on renewable insulation products. There are numerous market drivers to support this optimism, particularly climate change, healthy buildings and sustainable construction as well as reduced building costs.

Cost remains the main barrier although those surveyed in the research felt that a 10% to 30% price premium would be attractive to the general market (premiums in the research ranged from 0% to 500%).

The technical capability of many of the available products is impressive, even if there is limited experience of their application in the UK. Of course, they need to be specified correctly to optimise the overall thermal properties of the building and are more suited on the whole for breathing buildings (or breathable elements of the building). ❖

Further information

Further details can be found in 'Renewable Insulation Materials, A guide' published by Impetus Consulting. This contains:

* *Information on thermal conductivity, density, u-values and energy consumption in manufacture*

* *Feedback from users of the different materials*

* *A product use comparison table and*

* *Examples of stockists*

The report from which this information is extracted was created with some funding from the Pilkington Energy Efficiency Trust. This culminated in the production of a guide to using these materials. The key points from this research are summarised in this article.

The full report is available by emailing info@impetusconsult.co.uk.

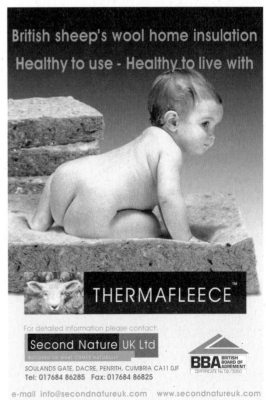

The ecological design of timber buildings

Timber is a funny one. On one hand it is the epitome of environmental design, and on the other, the indiscriminate use of timber is responsible for some of the worst excesses of environmental degradation. Timber is renewable, unlike most other modern building material components, but this implies only a potential advantage. To realise this potential, there is a bit of work to do. **Chris Morgan** explains ...

To attain any semblance of 'sustainability', the use of timber on a building must compare favourably with four criteria. These are: **source, transport, treatment and detailing**. If any one of these four criteria cannot be met, then the term 'sustainable' should not be applied.

Source

Timber must come from a sustainable source. Easy to write, but very difficult to define and establish in practice.

A sustainable source is one where the growing, management, harvesting and re-planting of trees is socially, environmentally and economically sustainable. The forestry must be profitable enough to sustain communities, who can afford to stay, raise families, manage and re-plant appropriately, maintain and even enhance soil conditions, avoid erosion and nutrient loss and generally improve the conditions of the local area.

Experience all over the world, and throughout history, suggests that this is not easy to achieve. De-forestation due to lack of replanting, soil erosion, fires (and firewood collection) conversion to agriculture, lack of management and a host of other reasons, along with subsequent de-population of rural areas is often the norm.

Certification schemes have developed to try to account for these many variables because of widespread global concern of the damage being caused, and there is no doubt that great advances, not least in understanding of the issues, have been achieved. None of the schemes claim to be 100% water-tight, and there is still a very long way to go.

The main scheme operating in the UK is the FSC (Forest Stewardship Council) and it is worth noting that all Forestry Commission forests in the UK are certified under this scheme.

Transport

Transportation of timber is an issue largely because of the pollution associated with it, but also because of the failure to realise the potential of (re-) vitalising local economies, which is inherent in the worldwide trade in bulk timber.

The scale of the pollution associated with transported timber is often under-estimated.

Table 1. Energy Requirement for Manufacturing and or Producing Selected Building Materials
(source: Whole House Book)

Material	KWh/tonne	KWh/cu.m
Timber-local air dried	200	110
Timber-local green oak	200	220
Timber-imported softwood	1,450	754
Non-fletton bricks	860	1,462
Lightweight blocks	500	600
Steel	13,200	103,000

Consider the information in Table1.

In other words there is more pollution associated with imported timber than there is with other, supposedly 'less green' materials. And so, it makes sense to look at the use of UK sourced timber because only then can it be said with confidence that the timber is anything like sustainable. In doing so, a number of other advantages become clear. Using homegrown timber:

- stimulates UK forestry and related rural industries,
- creates and/or maintains employment in rural areas, and promotes good woodland management in the UK, which also benefits the local ecology.

Such considerations rarely show up on 'green building' checklists and assessment schemes, but these aspects are important, and the potential capacity of the construction industry to engage with and benefit local forest industries is vast.

There is no doubt that homegrown timber is the 'greenest' choice for UK construction, but there is a snag...

There is no way in which the UK construction industry (let alone the paper, fencing, pallet and other industries) could source all its own timber from within the UK.

Annually, the UK consumes around 50 million cubic metres of timber. In the same period, it produces only 7.5 million cubic metres of timber. In other words, we produce only 15% of what we consume, and we import the remainder at an annual cost to the nation of around £7 billion (not to mention the environmental cost in CO_2).

This may seem a lost cause, but there are reasons to be positive about the future. First, the amount of timber produced in the UK is set to increase from 7.5million to 16 million cubic metres by 2020. The challenge is to create a larger market share for this timber in the construction industry.

Most of the timber used in construction (by

Far left: This 1200m² building in Scotland used all Scottish timber for its construction, and all of that was untreated. This was achieved through careful detailing and species choice, along with the use of 'breathing' construction to ensure the timber was adequately protected from decay.

Right: The use of poor quality softwood as cladding, while natural paint finishes do the work of keeping off the moisture and innovative 'non-touching' cladding allows the boards to dry out quickly. Using lower quality timber enables locally supplied wood to be used. This project is in the extreme North-West of Scotland, on the coast.

volume), does not need to be particularly good quality, studs, joists and rafters, battens and so on could all be readily sourced from homegrown softwood, though designers may need to alter their practices to account for weaker timber, by specifying lower strength classes, closing up on spacings, increasing section sizes and so on. Choosing to use C16 grade timber at 450mm centres rather than C24 timber at 600mm centres, for example, is a small price to pay for being able to cut all the pollution associated with importation, and benefit our own forestry industry.

Some have already started to look at initiatives to realise the potential of this extra timber, and various investigations are underway such as high-tec jointing, gluing, de-knotting, heat treatment and so on. These initiatives will doubtless benefit the industry, but there is far greater potential simply by adjusting our expectations and design practice to suit the material we have to hand.

One excellent technique, particularly suited to the UK timber supply, is solid wood panel construction. Pioneered on the continent where it is usually known as 'Brettstapel' construction. One London practice specialises in the technique, but the potential to produce very strong, insulating, structural panels with excellent environmental credentials is huge.

Insulation can be made direct from timber

– one product on the market now is timber based and imported from Finland,[1] even the binder is timber based. Woodchip and sawdust can be combined with clay and lime to produce insulating wall mass, as described in the article on low impact construction elsewhere in this book. Locally supplied woodchip can also be used for fuel. Insofar as this normally replaces fossil fuel alternatives, it is one of the most significantly beneficial uses of timber now available in the UK. Almost all wood pellet fuel is currently imported. With only 12% of the land in the UK under forest, just one third of the EU average, we could always plant more trees...

Treatment

The chemical treatment of timber makes it unsustainable for two reasons. First, these chemicals can be harmful to human, as well as other biological life. Second, treatment takes a completely natural, biodegradable material (one of the few available to the modern designer), and turns it into toxic waste which at the end of its useful life will have to be disposed of at approved sites. The UK has a huge waste disposal problem which is becoming worse, and timber treatment adds to it.

Apologists for the treatment of timber will argue that this is all very unfortunate but sadly unavoidable. Others claim that treatment makes

Fig.1 VOC emissions from building products: Source: VOC emissions from building products: BRE Digest 464 Part 1

The possible emission of VOCs and formaldehyde should be an important consideration during selection of a building product. Timber studs, frames, and beam supports usually have been treated and can contain organic solvents in the timber fibres as preservatives and natural terpene compounds. High VOC emissions can be released from the treated timber and from coatings.

Materials	1 day TVOC emission rates ($\mu g\, m\text{-}2h\text{-}1$)	Typical VOCs
Timber beams, frames & studs	145 - 25,648	Aldehydes (eg formaldehyde, acetaldehyde, C4-C,, aldehydes, benzaldehyde) ketones (eg acetone, MIBK, 2-heptanone, pentan-3-one, pentan9-one, 2-methyC2-butanone, cyclohexanone, acetophenone), terpenes(eg pinenes, carene, myrcene, limonene); linalool; geraniol; a-terpineol; a-cedrene; linalyl acetate; acetic acid; propanoicacid; pentanoic acid; hexanoic acid; benzoic acid; C,-C, alcohols; cyclohexanol; 2-ethylhexanol; benzyl alcohol; 1,2-propanediol; esters (eg ethylacetate, butylacetate, isobutylacetate); C,-C,, alkanes and branched alkanes; cyclohexane; methylcyclohexane; benzene; toluene and alkylbenzenes; styrene; glycols (eg carbitol, triglyme, butyl glycol, 2,2-butoxyethoxyethanol, 2-phenoxyethanol); 2-ethoxyethyl acetate; 2,2,4-trimethyl-1,3-pentanediol monc-isobutyrate; phenol; 2,6-di-tert-pcresol; naphthalene; acenaphthene; trichloroethylene; tetrachloroethylene; chforobenzene; dichlorobenzenes; 1,I,I-trichloroethane

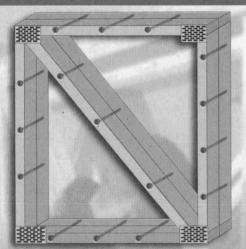

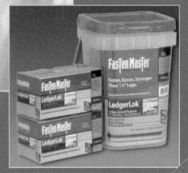

timber more durable – so fewer trees have to be cut down – and people like me ought to be very grateful for it! The answer to both these points is that, with a few exceptions, the treatment of timber is avoidable, and once you know how to avoid it, the continued use of it all around you appears unforgivable.

BRE Digest 464 Part 1 (see Fig.1) gives an indication of the chemicals to be found in all that innocent looking, 'environment friendly' treated timber.

The possible emission of VOCs and formaldehyde should be an important consideration during selection of a building product. Timber studs, frames, and beam supports are usually treated and can contain organic solvents in the timber fibres as preservatives. High VOC emissions can be released from the treated timber and from other coatings.

There are locations and uses where timber is unavoidably at risk and chemical treatment is one answer. Choosing another material which is not liable to decay is also possible, and often preferable. However, the majority of situations can be designed so that timber may be used safely without treatment. There are three main tactics to avoid treatment and these are covered in the next section, which deals with good practice in detailing more generally.

Detailing

Good detailing and specification are critical. If the timber installed only lasts a few years because of poor detailing, most of the effort (and money) has been wasted, and the whole affair can hardly claim to be sustainable.

There are three main tactics worth following to avoid timber treatment and still ensure good durability of timber, all of which need to be considered at the design stage, though of course some of the following is applicable for existing buildings.

The first and by far the most important is good design detailing and specification, the second is moisture transfusive construction and the third is species choice. This is in some ways part of the first, but is worth mentioning separately.

Good detailing for durability is well covered by organisations such as TRADA, BRE and others.

Many specialist publications offer guidance, as well as magazines, trade literature from manufacturers, conference proceedings and other sources of advice. The references list, at the end of this article, gives some of these sources.

The key to good detailing in general is to avoid any build-up of moisture which cannot escape. It doesn't matter too much if timber gets wet, but it matters very much if it stays wet. Stopping it getting wet is normal, but making sure that once wet, it can easily and quickly dry off again can be more important. One of the most common ways timber stays wet is because it is touching, or within about 4mm of another material. Where this happens capilliary action can keep moisture in, and so this sort of detail needs to be avoided wherever possible. Since timber usually has to be fixed to something, it is clear that different forms of detailing start to emerge.

It is also important to allow for movement of timber as it responds to varying ambient humidity levels. Grooves can help reduce shrinkage cracks, which externally at least can be a significant cause of decay, leaving at least 6 or 7mm between boards externally will overcome capilliary action (even allowing for board expansion), and sawn faces tend to evaporate moisture more readily than planed finishes, so may be used with advantage on external boards and cladding.

The important thing about timber coatings in external situations is that they are vapour permeable and allow the timber to move without peeling off. Some coatings achieve this by being somewhat elastic, others, like oil and wax based coatings do not form a skin in the same way and so are not vulnerable to movement. Light, opaque coatings protect timber better (from UV and thermal movement) than darker and more translucent coatings.

Moisture transfusive construction – well known as the 'breathing wall' is a useful tactic not only in controlling moisture movement, but in so doing, protecting the timber used from decay. Because moisture in a 'breathing' wall, floor or ceiling will tend toward the outside and safely evaporate, there will be no build-up of moisture which could lead to decay, and so timber studs and so on may be safely left untreated.

Species choice can have a significant effect on

the durability of timber elements, and in many cases the cost difference is negligible since most of the cost is in the machining of elements. Oak and European larch heartwood, for example are quite durable externally and may be used without preservative treatment for decking, cladding and so on. Softwood external joinery normally needs to be treated but some hardwoods do not, though bottom beads on windows are best protected, or replaced with aluminium, and cills, which are more prone to the destructive effect of UV radiation, need extra protection.

Conclusion

Perhaps the defining aspect of the environmental design movement at present is how it manages to remain true to its ideals whilst acknowledging the need to mainstream and influence the majority. The use of timber in buildings, particularly the use of homegrown timber is a useful gauge of this process, but the movement must also develop and deepen its understanding of the issues, and at present there is a great deal of timber used unwisely and unsustainably. We still have a lot to learn on the subject.

Postscript

One interesting development, which could have huge repercussions for the forest and timber industry in construction and elsewhere, is the idea of timber use as a carbon store. Initial work in Norway and Scotland suggests that using mass timber, and indeed timber generally, contributes more than you might imagine to storing carbon in the medium term, more even than installing pv cells on your roof, for example and this notion may have some currency in the wider carbon sequestration debate. Of course, it depends where it comes from...! ❖

References.

1. 'Timber based insulation "Vital" is available from Construction Resources - *www.constructionresources. com*

Websites.
Forest Stewardship Council *www.fsc-uk.info*
PEFC Council *www.pefc.org/internet/html*
Forestry Commission *www.forestry.gov.uk*
UK Forest Products Association *www.ukfpa.co.uk*
TRADA *www.trada.co.uk*
British Biogen *www.britishbiogen.co.uk*

Publications
Affentranger, C New Wood Architecture in Scandinavia Birkhäuser, ISBN 3 7643 5458 5

Borer P & Harris C Out of the Woods: Ecological Designs for Timber Frame Houses CAT Publications / Walter Segal Trust

Dinwoodie, J.M. Timber: Its Nature and Behaviour E & FN Spon, ISBN 0 419 23580 9

Forests Forever Responsible Timber Purchasing Forests Forever, 2001 (Contact 0207 839 1891)

Forests Forever Timber in Buildings: The Environmental Choice

Forests Forever, 1999 (Contact 0207 839 1891)

Gutdeutsch, G Building in Wood: Construction and Details Birkhäuser, ISBN 3 7643 5277

Hislop, P.J. & TRADA External Timber Cladding

TRADA Technology Ltd., 2000 ISBN 1 900510 30 8

Rideout, B Timber Decay in Buildings: The Conservation Approach to Treatment E & FN Spon, ISBN 0 419 18820 7

Stungo, N The New Wood Architecture Laurence King, 1998

TRADA British Grown Hardwoods: The Designers' Manual TRADA Technology Ltd., 1996 ISBN 1 900510 02 2

TRADA Timber Frame Construction TRADA Technology, 2001 ISBN 1 900510 32 4

Wachsmann, K Building the Wooden House: Technique and Design Birkhäuser, ISBN 3 7643 5134 9

TRADA Technology Ltd has published a revised version of its Wood Information Sheet 'Durability by design'. This Wood Information Sheet contends that the life of timber components can be extended considerably by attention to detail at the design stage. It urges designers first to target and define performance and maintenance expectations, then to specify and detail appropriately.

Principles for protective design detailing are included and expected life and component sensitivity are discussed, along with specification strategies.

Members may download a pdf file of 'Durability by design' free-of-charge from *www.asktrada.co.uk*. Non-members may purchase a copy at a cost of £5.00 plus postage & packing from the online bookshop, or by contacting the publications department on 01494 569602 or email info@trada.co.uk.

Merchant on a mission

Demonstrating social responsibility is fast becoming a fundamental requirement of organisations in the timber trade. As demand for chain of custody approved materials increases and the attention from media and non-Governmental organisations intensifies, leading UK timber merchants, such as Travis Perkins (TP), have embarked on a crusade to prove their commitment to the environment.

Ian Goldsmith, Group Planning Director of TP, assesses the first steps taken by the merchant to satisfy its own ethics and that of the timber trade.

The amount of work involved in procurement of certified timber products and achievement of chain of custody is substantial. It is agreed, however, that it is the responsibility of the industry to raise the profile of such products and educate customers as to the benefits of using timber from well-managed forests. With growing awareness of the importance of using certified products, future demand will undoubtedly increase; suppliers will be encouraged to invest to produce greater volumes at lower costs, and the mindset of the trade and end user will change.

The reputation of a business dictates its responsibility and accountability to customers for the products sourced and supplied. Travis Perkins has, over the last few years, implemented a major programme of continuous improvement relating to social and environmental performance. It has worked closely with non-Governmental organisations, shareholders and suppliers to understand their view on environmental issues and therefore guide its actions in implementing good practice over and above that required by legislation. This culminated in the accomplishment of an Environmental Management System and the achievement in November 2001 of ISO14001 certification – the first national merchant in the UK to do so.

A range of policies and procedures ensures that environmental issues are considered in all aspects of decision-making and a continuous improvement plan includes targets to increase the percentage of certified timber products available in branches - more than 270 have achieved chain of custody certification nationwide with a roll out to all branches intended by the end of 2004.

In addition, a programme of independent audits on all sources of timber from higher risk areas that are not currently certified has shown that merchants such as TP can encourage and assist suppliers to achieve certification over time. An excellent example of this is the Compensados E Laminados Lavrasul mill in Brazil, which has now achieved FSC certification for its Elliottii Pine Plywood.

Although the UK Government has not made it mandatory, TP has adopted CE marking in its timber procurement as this is deemed the most effective method of meeting the Construction Product Directive.

Travis Perkins has whole-heartedly accepted its environmental obligations; after all, a good business should also be a good citizen. It is also ethically the correct path for the trade to follow and a strong element of a broader social responsibility programme. TP has started its mission and aims to continue leading other merchants by example.

TP is one of the largest suppliers of timber and building materials in the UK with more than 740 branches nationwide. The company supplies more than 100,000 product lines to trade professionals and self-builders. For details of your nearest branch call the Customer Careline on 0800 389 6611 or log on to: www.travisperkins.co.uk.

Modern earth building

The benefits of unfired earth as a building material are increasingly being recognised in modern construction projects. Low environmental impact and the capacity to beneficially regulate environmental conditions of internal spaces are just two benefits. Unfired earth elements can satisfy the requirements of building regulations in a wide range of applications, including loadbearing walls, infill panels, external and internal walls, plasters and renders, floors and cladding. **Pete Walker** introduces us to the most common techniques employed ...

Rammed earth, mud-block, cob and clay plasters are some of the growing array of techniques employed in modern earth buildings.

Rammed earth

Rammed earth, or pisé, construction is primarily an in-situ form of earth building, in which moist sub-soil is compacted in layers between temporary formwork supports. Unlike most other earth wall techniques, rammed earth is often left without renders or plasters. Recent applications, especially by Martin Rauch, express the aesthetic qualities of rammed earth construction.

Mud-block

The traditional form of earth block construction, adobe, comprises air-dried moulded heavy-weight mud blocks laid in a mud mortar. Similar manufactured cob blocks are available in the UK. Modern mud-block construction also uses both dry-pressed and extruded unfired clay units. Unfired standard sized clay bricks, such as Errol Brick Company's 'Eco-brick', are also available. Alternatively solid compressed earth blocks may be made to requirements using mechanical presses. Lightweight clay blocks, containing fibres such as straw and hemp, offer infill masonry alternatives for non-loadbearing panels in timber frame construction. Vegetable fibres reduce weight and improve insulation qualities. A variety of imported lightweight products, such as the Karposite blocks, are available from NBT (see refs).

Cob

As with rammed earth, cob is an in-situ mass wall technique, though like adobe it uses a wet mixture of mud and straw. Following preparation, cob walls are formed by stacking the mud-straw mixture in a progressive series of layers. As a wet technique cob lends itself to non-linear forms and sculptural expression. Cob is usually rendered or plastered for protection.

Other methods

Light earth construction combines a clay slip

Entrance to the reception building at the Eden Project in Cornwall, rammed earth walls

and vegetable matter fill, such as straw, woodchip or hemp shive, to form a solid wall infill material. Panels are built within a timber frame to provide internal and external walls. Alternatively blocks may be preformed and stacked. The material is lightly compacted between temporary forms supported off the timber frame. The clay slip coats the lightweight fill material to bind it together and provide some protection against decay and fire. On completion the walls are usually plastered or rendered.

Clay plasters have been used for many centuries. As well as protecting the material beneath, clay plasters provide an attractive hygroscopic finish that can make a significant contribution to building performance. A range of proprietary clay plasters, from Bayosan, Claytec and Tierrafino, are currently available from Construction Resources. Clay plasters can also be used on a variety of substrates other than earth walling.

Rammed earth, cob and mud-block, including tiles, are all also suited to floor construction. Beautiful and durable floors may be provided by protecting the earth using coatings such as natural waxes and oils.

New cob earth extension near Newport in Ceredigion being built by earth builder Steve Wilson. Steve plans to leave the exterior of these extremely well finished walls unplastered.

Materials

The bulk raw material of most earthen building is inorganic sub-soil. Soils suited to earth building should be well-graded, containing appropriate proportions of gravel, sand, silt and clay. Gravel and sand contents provide the structural matrix for the soil bound together by clay, soil's natural binder. Too little clay and there is insufficient cohesion; too much clay the soil is difficult to work and will shrink excessively on drying.

Traditional vernacular techniques have evolved to make best use of local soils. Mud, or wet moulded techniques such as cob and adobe, is best suited to soils with relatively higher clay contents; drying shrinkage is controlled by the addition of natural fibres such as straw. Rammed earth, compressed earth blocks and other compacted techniques are more suited to soils with lower clay contents; drying shrinkage

is controlled by having less clay and using less water during construction.

Many people attracted to earth building see it as a means of maximising the use of locally sourced materials. In some projects, such as the Eden Project's Visitors Centre and the Kindersley Centre at Sheepdrove Farm in Berkshire, this approach has worked successfully.

A variety of proprietary earthen products, including blocks, plasters, renders and mortar, are available. Unfortunately at present many of these are imported from overseas. Material testing and consultation is recommended when using unproven materials and appropriate resources, in particular time, should be allocated for this. Some unsuitable materials can be improved by blending with others.

Some benefits and limitations of earth building

Earth building materials offer a number of significant advantages for modern buildings. Natural clays are hygroscopic, absorbing and releasing moisture in response to changing air conditions. Their presence in walls, floors and plasters regulate the internal environmental conditions of

Earth is a wonderful material. Here, in this rammed earth building designed and built by Natural Building Design, its natural mouldable properties are used to good effect.

Though the durability of earth building is well proven, unfired earthen materials will deteriorate and decay in the prolonged presence of water. Consequently walls are normally built on raised plinths and with surfaces protected by renders, plasters or coatings. External walls are often further protected by extended roof projections. This susceptibility to deteriation in the presence of water must be addressed in design and construction.

Walls, especially in-situ techniques such as cob and rammed earth, are frequently thicker than many alternative forms of construction, especially for internal walls.

Costs of earthen construction are influenced by technique, application, design, and material selection. Finished costs of earth walling are comparable with competing methods such as fired clay brickwork.

Guidance

Development of earth building in the UK has been restricted by the lack of authoritative guidance for designers, builders and building occupants. Three recent projects sponsored, under the DTi's Partners in Innovation scheme, have been working towards addressing this problem. A design and construction guide for rammed earth construction, developed by the University of Bath together with Insitu Rammed Earth and others, is to be published soon. Guidance on the use of unfired clay bricks, mortar and plasters has recently been produced by Tom Morton at Arc Architects, with further guidance available in 2005[1]. Published guidance on use of light earth construction is already available from Chris Morgan of Gaia Architects[2]. These publications, together with other future innovations, provide the foundation for greater and wider use of modern earth building in the UK. ❖

1. Tom Morton - *www.arc-architects.co.uk*

2. Chris Morgan - *www.lightearth.co.uk*

Steve Wilson - earth builder - 01348 837 007

Natural Building Design - 01695 729603

Construction Resources - 020 7450 2211
www.ecoconstruct.com

Natural Building Technologies (NBT) - 01844 338338
www.natural-building.co.uk

In-situ - *www.rammed-earth.info*

buildings, in particular relative humidity, removing many of the triggers associated with medical conditions such as asthma.

Unfired earth materials generally have very low embodied energy (and carbon dioxide); transportation is perhaps the greatest contributor to environmental impact. On the whole earthen building materials have low toxicity, though some surface treatments may emit high levels of volatile organic compounds. Earthen materials are also readily recycled or easily disposed of at the end of their life.

Earthen materials do not on the whole possess good thermal insulating qualities. External earth walls will therefore normally require further insulation measures. However, earthen walls and floors can make a significant contribution to building performance through their thermal mass, storing and releasing heat energy passively.

The Natural Plaster Book Book review

Editor's favourite

Although this book is all about natural plasters, it dedicates a number of chapters to the natural buildings that are most likely to be adorned with these finishes - mainly straw bale but cob, rammed earth and tyres (earthship style) are also included. It is fascinating reading and makes the book even better value. The authors go into quite a lot of detail, certainly for the straw building. So much so that the book could just as easily have been titled 'The Natural Building and Plaster Book.' If I have a criticism it's that they do not seem to be telling all homeowners that, regardless of their house type, they can have beautiful natural plastered walls in their home too. One could almost get the impression that you need to build yourself a completely natural home before you can naturally plaster it. This certainly isn't true and probably the authors assume that we will all take from the book just what we can use. There is a full colour section that beautifully illustrates what can be achieved and certainly helps drive home the claim that natural building allows personal expression to emerge in all of us. It certainly inspired me.

The book is nicely laid out for those of us (me included) who just like to dip in at will or as the need arises. Straightforward chapters and bite sized subheadings take you straight to the point. Warnings, tips and ideas are included in clearly highlighted boxouts.

The authors, Cedar Rose Guelberth and Dan Chiras, certainly know their stuff and practice what they preach which I always find makes the most interesting reading. There are so many theoretical eco-building books around that it's often difficult to spot the real gems among the chaff. Cedar Rose has practised natural building and plastering for over 25 years and even has her own retail company in the States where she makes and sells the products she obviously so enjoys using.

Dan is a name you may well have heard before. He has written extensively on natural building, solar energy and environmental homes. He lives the story in a passive solar/solar pv home built of tyres, straw bale and earth in Colorado.

I am so impressed by this book I have added it to the small selection of specially selected titles that we sell at our website: www.newbuilder.co.uk.

Reviewed by Keith Hall

Just £26.00 inc. p&p
Go online to
www.newbuilder.co.uk
and pay by credit card.
Alternatively send a cheque (or
your credit card details) to:

Green Building Press, PO Box 32,
Llandysul, SA44 5ZA

More about cob

Edward Moss explains what cob really is and points out some of its endearing features ...

Cob is a building material made from clay rich sub soil, mixed with sand (to reduce drying shrinkage) and straw. Straw acts as reinforcement and allows cob to be easily pitched up to higher lifts. It is mixed into a moist, consistent and cohesive material. Cob is a non-toxic resource and can be 'returned' to the earth or reused after the original building's life ends.

When dried out cob becomes very hard and can last hundreds of years, as long as the cobber's rule is followed,

"a good hat and a solid pair of boots".

This means a leak free roof with a good over hang and a solid footing. The footing acts as a splash barrier or boot to stop bottom up erosion. The roof acts as a rain guard or hat to stop top down erosion.

The properties of clay

Clay particles are shaped like a disc. This composition allows the material to absorb water and swell or dry out and shrink. Some clays are more prone to swelling and shrinking.

Types of cob

Mass cob – This is cob made in a large volume. It is built in lifts or layers and then trimmed or pared with a shovel. Mass cob is used to create free flowing walls and sculptural building because it requires no shuttering / formwork. When using mass cob, drying shrinkage must be allowed for.
Cob bricks – These are pre made cob building blocks and are usually the size of a concrete block or smaller. Cob is mixed and then placed in moulds and allowed to dry. The blocks have already undergone shrinkage and are ready to be used. For this reason they are usually used for renovation work.

Why build with cob?

Cob buildings have smooth, organic lines and the thick solid walls give it strength. It is quite a magical experience when surrounded by cob. Cob also regulates the internal environment, in other words it acts as a natural air conditioner. This means it will regulate temperature and humidity (water vapour content in air). Cob (and all earth walling techniques) behaves in this manner because it has a high thermal mass. This means it absorbs heat when warmed and releases it over a long period of time. The opposite is true for cooling. For example in hot African countries mud huts are built with thick mud walls which absorb the heat making it comfortable inside. Air can hold more vapour when cold and therefore when it is warmed the atmosphere dries out. This warming/drying effect is one of the factors in sick building syndrome. This will not happen with cob, for example heating internally will warm the air making the room warmer. Natural moisture movement through the cob will then humidify the warmer air.

Why cob goes wrong

Unsympathetic restoration of cob has given it a bad name. Cob houses have tended to be associated with damp cold dwellings. The reason cob has acquired this stigma is because modern non-breathable materials have been used to repair it. For example cement render does not breathe like lime render. Hairline movement cracks start in the cement render because it is a rigid, modern, unforgiving material. The hairline cracks allow water to get in behind the render and soak the cob, which stays wet because it cannot breathe. This is a cyclic process and eventually the render and wall will fail. All this could be prevented if cob was better understood. As long as you let the moisture move through cob it will stand for many, many years.

Conclusion

Things to remember about cob
● Cob building is nothing new, it has been practiced in the UK (mainly Devon) for hundreds of years

- Cob needs a good hat and a solid pair of boots
- Cob is natural and non-toxic
- Cob moderates the internal environment – but breathable materials must be used with it, such as lime renders, mortar and plasters to let it breathe! ❖

Suggested reading

Cob Building by Jane Schofield and Jill Smallcombe, ISBN 0 9524341 5 6

The Hand Sculpted House: practical guide to building a cob cottage by Ianto Evans, Linda Smiley and Micheal G Smith

The above books are available from The Green Shop **www.greenshop.co.uk** *01452 770629*

New cob home in Devon built by Kevin Mccabe. An in-depth story about Kevin's home can be found in Building for a Future magazine Vol 13 No 3 Winter 2003/4 ' **http://www.newbuilder.co.uk/bffmag/**

Sculptural artistic cob – potting shed at the Falmouth Green Centre

Straw bale building

Using straw in building is not a new concept. It has been used for over 100 years in America and for a similar length of time in the UK where it tended to be limited to thatching and 'reinforcement' in cob walling. **Edward Moss** offers us a compressed briefing on the straw bale building world ...

American pioneers were building homes with straw bales 100 years ago but In recent years building with straw bales has been going through a renaissance in the UK thanks to a few passionate 'straw baler' pioneers.

The properties of straw

High quality straw has minimal organic matter in it and it's a renewable resource. It also has extremely low carbon and embodied energy. Straw has extremely good thermal properties, it is nature's insulator. This means that a building built using straw will be kept cool in the summer and warm in the winter.

Straw bale myths

Do straw houses rot? The first straw bale house was built about 130 years ago. There are some straw houses in USA nearing 100 years old which are still inhabited. Straw will only rot when it gets wet and stays wet. To prevent rotting you should have a self-draining footing, good eaves and over hang to stop driving rain saturating the wall.

What about rodent attack? Straw has no particular attraction for mice and rats because it contains no food. It is the stems of baled cereal crops, unlike hay. But rats and mice like to live in spaces, i.e. wall cavities and floor voids. Once the straw bale walls have been lime rendered there are no gaps to encourage the mice and rats in.

The three little pigs' myth? Straw bale buildings are structurally 'pinned' together at the base, between courses and at the top of the wall. Chestnut or other local wood is used for structural 'pinning'.

Straw bale building is a very social occasion. Groups of friends can gather at weekends to build or plaster straw bale buildings as they are so natural and user friendly. Photo: Chris Morgan

Building with Straw Bales

What about the fire risk? Research in the USA and Canada concluded that: "Straw bales hold enough air to provide good insulation value but because they are compacted firmly do not hold enough air to permit combustion" (Bob Platts 1997)

Hay can spontaneously combust, but straw is a very different material. There have been no cases of spontaneous combustion. When walls are rendered both sides the risk of fire is reduced even further. However loose straw on site can burn and should be tidied up.

Methods of straw baling

Nebraska – this was the method pioneered by the Nebraskan settlers in USA. The bales take the load and are pinned with hazel stakes at the footings and have timber wall plates. The roof is secured to the footing with coppiced hazel and strapping.

Load bearing with temporary lightweight frame - a lightweight frame with a roof is constructed. Temporary bracing and props are used to keep it in position. The roof is suspended about 100mm above the finished wall height. The bale wall is constructed in much the same way as Nebraska. Once the walls are complete the roof is lowered onto the finished wall and the frame taken away.

Infill - the roof load is taken by a structural frame and the bales are used to infil the gaps between the structure. This approach requires carpentry skills and has cost and environmental disadvantages over the others. ❖

Suggested reading

Building with straw bales – a practical guide for the UK and Ireland by Barbara Jones

Serious strawbale: A home construction guide for all climates by Paul Lacinski and Michel Bergeron,

Building for a Future magazine - Volume 14 No 3. (Winter 2004/5) features an in-depth article looking at the UK's first, two storey straw bale house. **www.newbuilder.co.uk**

A Practical Guide for the UK and Ireland

This is a book that concentrates specifically on techniques for straw building in the UK and Ireland. It is written for self-builders and the construction industry.

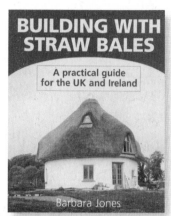

However, its clear, non-technical language also makes it suitable for the amateur. It is written by an English builder, Barbara Jones, who has studied American straw bale building techniques and adapted and developed them for the UK climate. A builder by trade, she has been constructing in straw and teaching others how to use this material for over ten years. She has been involved with designing and building many straw bale projects in the UK and is considered an expert on the subject.

The book is certainly practical. It explains the different methods of straw bale building: load-bearing, framed and hybrid. It also includes useful information on planning and building regulations. She explains what makes a good building bale, and there's a section on tools, some guidance on costs and a chapter on lime rendering. It not only tells the reader what to use and how, but most importantly, it explains why.

There are plenty of clear detailed drawings but some details do reveal some potentially nasty cold bridges and air leakage problems that would need to be dealt with.

£9.95 ISBN 1-903998-13-1 (available from The Green Shop www.greenshop.co.uk 01452 770629)

Earthships

A new cost effective strategy for people building their own homes has taken a big step forward with the construction of the first two Earthship buildings in the UK. Earthships offer ingenious yet simple alternatives to the traditional bricks and mortar approach. **Keith Hall** reports ...

Brighton is the location for Europe's first major Earthship which offers inspiration to tackle Europe's growing waste tyre mountains and to build communities with minimum impact from carbon dioxide emissions and global warming. The UK generates 40 million used tyres each year. With each Earthship taking around 2000 tyres to build, just 20,000 new Earthships each year would use all of this growing tyre mountain as well as saving millions of tonnes of carbon dioxide from being pumped into the atmosphere.

The Low Carbon Network, the group behind the Brighton project, is also pioneering a new approach to development which is applicable to any project whatever the scale. By assessing the carbon footprint of the building and compensating for this through reforestation, Earthship Brighton is the first carbon balanced development in the UK. Low Carbon Network is also experimenting with a radical new form of cement, which dramatically reduces CO_2 emissions, and again could be applied to any project. This magnesia based cement is called ecocement, and originates from work in Australia (**www.tececo. com**).

Earthships are solar powered 'low carbon' homes and work spaces, built from a massive waste problem - used tyres. They are buildings that work with the planet's natural systems - using the sun's energy and rain to provide heat, power and water. They do not make use of greenhouse gas emitting power stations, nor do they rely on mains water or waste services. This makes them autonomous and therefore cheap to run.

Earthship Brighton, built in collaboration with Mike Reynolds, the originator of the Earthship concept, and his crew from the United States, provide a unique opportunity to inspire innovation in the face of climate change while also offering a new model for affordable home building with minimum impact on the environment. Low Carbon Network is now offering training to groups and individuals who are interested in learning more about this new way of approaching development. Courses can be booked through their website.

Daren Howarth, Earthship project manager commented: "We live in a time where there is a desperate need for bold experiments to tackle our social and ecological imbalances. We must rapidly identify alternatives, try them out and switch them on. Earthships offer massive potential and we are putting massive energy into making them happen."

Scotland's first Earthship is now officially open to visitors. This is a building made completely

from reclaimed materials using old car tyres and drinks cans as the basic building blocks, with the typical Earthship principles of thermal mass and passive solar design. It is a fully autonomous building providing its own heating, electricity, water and sewage treatment.

Paula Cowie of Sustainable Communities Innitiative (SCI) said "It is now open as a resource centre and we have a library of eco-building and sustainable living books and videos. Tours are currently available on request but anybody is free to come and look around the building and see how it was built. If anyone is intererested in visiting then please contact me".

Although these are the only the two Earthships so far in Britain, this bold experiment has already attracted significant interest, and the Low Carbon Network and SCI are helping a number of other projects to prepare to launch. Most of these will be community centres based on the Earthship model, and the network will be looking to empower the communities themselves to help with the buildings. ❖

Low Carbon Network
www.lowcarbon.co.uk

Sustainable Communities Innitiative
Tel 01592 891884
www.priority@sci-scotland.org.uk
www.sci-scotland.org.uk

Want to know more about earthships? Book review

The Earthship series of books from the inventor of the concept, Michael Reynolds, have been in circulation since the early 1990's.

So what is an Earthship? The general idea is that the building will be totally autonomous. Earthships are built largely using unwanted tyres whose tread has been worn down to the requisite 1.6mm. The tyres are stacked and stuffed with subsoil from the building site. The whole of the southern elevation of the building is a conservatory (greenhouse) in order to bring in as much solar gain as possible. The massive nature of the floor and walls is expected to store heat for later.

As far as we know, the Earthship books are the only ones dedicated to this subject. Volume I gives you everything you need to build the basic shell, from the 'U' shaped tyre walls, the roof, the greenhouse, as well as detailing and finishes. Chapters on the concept, location and design are also included, as well as some general advice on how to live in an Earthship. Although many uses have been discovered for unwanted tyres over the past few years, the Earthship is one of the most imaginative. >>>

Volume II is all about systems and components. Systems include solar electric and hot water, domestic water (from rainfall), waste and lighting. The components section has details on fireplaces, stairs, gravity skylights, bathroom fittings, doors and cabinets. A final section looks at appropriate landscaping. Although many of these subjects have been covered in other books you may be more familiar with, the Earthship version does give a new slant on many of the ideas.

Volume III is subtitled 'Evolution beyond Economics', and my initial thoughts were along the lines of 'what can they possibly have left out of volumes I & II?' The general idea of this volume is to extend the ideas and concepts of the first two books. Part one gives plenty of extra thoughts on the structure and mechanics of the building itself. Part two adds new components and concepts such as a thermal mass refrigerator, and a solar toilet. Part three explores community concepts and the possibility of urban Earthships, while the final part looks at related ideas such as a tyre building code, and building domes using waste drinks cans.

The three books have a fairly homespun feel, but have a mass of detail and excellent diagrams which leave you in no doubt about how to proceed. The only let down is the quality of the photographs, which suffer from mediocre monochrome reprinting. Another consideration for UK readers is that many of the concepts rely on a fairly dry and sunny (though not necessarily warm) climate. Information should be sought on the experiences of the designer/builders of the Fife and Brighton Earthships to supplement the excellent detail in these three books.

Reviewed by Jerry Clark

£25 each, ISBNs 0-9626767-0-5, 0-9626767-1-3, 0-9626767-2-1 respectively, Solar Survival Press, available from Green Shop, www.greenshop.co.uk, 01452 770629

Book review continued

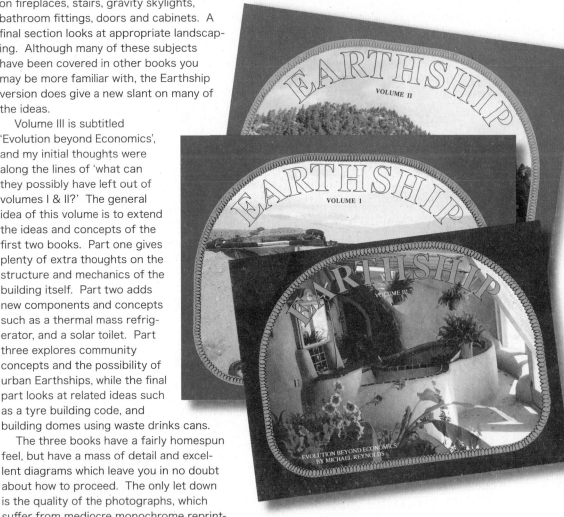

The real cost of decoration

High-performance natural paints and finishes: a sensible investment or just ludicrously overpriced? The average contractor, paint merchant or buyer may entertain the possible advantages, but these considerations often go out of the window when the issue of price comes up. **Richard Handyside** believes they are worth the investment ...

Litre for litre, natural paints almost invariably appear more expensive than their conventional competitors – sometimes double the price or more. Why are natural products often more expensive to buy? Economies of scale is certainly part of the explanation. Natural paints and finishes have a market penetration of less than 5%, even in the markets where they are most successful, such as Germany and Holland. So their manufacturers generally lack the opportunities for cost reduction available to the chemical giants, in procuring raw materials, in manufacture, in marketing and in distribution.

The cost of quality

The quality of ingredients and the high cost of some natural raw materials are other factors. Natural paints use very finely milled pigments, and many of these are not in such relatively cheap and abundant supply as classical yellow ochre or burnt umber. Natural ultramarine blue, a particularly popular choice, is fearfully expensive compared to the synthetic alternative.

Natural paints use not just any oil, but selected quality linseed oils, often organically cultivated, and not just any balsamic turpentine, but highly selected turpentine, tested for the lowest possible delta-carene content to minimise harmful emissions.

The quality of the products is another key factor. Skilled manufacturers of natural paints, bringing thoroughly modern technology and knowledge to bear on long-proven traditional raw materials and recipes, create finishes of a quality which can stand up against the very best conventional products – and a performance which far exceeds that of the cheaper conventional products which are typically brought into the equation when a specification reaches the pricing stage. This quality translates into coverage and obliteration, which can be measured and proven in practice, but are typically left out of the crude price-per-can equation. Very often the benefits to the total cost of the finished job will more than out-weigh the bare price difference.

The quality of natural paints, oils and waxes also translates into such terms as softness, sheen, subtlety, transparency – 'merely aesthetic' considerations, not measurable like coverage and opacity, but very real to the appreciative users of the building. In a hospital, every element that increases the general sense of well-being is a positive benefit to the healing process.

In offices, shops and other workplaces, study after study has proven beyond doubt that buildings with natural finishes and natural insulation and natural ventilation – bring major benefits in comfort and significant benefits in reductions in costly employee sickness and absenteeism.

The cost of health

Ecological quality is much more than a question of subjective aesthetics. The sick building syndrome is still not fully recognised by all designers and developers, but there is now a wide public and professional awareness of the link between indoor pollution and environmental diseases. Healthy buildings breathe, and natural paints and finishes play an important part in maintaining that breathing quality, rather than sealing surfaces like most conventional finishes.

Paints and finishes cover such a major proportion of the surface area of everyone's living and working environment that their part in the complex chemical environment has to be a cause for concern. Increasing numbers of people suffer from skin problems, allergies and multiple

Natural finishes can provide opportunities for artistic shading, striking or subtle designs! Here coloured lime wash has been used for the walls and natural varnish for the wooden floor.

chemical sensitivity, and quite simply need to reduce the number and complexity of chemical compounds in their environment. Natural paints and finishes, using a much smaller range of well-proven raw materials than conventional alternatives, offer one way of reducing these problems.

An important feature of natural paints, absolutely NOT shared by conventional paints, is their manufacturers' general practice of declaring ingredients, which enables purchasers to form their own judgment about potential health hazards. Occupational health is an equally important consideration.

The true environmental costs

When it comes to overall environmental impact, true costs are not adequately reflected in selling prices. Manufacturers of natural paints and finishes choose renewable raw materials wherever possible – natural oils sustainably harvested from plants and trees rather than petrochemical compounds from finite resources, often extracted at huge cost to the environment. They deliberately seek to exclude toxic ingredients from their products – and toxic by-products from their manufacture.

Legislation does theoretically impose restrictions on discharge of toxic waste from manufacturing processes. But in many countries this legislation is only loosely policed, if at all, and penalties for infractions are generally visibly low. Because of the materials used, it is clear that an accidental discharge from a natural paint factory would be less likely to kill thousands of fish downstream than a discharge from a conventional paint manufacturer. The true costs of pollution are all too often ignored, and these costs, direct and indirect, end up being paid by the tax-payer, and society at large. These costs are not included in the selling price of a can of conventional paint.

At the other end of their life cycle, many products of the petrochemical paint industry cannot be disposed of as anything other than toxic waste. This is becoming increasingly expensive to handle officially, so large amounts are disposed of illegally, whether locally or by shipment to poorer countries with no shortage of corrupt officials keen to turn a blind eye. Natural

paints and finishes are designed to be bio-degradable, so these problems do not arise. The true costs of illegal waste disposal are paid by society as a whole: they are not included in the selling price of conventional paint. At the centre of paint's life cycle, the predominant issues are those of personal and occupational health, and of a healthy living and working environment. Some costs of a poor working environment fall on employers who suffer high levels of sickness leave and absenteeism.

Most costs, however, fall on the individuals whose health suffers, whether at work or in the home, or as workers in the painting trade – and as often as not these individuals will have had no say in the original choice of the product/s that affect them. Here once again, true costs are not included in the price of a can of conventional paint.

Balancing the costs

For conventional paints – as for other synthetic building products – current selling prices badly understate the true, overall cost to us as individuals and as a society. Our 'free market' is a very inadequate mechanism for reflecting even direct costs, let alone indirect ones.

The prices of natural, healthy, non-polluting paints and finishes come much closer to reflecting their true costs. When conventional materials start to bear their true costs, the natural alternatives will become the only sensible and economic choice. Legislation, in forms such as energy and waste disposal taxes, is starting to move towards a more level playing field, but painfully slowly. Until that happens we need to strike our own individual balance between buying products that seem cheaper now but will be costing us more in the long run and natural products whose selling price comes much closer to including all their costs. ❖

The Natural Paint Book

Book review

Don't confuse this book with other DIY or decorating books currently flooding bookshops. As well as being a hands-on 'how to do it' book it is also a recipe book that will teach you how to concoct your very own paint recipes from natural organic resources and minerals.

Our modern way of living keeps us indoors 80% of the time and indoor pollution can be up to 10 times higher than that found outdoors. Not only will natural paints enhance the ambience of your rooms, but, through the avoidance of chemicals, their use will lower the toxic load in your home and help to reduce the chemical burden that the paint industry places on the ecology of the Earth.

Even to those people for whom health and ecology are not their main issue, the exciting decorative properties of natural paints and finishes bring them into a class of their own.

The book begins with a history of paint and decoration, then it outlines what paints are made up from with an emphasis on natural ingredients, some of which you will probably have to hand in the kitchen. Two further chapters explore over 20 home-made paint recipes and over 25 techniques for the creative application of these products. Other sections look at the use of colour in Feng-shui, colour therapy and the use of space and light to enhance various decorative effects, suggesting possibilities for each room in the home.

This is a delightful and lavishly illustrated book, inspiring the reader to be adventurous in creating harmony in the home without compromising the harmony of Planet Earth.

Written by Lynn Edwards and Julia Lawless
ISBN 1 85626 432 7 Published by Kylie Cathie Ltd.

**Order now online for just £12.99 www.newbuilder.co.uk/books
or call 01559 370798 to order by phone.**

Choosing and using natural paints

Most people would not regard paint to be a very interesting subject, but just consider what this material means to us. Used by humans for thousands of years, it's something we are virtually surrounded by 24 hours a day. With the boom in synthetic paints since the 1950s we are only now realising the effect these modern materials are having on the global environment and our own health. **Jamie Anderson** considers some of the issues surrounding petro-chemical paints and the viable alternative in the form of natural paints and finishes ...

When selecting paint one usually considers durability and cost. Other aspects to bear in mind however, are the damage caused to the environment during the production and use of chemical paints, and the potential damage to human health during and after their application.

Durability

If we look first at durability, one of the main causes of paint failure is trapped moisture beneath a paint skin. This makes the timber rot and the paint layer flake and blister. Natural paints, by virtue of their ingredients, are microporous, meaning moisture is allowed to pass through them, whilst still being waterproof. This is akin to a built-in ventilation system for your walls, ensuring there is always fresh air in the room. You may have noticed how the woodwork you painted last year has cracked and water has penetrated into the wood. Chemical paints often sit on top of a surface or penetrate just below it. Again, with natural paints the oils used - particu-

larly linseed oil which has a tiny molecule size - penetrate deeply into the surface of the timber, nourishing it and deflecting water.

Synthetic paints may attract dust and bacteria as their ingredients are electrically charged and contain plastic, whilst natural paints use plant resins and other ingredients that act anti-statically. By repelling dust and bacteria natural paints enhance the room climate and keep their true colour longer.

Cost

The cost of natural paints – or the perceived cost - is what seems to put many people off even considering them. On paper, the difference can be between two or three times more. However these comparisons are usually made with the cheapest trade paints, whereas when comparing quality natural paints with top of the range, chemical-based paints, we actually see a fairer comparison.

Environment

Whilst financial considerations are one aspect of cost, we need to look at the implications for the environment. Production of synthetic paints gives out nearly as much atmospheric pollution as vehicle exhausts and often results in 10 to 30 tonnes of waste per tonne of product. With a dilution ratio of 40 million to 1, once these products enter the sewage system the damage becomes even harder to calculate.

Health

The cost of synthetic paints continues to increase when we consider the health implications for the user. In 1989 the World Health Organisation reported that painting as an occu-

pation is carcinogenic.

The use of paints and their in-can chemical cocktail of ingredients can also cause and aggravate allergies, particularly skin and respiratory disorders. Media advice in national newspapers on pollution, health and chemical issues is to seek out safe, quality alternatives.

VOCs

You may have noticed information on paint products mentioning the 'VOC' content of the product. VOCs (Volatile Organic Compounds) are a class of carbon-based chemicals which, when released into the atmosphere, produce ground level ozone. According to the American Environmental Protection Agency, 9% of the airborne pollutants creating ground level ozone come from the VOCs in paint.

VOC levels are consistently ten times higher indoors than outdoors – this number rises by 1,000 times directly after a new coat of paint... something to be avoided if possible! More alarmingly, VOCs have been linked to many different physical ailments. The staggering list of the serious effects VOCs have on humans includes: irritation to the skin, eyes, and respiratory system, headaches, fatigue, nausea, difficulty with memory, dizziness, damage to the liver, kidney or central nervous system.

Studies show that up to 90% of the internal surface area of a building may have a synthetic covering. The indoor environment can be up to ten times more polluted than the external environment, yet we spend up to 80% of our time indoors.

Living in a safe, natural environment

Fortunately, there is something you can easily do to avoid generating pollution and unsafe living spaces. You can still have beautifully finished, colourful walls without poisoning yourself or the environment. Choose natural paints. Natural paints contain natural, mainly renewable, ingredients such as seed oils, tree resins, natural pigments, inert mineral fillers and more.

Paints for your walls

The most popular and readily available natural paints are emulsions, clay paints and casein paint. Each of these paints is easily applied using brushes and rollers and is available in a range of colours. If you are brave, a little experimentation with mixing your own pigments can increase the choice of colours. The distributors and manufacturers of natural paints in the UK are constantly expanding the range of colours offered, and Villa Natura, the UK's distributor of Biofa paint, have recently introduced a mixing machine that can mix up to 750 colours!

Natural emulsions give a lively matt finish as the natural pigment particles diffract light. They are wipeable and have excellent dirt and stain resistance. You can choose from paints that are washable or for heavy wear areas paints with a soft silk sheen that are scrubbable. If you want to add protection and keep a matt finish you can apply a clear matt wall glaze.

Clay paint is a clay-based emulsion suitable for walls and ceilings. It is solvent free, antistatic, and has very good obliteration, making it a good choice when painting with a lighter colour than the base colour. Clay paint has all the qualities of natural clays, and allows surfaces to breathe and absorb variations in humidity, making for a more comfortable living environment.

Casein Paints come in powder form and are mixed on site. Casein is a very ecologically sound paint using nearly a dozen natural substances that render the use of titanium dioxide, solvents and preservatives obsolete. It is washable after it has dried and has a soft matt chalky finish. Casein can be coloured with pigments or colour concentrates and is suitable for children's bedrooms and nurseries.

Doors and woodwork

Eco-solutions Home Strip paint and varnish remover removes water and oil based paint, acrylics, polyurethanes, varnishes and fire-protective paints. This water-based product actually works and does not harm users or the environment. In addition to this, Eco-solutions is the only company known to be marketing a paint stripper with a CE-mark for safety for use on children's toys www.ecosolutions.co.uk.

Finishing off the job with natural gloss and eggshell is growing increasingly easier. The advantage of these natural oil-based products is that they are flexible and the absence of acrylic constituents mean they do not crack or flake. >>>

Companies are now offering colouring-matching services which allow you to choose the perfect colours to compliment your freshly painted walls.

Plaster

Tierrafino clay plaster is a natural clay plaster with breathable qualities and a beautiful finish, to which pigments and mother of pearl can be added. The clay constituent of this comes from various European quarries and provides the breathtaking, matte structured finish. The colours are rich in atmospheric tones.

For new plaster, colourless, water-based sealants are available. Alternatively, you might choose to apply a thinned-down mist coat of emulsion as a sealing coat.

Outside or in

Silicate paint – this paint is suitable for use on mineral-based surfaces such as stone, concrete, plaster and masonry that has not been previously painted, for interior and exterior use. It is based on stabilised sodium silicate which enables the paint to bond chemically with its substrate. This results in a breathable coating, which is far less likely to flake or crack. The working principal of silicate paints is their petrification with the substrate. The paint both penetrates and chemically reacts with the mineral substrate onto which it is applied. In contrast to chemical paints which form a skin on the surface, natural silicate paint becomes an integral part of the surface. The resultant pore size allows the free passage of vapour but water penetration is prevented. Silicate paint is highly resistant to harsh weather conditions and is exceptionally fire resistant.

Linseed oil paint, produced from flax seed, offers a very beautiful finish and is particularly suitable for external application. It is also suitable as a first-stage protection of all natural porous surfaces, such as timber and terracotta tiles. It can also be used as a pre-treatment for surfaces that are to be waxed. The deep protection against water and dirt by linseed paints still allows the surface to breathe naturally.

With time when Linseed oil paint starts to show its age and the paint becomes chalky as the pigment begins to be released, simply by brushing the surface and adding new cooked linseed oil you can help the surface regain its former lustre and function. A truly renewable resource!

Limewash is becoming increasingly popular and more readily available. Being a hygroscopic material, lime allows the internal relative humidity to be stabilised by absorbing and releasing moisture. Due to its alkalinity fresh lime is caustic and limewash is used for its disinfectant qualities. The finish offered is velvety matt which can be given depth by adding further coats.

If you want to feel good, make a difference and be inspired then why not start with using natural paints and finishes for your next home decorating project? Make the right choice, purify your atmosphere! ❖

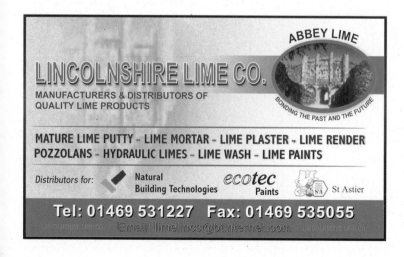
© Green Building Press

There are four simple ways to make your buildings greener ...

Subscribe to Building for a Future magazine **for a year**

and we will send you one of them every three months!

Just £20 per annum

Subscribe now online at **www.newbuilder.co.uk**

or telephone 01559 370798

Green Building Press ...

promoting energy efficient, healthy and sustainable buildings

Maximising daylight and solar gain for your building

Exploiting beneficial light and heat from the sun within buildings may be a rather obvious priority for environmentally conscious building designers. However, it is one that is often misunderstood or inadequately applied. **Stephen Lowndes** examines the issues and options ...

An appreciation of how best to manipulate nature's energy source to ensure maximum benefit of the sun's heat and light when it is available and at the same time ensure discomfort is avoided during periods of excess, is fundamental to successful building design. Here we examine the key concepts behind effective use of daylight and solar heat, which should be adopted at the earliest stages in planning a project.

Passive solar design

Most people have at one time or another stood next to a brick wall on a warm summer's day and felt the radiating heat. You are feeling some of the radiant energy that the masonry has absorbed from the sun. This energy is felt more directly next to a window, the epitome being the heat one can experience, even on a cold, bright winter's day, within a greenhouse. A greenhouse is of course designed to maximise the capture of the sun's radiant energy and is an example of a building designed to optimise solar energy in terms of heat and light. Passive solar buildings are designed specifically to exploit this "free" energy, making use of the sun's heat especially in the winter for warmth and to mitigate the extremes of heat experienced in the summer. Usually buildings designed to maximise beneficial solar heat will simultaneously optimise daylight utilisation, although this is not always the case and the use of solar heat and daylight are not necessarily mutually inclusive. The energy utilised by the building is passive by definition since the building has not generated the energy itself or exclusively by artificial means, rather it is effectively capturing, transferring or (in the case of heat) storing the energy from the sun.

You may be forgiven for thinking that the climate in the UK would not make passive solar design worthwhile. Studies undertaken in this country show that even conventionally designed housing with primary glazed elevations specifically orientated towards the south will achieve annual energy savings of the order of 3%-4%[1] and that if conventional housing layouts are planned so that most principle rooms face south, further annual energy savings of 1%-2% should be possible[2]. These savings relate to applying the first steps of passive solar design to contemporary housing without incurring any additional construction costs. Specifically designed passive solar housing schemes have demonstrated annual energy savings in excess of 8% - 10%[3]. The additional monitory costs for implementing

Re-radiated heat

passive solar design over and above conventional build cost can be negligible, depending on the extent of design solutions adopted and the nature of the project. These solutions will revolve primarily around the parameters of building **orientation, shading, window design, thermal mass, ventilation and air-tightness**.

Orientation

Imagine the ultimate passive solar house, which, rather fantastically, is constructed upon a large revolving turntable. It slowly rotates so that the primary occupied rooms are continually facing the sun throughout the day during the winter and in the summer, the house rotates so that these areas are continually in the shade. Unfortunately such a fantastic proposition is impractical and likely to be somewhat disorientating for its occupants! This illustration shows, however, that passive solar buildings need to be designed so that rooms occupied for most of the day are exposed to optimum sun for winter warmth and daylight as well as recieving benefit from seasonably available shade during the summer.

The maximum incident solar radiation on a vertical wall occurs for an orientation facing due south, typically 5 kWh/m² in January, which drops to about 2 kWh/m² if the wall faces due north[4]. Fixed room orientations up to 30° east of south result in exposure to the sun in the morning, whereas orientation up to 30° towards the west of south achieves maximum exposure in the afternoon[5]. This diurnal variance in optimum solar exposure tends to dictate the layout of passive solar buildings. As a result it is usually recommended that living rooms and major bedrooms in dwellings achieve an exposure within 45° of south[6].

Shading

Passive solar buildings need to take optimum advantage of the different sun altitudes throughout the year. In the winter, the sun's altitude is low, which may mean adjacent buildings obscure beneficial direct solar radiation. Ideally, the building would be positioned clear of the obstructions. The reverse is true in the summer, when an adjacent obstruction is beneficial, providing shade at the start or end of the day. There are a number of ways to solve this dichotomy. For example planting deciduous trees on southerly aspects, enabling solar penetration in the winter months when the tree's branches are bereft of foliage and giving shade in the summer from a renewed green canopy.

External shading devices that are part of the building structure can be used, such as large overhanging roof eaves or deep window reveals, although care should be exercised to ensure external shading does not preclude too much daylight. These structures could also potentially provide other useful functions, such as use as a balcony or doubling up as an external light shelf to help reflect more daylight into the building, reducing reliance on artificial lighting. External shading devices offer the advantage of an increased external viewing amenity when compared to internal shading such as Venetian blinds. Internally located blinds are less effective in terms of reducing summer heat gain and can

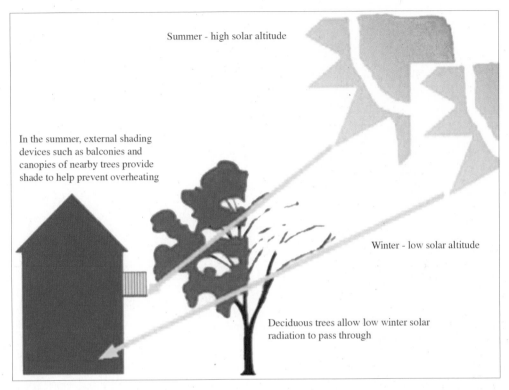

Summer - high solar altitude

In the summer, external shading
devices such as balconies and
canopies of nearby trees provide
shade to help prevent overheating

Winter - low solar altitude

Deciduous trees allow low winter solar
radiation to pass through

reduce the effectiveness of natural ventilation through the window that they are covering.

Thermal mass

The effect of a shelter offering the advantages of thermal mass would have been experienced by our earliest ancestors dwelling within caves and has been utilised within vernacular architecture throughout the world. For most of the twentieth century, the use of mass produced building products combined with modern commercial construction methodologies and timescales, has tended to favour the use of lightweight materials. Yet the ability of thermally massive materials to store or release solar heat when used as part of a building's structure for subsequent beneficial release later in the day, is recognised as a fundamental principle of passive solar building design. Buildings that make use of thermal mass tend to take longer to heat up from cold, but retain their heat for longer once warmed. This behaviour suits continuous or regular occupation patterns in the winter, enabling occupants to take advantage of available solar heat received in the day, reradiated slowly during the colder

evenings, when there is greatest need for heat. In the summer the thermal mass acts as a buffer, with the same thermal storage properties helping to attenuate the peak solar gain to the space, minimising overheating.

The physical property of a material that governs its ability to store heat is its specific heat capacity. This is the amount of energy (kJ) required to raise the temperature of 1 kg (or 1 m^3) of a material by 1°C. Materials such as soft wood have a heat capacity of about 730 kJ/m^3 °C and brick 1360 kJ/m^3 °C. These have a lower heat capacity and hence lower thermal mass than dense concrete with a heat capacity of 1760 kJ/m^3 °C [7]. Other more environmentally friendly thermally massive materials, such as locally sourced stone or even rammed earth and clay adobes are increasingly being used. For the thermal mass to be effective it needs to be exposed to the occupied space and not completely shrouded with light-weight finishes. This means that the proportion of exposed thermal mass should be as high as possible, which might require for example, the exposure of areas such as floors that receive direct solar radiation, as well as

Solar courtyard

Passive solar roof and wall glazing on a farmhouse in Wales. Also note the thermal active solar water heating panel below the windows. Note: the roof is triple glazed - 2+1 (double glazed below a single pane rain-screen).

areas receiving indirect solar radiation such as ceilings. Placing an insulating layer or an air cavity in front of a heavy weight material isolates the mass from the internal environment and will reduce the material's ability to exchange heat with the surroundings. A compromise between acceptable finishes, poor acoustic environment (often a problem with excessive hard surface exposure) and adequate thermal coupling with the building mass needs to be struck.

Windows and buffer zones

To minimise the requirement for space heating, passive solar housing designs usually incorporate reduced glazing areas on north, east and west elevations in comparison to the south. The associated reduced winter heat loss from reduced glazing on these elevations is usually always greater than the potential solar gain, even when low emissivity glazing is utilised (i.e. a low E coating allows the shortwave energy from the sun to enter the building, but acts as a barrier to the escape of long-wave energy from internal heat sources). Increasing the southerly aspect of the glazing using low E specification glass will usually always provide a net winter day-time heat gain in most parts of the UK[8].

Conservatories, atria, entrance lobbies and porches provide a cushion or barrier between the occupant and the external environment. These so-called buffer zones act as the first line of defence against the elements and in the context of passive solar design, they make use of solar radiation to increase the temperature relative to the outside. This means that the conductive heat losses through the separating wall from the occupied space and the heat loss due to natural infiltration is reduced because of the reduced temperature difference between the inside occupied space and that of the buffer zone.

A judgement on how big windows need to be to maximise beneficial utilisation of daylight will be a function of the amount of visible or unobstructed sky potentially available, the room depth, room height and internal finish of the room walls. Formally, the measure of acceptable daylight within a room can be expressed in terms of a daylight factor. In theorical terms this is (simplistically) the ratio of internal daylight level to external daylight level within a room, expressed as a percentage. It is possible to calculate this using formula found in most building science text books and obtain an optimum glazing area for a particular room design. Typically, living rooms should achieve minimum daylight factors of 1%, kitchens 2% and bedrooms 0.5%[9]. In practical terms, good design that aims to encourage maximum daylight penetration within a room should be pursued wherever possible:

- consider roof lights - about twice as effective as the equivalent area of window within a vertical wall (although they may lose more heat)
- allow windows that open onto conservatories and atria to be larger than normal - the heat loss is reduced by the buffer zone effect
- incorporate splayed window reveals, light-shelves and light coloured internal finishes to ceilings and walls - all help to provide increased reflective surface areas and bounce light further into a room
- provide dual aspect windows - maximise light source throughout the day, depths greater than six metres are difficult to light from one glazed elevation.

Air-tightness and ventilation

A building that has been designed to optimise the beneficial utilisation of passive solar heat should not overlook the integrity of the building thermal envelope. The contribution from solar heat in the winter will be more significant within a building that is designed to minimise heat loss with enhanced levels of thermal insulation, airtight construction and controlled ventilation.

There is an emphasis on well sealed buildings that minimise uncontrolled infiltration of cold outside air by avoiding ill fitting windows and doors and generally poor building details. This has raised awareness of the importance of ensuring energy efficient ventilation is provided for a healthy, habitable environment. Passive solar design can be adapted to further promote this using naturally ventilated cavities or Trombe walls. An air cavity separates an internal wall from a series of glazed panels. Outside ventilation air enters the cavity at low level. Solar radiation heats both the air within the cavity, as well as the mass of the wall, which conducts heat to the adjacent space. The buoyant, heated air is displaced to the top of the cavity by cooler incoming outside air of greater density. The heated air at the top of the cavity flows into the adjacent internal space for ventilation.

Regulations

All new and modified buildings constructed in the UK must comply with the current Part L building regulations[10] (Part J in Scotland). Passive solar buildings may not always be able to show compliance based upon the "elemental method" cited within the regulations, because this method stipulates that the combined area of windows, roof-lights and doors must not exceed 25% of the total floor area[11]. However, the regulations allow two alternative approaches that may be better suited to passive solar designs. The "target U-value" method does not stipulate maximum glazing areas, but gives credit within the target U-value calculation where south facing glazing exceeds that facing north. The "carbon index" method may be the most explicit method by which a passive solar building may show compliance, since it specifically takes into account schemes that incorporate passive solar heating.

In the case of dwellings, SAP ratings (often required by local authorities and housing associations to give an indication of the energy efficiency of an individual house design) have the potential to be improved when passive solar design techniques are correctly adopted.

The weakest link

Buildings that exploit the sun's heat and light to their optimum beneficial effect have the potential to offer significant savings in energy and ultimately CO_2 emissions. It is important to understand that the concepts that drive the successful application of passive solar building design are intrinsically linked. There is no weakest link as such, since building orientation, window design, solar shading, thermal mass and building envelope are all influenced by each other. A badly orientated building, for example, affects the performance of each of the other parameters, requiring their re-optimisation to compensate. Similarly a building with optimised orientation but limited thermal mass may require other enhanced measures to help maintain comfortable tempera-

tures during the extremes of winter and summer. In the UK we have to design to accommodate the excesses of potentially cold winters as well as hot summers and this will always dictate how far the designer is able to pursue each particular parameter. ❖

References

1, 2, 3 Energy Efficiency Best Practice Report 27, Passive solar estate layout, p2, table 1, BRECSU, Building Research Establishment, Watford.

4, 5, 7 Baker N, Steemers K, (2000), Energy and Environment in Architecture a Technical Design Guide, pp20-24, and 36-37, E & F N Spon, London.

6 Good Practice Guide 79, 2001, Energy efficiency in new housing – a guide to achieving best practice, p8, BRECSU, Building Research Establishment, Watford.

8 Energy Efficiency Best Practice Report 27, Passive solar estate layout, p9, BRECSU, Building Research Establishment, Watford.

9 Borer P, Harris C, 1998, The Whole House Book, p37-38, (available from The Green Shop, www.greenshop.co.uk 01452 770629)

10, 11 UK Government, (2001), Approved Document L, L1 Conservation of fuel and power in dwellings, pp5-13, The Stationary Office, Norwich

© Green Building Press

Solar heating

Name the only heating appliance that costs you virtually nothing to run, increases the value of your house and runs on the only safe form of nuclear energy? Answer - a solar water heating installation. So why is there still so little interest in solar water heating in this country? One reason may be the widespread but incorrect assumption that the British Isles is not sufficiently sunny to make this worthwhile. However, research has proven that there is sufficient solar energy available in Britain to make an investment in solar heating a sensible financial move. **Barbara Grantham** explains ...

Each year in the British Isles over 1000kWh of energy is received on every square metre of surface. The energy requirement of the average British home for hot water supply is 3000kWh and a well-designed solar thermal heating system could deliver between 1200 – 2000 kWh.

From a properly installed system, in a normal summer, the average household can expect to produce 90-100% of its domestic hot water, 50 - 60% in the Spring and Autumn and 25 - 35% in winter. These figures are the minimum to be expected from a properly designed and installed system. Even on a cloudy day, the amount of radiation that gets through is about 60% of the total available, so on an overcast winter's day the water will at least be pre-warmed.

It is a common misconception that solar water heating is a poor capital investment. An interesting way to evaluate this is to consider the savings made in reduced heating costs, compared to the amount the same money would earn if invested in a building society. How much interest would that sum earn, taking into account that a well-designed and properly installed system will last at least 25-30 year? In addition the value of an investment in solar energy increases if inflation is taken into account and the cost of conventional fuels continues to rise.

Also the capital cost could also be reduced by joining or forming a Solar Club or taking

advantage of the DTI Clear Skies funding (<u>www. clear-skies.org</u>).

How does it work?

A conventional solar water heating system consists of an absorber - a heat-collecting panel that is connected to simple plumbing system with hot water being taken to a heat exchange coil in a hot water cylinder, and cold water being returned to the panel, similar to a standard domestic hot water system.

There are three basic types of solar water heating collectors: -

Matt black unglazed un-insulated - suitable for swimming pools, which require lower operating temperatures.

Flat plate collectors in a box - which is glazed on the side facing the sun and insulated behind. These can be either matt black as in older types or with a selective coating applied. The selective surface appears to be black in colour and absorbs heat well in the light radiation spectrum but less heat is radiated away from the collector in the long wave (infra-red) spectrum. The selective coating greatly increases the efficiency of the panel.

Evacuated tubes - vacuum glass tubes enclose each pipe and its associated absorber plate. The heat pipes use a very low boiling point fluid, which evaporates, rises to the manifold and transfers the heat of condensation to the water system. This type is more efficient especially in the winters that we experience in the UK.

The more efficient the method of collection, the smaller the size of the absorptive surface needed. As a guide, for an average sized house you would need 5m² of single glazed matt black flat plate collector, 4m² of selective-surface flat plate collector or 3m² of selective-surface evacuated tube collector.

As the collectors are generally located higher than the hot water cylinder, a pump will be necessary to circulate the water. The pump is controlled by an electronic controller, which measures the difference in temperature between the panels and the cylinder, bringing the pump on when the panels are hotter than the cylinder. Some systems use photovoltaic pumps which means the system can run independently of mains electricity and is totally solar powered.

In indirect systems the hot water from the solar collector is separate from the domestic hot water and a separate heat exchange coil in the hot water cylinder makes the heat transfer. This will usually entail the installation of a new solar cylinder with an additional coil. Some systems use the existing hot water cylinder and plumbing, but as with all direct systems there could be problems of lime scale build up in hard water areas.

All systems need to be frost tolerant and manufacturers approach this in different ways.

Some use a drain-back system, others use anti freeze or rubber pipe work.

How much does it cost?

Over the last few years prices have come down considerably with the cost of an installed system ranging from £2,100 for a flat plate collector to £4,000 for a system using evacuated tubes installed for a large house. The type and design of the system will depend on your location, the orientation of your home and the likely amount of hot water required. These prices should include plumbing and all other necessary equipment. Over the years there have been cases of high-pressure sales people quoting exorbitant prices and if you should receive an estimate in excess of these figures, shop around. There are now many reputable installers who will ensure you get value for money. A list of approved installers is available from **www.clear-skies.org**.

The type of collector that is best for you depends on your current water heating arrangements. If, for instance, you have an Aga or a woodstove that provides plenty of hot water all winter it makes sense to have a simpler and cheaper collector for summertime use only. If you were looking for savings all year round you would need to consider using evacuated tube systems.

In the UK a collector that is set anywhere between SE to SW with a tilt of 10 to 60 degrees and minimal over shading will operate efficiently.

The Centre for Alternative Technology (CAT) at Machynlleth in Wales has a demonstration solar roof which incorporates a number of systems.

The output will be around 1200 kWh per year, which is about 40% of the average total hot water needs. The amount of money saved on water heating bills will vary from £30 - £150 per annum depending on the type of fuel you are using.

What is a solar club?

The 'solar club' concept helps householders who want to install a solar hot water system at a reduced cost. The Club uses the purchasing power of its members to buy equipment at bulk discounts. It also provides training for those members wishing to install their own solar collector. Members can provide support to each other by sharing skills, labour, tools and equipment.

This can lead to considerable savings on the normal installed prices, with typical systems averaging around £1,100 and £1,800. With basic DIY skills and expert training most people are more than capable of installing their own solar hot water system.

The Centre for Sustainable Energy (CSE) in Bristol along with Environ in Leicester (both registered charities) developed the concept of Solar Clubs, which is a non-profit initiative, supported initially by the Department for the Environment and currently by Shell Better Britain Campaign and the Mark Leonard Trust. They have negotiated bulk discount schemes with five manufacturers (FILSOL, AES, Solartwin, Thermomax and Imagination Solar Ltd) to

purchase equipment at reduced prices. The intention is to set up a UK-wide network of Solar Clubs. There are already around 20 clubs in various locations in the UK. If there is not one in your area why not form one? The first step is to contact the CSE or Environ to find out if there is one; if not they will give advice on setting one up.

What is the Clear Skies initiative?

The DTI Clear Skies Initiative has been set up to encourage homeowners and communities to take advantage of all forms of renewable energy by providing grants and advice (see www.clear-skies.co.uk/). Practically speaking for domestic solar water heating this means a grant of around £500 regardless of the size or cost of the system, but can be 50% for community projects. However, unlike the solar club this is not a DIY option. The system has to be on the Clear Skies recognised product list and installed by an approved installer.

Planning

People who are considering installing a solar hot water system sometimes worry about planning restrictions. Most systems fitted to existing buildings do not need to involve planning controls. The exceptions are in conservation areas, national parks and listed buildings. In these cases the first step is to talk with the relevant local planning officer. >>>

Conclusions

In conclusion solar energy is clean, renewable and as the price of oil increases, affordable. It will add value to your home and give you a sense of well-being. It is a wonderful feeling soaking in a hot bath in the knowledge that the water has been heated by the power of the sun, an energy that is older than the earth itself. ❖

(The price guides used in this article are all exclusive of VAT, which is 5% for installed systems and 17.5% for DIY)

Acknowledgements

Thanks to: Chris Lord-Smith and Andy Burroughs for assistance and advice.

Solar energy advisory organisations

Centre for Alternative Technology 01654 705950
www.cat.org.uk

Centre for Sustainable Energy 0117 929 9950
www.cse.org.uk

Environ, Parkfield 0116 222 0222 www.environ.org.uk

Solar Trade Association Ltd 01908 442 290
www.solartradeassociation.org.uk

Grant aid for your renewables

Clear Skies is a £10m fund for homeowners and small community projects. Homeowners can obtain grants of between £500 to £5000 whilst community organisations can receive up to £100,000 for grants and feasibility studies. Clear Skies supports projects from homeowners and community groups in England, Wales and Northern Ireland.

Grants will only be awarded where an accredited installer is to be used. These installers will work to a code of practice, be vetted beforehand and at least two of their installations will be inspected by Clear Skies inspectors to ensure homeowners and community organisations get the most appropriate system for their needs, correctly installed and at the right price.

The renewable energy technologies being promoted via Clear Skies are:

- solar thermal
- wind turbines
- micro hydro turbines
- biomass (wood fuelled boilers and automated pellet stoves)
- ground source heat pumps.

In the industry?

Then become an accredited installer. Applications are still invited from experienced installers of renewable energy technologies. Installers that have less experience can become accredited via a mentoring route, whereby their work will be commissioned by an experienced, accredited, installer. People, who are seeking mentoring are recommended to contact accredited installers. ❖

www.clear-skies.org or ring the Helpline on 08702 430 930

Benefit from installing photovoltaic (pv) solar panels

Kirk Archibald of the Energy Saving Trust tells us how we can get involved in the Solar Energy Programme...

The damaging effects of carbon emissions on the environment and public health are now widely acknowledged. This increased awareness of the pressing need to cut emissions and conserve energy is having a growing impact on the building sector. In the future both legislation, and public pressure should ensure that sustainability and energy efficiency become key factors within any building or housing project.

In a market increasingly driven by sustainable products and services, it is essential that the industry understands the technologies and programmes available to help cut emissions and ensure current and future developments are sustainable and safe for the environment.

One such scheme is the UK Department of Trade and Industry Major PV demonstration programme (MDP), established to encourage the use of solar pv in domestic and commercial sectors. The scheme, which is managed by the Energy Saving Trust (EST), is part of a wider scheme to encourage energy efficiency and the use of renewable energy sources across the UK.

What are the benefits of pv solar?

Solar power is a resource with huge potential. The earth receives enough energy from the sun in one day to supply all mankind's energy needs for one year. Daylight can be turned into electricity by installing solar photovoltaic (pv) panels on the walls and roofs of buildings. It would only take one solar panel on the roof of every household in Britain to produce enough energy to light every streetlight in the country.

Moreover, unlike fossil fuels, solar power is renewable, inexhaustible and does not produce any of the chemical emissions that contribute to climate change. Just ten square metres of pv saves at least half a tonne of carbon dioxide every year.

There is scope for individual households to negotiate agreements with electricity suppliers to sell excess electricity generated by pv panels back to the national grid.

In addition, pv solar is incredibly safe and reliable, and requires almost no maintenance. Installations rarely break down, and manufacturer's warranties far exceed those for fossil fuel energy systems.

What benefits can builders or property developers achieve from installing solar pvs

Installing solar pvs gives commercial operations a clear and visible means of demonstrating their environmental commitment. A solar installation will differentiate a business from its competitors and allows an organisation to take a leadership position on environmental matters within its community.

For house builders, these unique selling points have a direct impact on sales. Reports have indicated that 90% of people would prefer their home to be environmentally friendly; 40% of those are willing to pay more.

Importantly, installing solar can help developers comply with much of the forthcoming UK legislation on environmental planning and energy performance. Including solar pvs in developments may, in the future, also increase the likelihood of gaining planning permission for projects. >>>

How does the grant system work?

The grant scheme helps make solar power an affordable option. The grant programme is divided into two application streams based on the size of the solar pv system being installed. The size of a solar installation is expressed by its kilowatt peak (kWp) potential, which is an indication of how much electricity the installation could produce in peak conditions.

Who can apply?

New UK factory producing pvs

A new factory that produces photovoltaic (pv) products was opened in Wrexham in 2004. The Sharp Corporation, the world's leading producer of pv products, initially anticipated producing pv panels for residential and commercial installations at a rate of 20 MW worth per year. However

There are two application streams:
- stream one is for installations with an output potential of 0.5 to 5 kWp and is appropriate for small commercial properties.
- Stream two is for medium to large-scale installations greater than 5 kWp in size. Large commercial organisations, including housing developers, can receive up to 40% of the cost of an installation. ❖

Application forms can be downloaded from the Energy Saving Trust website at www.est.org.uk/solar/ or a hardcopy can be obtained by phoning 0800 298 3978.

orders quickly exceeded output, resulting in a second line of production in the same year doubling capacity. The UK produced around 4.25 MW of solar electricity in 2002 (about as much as one small wind farm or the consumption of one small town). We are seventh in Europe with Japan and Germany leading the market in pvs. Sharp has not come to Wrexham to supply just the UK market as most of its output is destined for elsewhere in Europe but its presence should raise pv's profile in the UK. ❖

Sharp 01978 853 939 www.sharp.co.uk

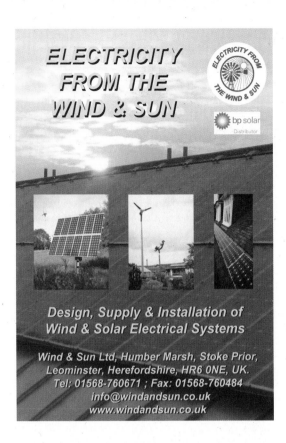

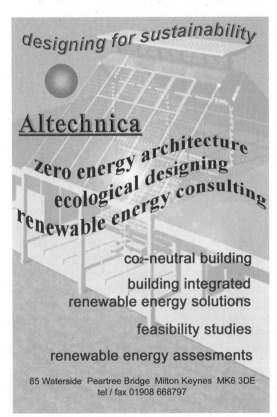

Water supply & demand management

The water flowing out of our taps has undergone a complex and energy consuming cycle that includes cleaning it ready for drinking and pumping it from the reservoir to our homes and places of work. This uses mainly fossil fuel based electricity that contributes to CO_2 emissions. Opportunities for saving water start with a change in our attitude to water utilisation. Here **Stephen Lawndes** reviews water saving techniques that can be incorporated into the design of our buildings ...

Water utilisation within buildings is of course required for washing, cooking, bathing and showering, flushing toilets and watering gardens. Other buildings, such as offices and community buildings, may consume water for large scale catering, swimming pools or even manufacturing processes. There are opportunities in all buildings to provide fittings, components and installations that help reduce water consumption.

Taps

Taps left running can waste enormous amounts of water. New installations should incorporate either self-closing or spray-head taps. These can of course be retrofitted to existing installations. Spray taps are particularly suited to wash hand basins and can save up to 50 per cent of water compared to conventional taps.

The slow flow rate achieved when spray-heads are applied to hot water taps can mean these savings are reduced if the tap has to be opened for a long time to obtain sufficiently warm enough water. However this is more likely to be a function of a badly designed hot water installation rather than the tap. "Dead – legs" i.e. lengths of pipe work with uncirculated hot water should be minimised so that hot water is readily available at all draw-offs. Where increased flow at the tap outlet is required, self-closing taps that close automatically after a preset period usually set between 1 and 30 seconds could be considered. These taps should significantly reduce the possibility of taps leaking or being left running. Some types incorporate an adjustable flow restrictor so that a lower flow rate can be set for even greater savings. Since water regulations require all outlets to incorporate an isolating valve, fitting a flow regulating service valve, rather than a standard isolating valve is a way of achieving this. The perception of good water flow can be achieved by fitting regulated aerators on tap outlets and these work well if water flow is unchecked, as long as there is sufficient water pressure.

There are a surprising range of sizes for wash basins and baths. The simple measure of ensuring wash basins and baths are not over sized will mean the amount of water used and time taken to fill them will be minimised.

Reduced flush toilets

Flushing toilets are usually the principal consumer of water, after catering, within most buildings. Since conventional WCs utilise drinking quality water and generate sewerage for processing, it is in the interests of those who wish to reduce water consumption to seriously consider ways in which use can be moderated. New dual flush (three and six-litre) toilets can save up to half the water used by old nine litre WC units, so replacement of older existing units during refurbishment projects is usually worthwhile. It is possible to install WCs with ultra low flush capacity utilising a four and two litre dual flush. Any lower than this and you are probably looking at installing a waterless or vacuum toilet.

If your loo flushes 9 litres (80% of houses still use this size cistern) then there is a retrofit kit available to fit to your your existing toilet syphon www.interflush.co.uk Once fitted, the averge houseold of 2.4 people could save 27,000 litres per year which equates to a saving £50 per annum and rising.

Composting toilets

Composting or waterless toilets compost the waste into a form that can safely be used as fertiliser. Human waste contains nitrogen as well as magnesium, sulphur, phosphorus, potassium and other trace elements that are, in the form of compost, beneficial for plants and help condition soil. Rather than flushing the waste away with water the user throws in a handful of "soak" (sawdust or shredded cardboard). A chamber under the composting toilet receives the waste and the soak and facilitates the composting process. Composting chambers range in size from a large box located within the toilet area or a chamber under the floor. In most cases more space needs to be allocated for a composting toilet compared to a conventional WC and access must be provided for final removal of the compost and for interim turning and raking. Because human faeces contain pathogens, care needs to be exercised and contact with waste in its raw state avoided. Of course there needs to be a ready use for the compost. Without a garden you might need to rely on your friends to take your compost away.

Other types of waterless WCs include vacuum systems, usually employed on trains and in aeroplanes. These systems can be expensive, maintenance intensive and require the operation of electric vacuum pumps. Generally their use within buildings has been restricted to large installations that cannot utilise conventional gravity drainage.

Urinals

Water flush urinals are commonly installed in public toilets and in toilets within commercial premises. Where urinals are installed, automatic flush control should be installed as a minimum. With the older type of automatic flush, the urinal stalls are only flushed if the automatic flush valve senses a change in water pressure. Newer devices enable flushing if movement in front of the urinal is sensed using an infra-red detector.

Although automatic flush control valves reduce water consumption, if you really want to save water in a urinal installation you might consider turning the water off to the stalls altogether. Waterless urinals in essence are just that – a urinal bowl without the flush. However they need to incorporate a syphonic trap, or an outlet in the urinal waste with a perfume impregnated pad, designed to reduce the smell of urine.

Urine-separating flush toilets are a variation on the waterless urinal and ordinary loo. Aimed at the domestic application these toilets separate solid and liquid waste at source. They usually work on the principle of accepting liquid waste at the front of the toilet bowl and solid waste at the rear. Because the solids and liquids are separated in the toilet bowl the former can be flushed in the conventional manner while the latter requires no water to flush away.

Hot water outlets

Although we have discussed general water outlets from taps, there are particular issues relating to hot water outlets and distribution pipe work which will affect efforts to conserve water. For instance the thermal insulation of all of the hot and cold water distribution pipe work is often overlooked. As hot and cold water pipes are usually run together the mains cold water may be warmed up by the adjacent uninsulated hot water pipe. Apart from the obvious energy wastage from heat lost from the uninsulated hot water pipe, users will waste water by running the cold water for prolonged periods trying to get a cool drink. There will also be condensation on the outside of the pipe. As previously mentioned if hot water pipe dead legs are too long a great deal of water will be wasted before the hot water comes through.

Showers and water pressure

Although taking a shower normally uses much less water than a soak in the bath, there is still scope to ensure that the water utilised by a shower is no more than it needs to be. The problem here though is that a low flow rate from a shower does not give a very invigorating experience. So whilst flow restrictors can be installed, their effect is likely to be at the expense of shower performance. The use of thermostatic shower mixer valves with a fixed maximum flow and mains pressure atomising shower heads can help maintain acceptable performance, even with low water flows. The available water pressure head plays an important part in water flow delivery. Direct mains fed outlets will almost always receive a higher flow pressure compared to tank fed outlets, unless you live in an area of low mains water pressure. The available pressure at outlets such as showers and taps fed from loft tanks, rather than direct from the mains, is dependant upon how high the storage tank is above the outlet. The higher the tank, the greater the pressure head and therefore the strength of flow of water from the outlet.

Mean machines

If you are fitting in new appliances such as washing machines and dishwashers you should be looking at "A" or "AA" rated units. In the case of washing machines and dish washers this label means that the appliance should be a low consumer of water, compared with a "B" or "C" rated machine. It is not always the case that an "A" rated machine is more expensive to purchase over a lower rated appliance and of course it always pays to shop around.

It is possible to purchase hand operated "pressure wash" devices, that are claimed to use only a very small amount of water and do not run on electricity. Hot water is poured into and sealed in an airtight washer drum. The heat from the water causes the air in the drum to expand, which builds pressure, driving soap and water into the clothing. Hand operation is required to agitate the clothes within the drum and effect cleaning. Whether in reality these sorts of devices use significantly less water to achieve the same result as a conventional "A" rated machine is difficult to conclude without reliable data.

Grey water systems

Grey water systems are designed to reuse the waste water from washing and bathing for other non potable purposes, usually flushing WCs. Systems usually comprise primary and secondary filtration, a storage tank with an electric pump being provided for transferring water from

filtered waste to the storage tank. Even though the water from grey water systems is not used for drinking, bacteria should be removed and this is usually done with an ultra violet (UV) light filter. Although reported water savings within the range of 30% are potentially possible, installation and equipment costs, reliability and maintainability issues have all meant that the overall cost effectiveness of such systems has usually limited them to large scale projects, rather than domestic applications.

Rain water harvesting systems

Rain water harvesting systems can be as simple as the positioning of a water-butt to collect rain water run off via a building's roof gutter down pipe to more complex systems integrated within a building's internal grey water system.

The water butt solution can usually be accommodated in most house – garden scenarios and if flat profile, wall mounted types are used, they do not need to take up too much space. More complicated systems are available that can be used to collect rain water run-off from larger roof areas, paved and hard landscape areas. These will usually need to drain via gravity to a collection point be stored for use later as required. A pump may then be required to transport the stored water to the point of use. A settling tank is provided to collect silts and ensure they do not block distribution pipes and pumps. Finer filtration, using in-line pipe mounted nylon cartridges can also be used prior to draw off points such as garden watering taps and irrigation hose connections.

It may be possible to integrate the operation of pumps with small scale renewable PV and wind generation, however don't under estimate the power that may be required from even fairly modest pumps. As with all grey water systems, the more complicated the system becomes, the potential for increased maintenance and costs can make systems unviable, particularly if the use of the water is limited.

On a larger scale, SUDS (sustainable drainage systems) are being implemented on many developments. SUDS concepts involve managing surface water run off within the site. Features such as swales (shallow, wide ditches channelling surface water overland from the drained area

natural paints
quality, safe, non-toxic
exterior & interior finishes

sunpipes
natural daylight to brighten
that gloomy corner

renewable energy
Solar hot water, photovoltaic
& wind power systems

books & magazines
to inspire & inform

the *Green* shop
PRODUCTS FOR A SUSTAINABLE FUTURE

The Green Shop

Bisley, Glos GL6 7BX
01452 770629
enquiries@greenshop.co.uk
www.greenshop.co.uk

rainharvesting
pumps, tanks, filters
& controls

water saving
low-flush loos
& matching basins

steel guttering
recyclable

Rainharvesting Systems

Bisley, Glos GL6 7BX
01452 772000
www.rainharvesting.co.uk
sales@rainharvesting.co.uk

RAINHARVESTING SYSTEMS LTD

to a storage discharge) and basins (designed to hold back storm runoff reducing peak flows to rivers and reducing flood risk). Ponds can also be designed to accommodate peak variations in water levels to provide flood-storage capacity.

Off grid drainage

Off grid drainage has conventionally been utilised in rural situations where sewer networks are limited and has utilised cess pools and septic tank storage with periodic emptying using sewage collection companies who tanker the waste away for processing. On some projects, more sustainable approaches are now being practiced that involve the natural processing of waste on site. The majority of these utilise reed bed systems, which incorporate one or two stages of passing the waste through planted reed beds and when properly designed, can be used for the full treatment of domestic sewage. Reed beds, using the common reed planted on a sand and gravel bed, act as a percolating filter, with the waste flowing from the top down.

The beds should be planted on a gradient to aid percolation and some form of primary treatment may be necessary, depending on the treatment demand and space available for the beds. Leach fields and willow trenches are other treatments that have been used as predominantly secondary on site sewage dispersal. Any on site system needs to be bio-chemically tested at various points to ensure effective and safe operation of the process. Any on site treatment of sewage will usually come under scrutiny of your local authority's planning or environmental health departments. Other bodies such as the National Rivers Authority and the Environment agency may also need to be consulted.

The end user

We have briefly looked at a some of the technologies and systems that could be incorporated into a project with the aim of saving water. Some of these systems can be complex. For instance, on site sustainable sewage treatment is likely to require the involvement of experienced professionals in order to implement it successfully. At the other end of the scale there are comparatively simple solutions such as the installation of water saving appliances that will go a good way to reducing consumption in a reliable and cost effective manner. The building user will ultimately have the biggest influence on the water consumption and occupiers need to be encouraged to adopt responsible usage patterns, so that water conservation can be optimised. With the cost of our water predicted to soar in the near future and the introduction of water meters on both existing and new buildings, the adoption of some of these technologies are likely to become a necessity and our approach to water use less blasé. ❖

Further information

"Sewage Solutions – answering the call of nature" by Nick Grant, Mark Moodie and Chris Weedon. This book deals with all aspects of non-mains sustainable sewage treatment.

"Lifting the Lid – an ecological approach to toilet systems" by Peter Harper and Louise Halestrap is probably the classic book on waterless toilets!

Both the above books available from The Green Shop, **www.greenshop.co.uk** 01452 770629

Heating your building without fossil fuels

The choice of alternative ways to heat your building using non-fossil fuels has never been greater. With conventional grid-supplied electricity and natural gas prices currently on the rise, maybe the time has now arrived for serious consideration of the alternatives. But just how easy is it to adopt non-fossil fuelled heating within our building projects? **Stephen Lowndes** looks at the options available.

Whether you are considering a cosy log burner in your renovated country retreat or a wood pellet boiler to run your office heating system, the first line of enquiry will usually start with an understanding of the required performance from your heating system. This will usually entail an assessment of your heating load – the amount of heat you need to maintain your building at a comfortable temperature, during the coldest period of the year. The overall heat demand may very well encompass the load associated with heating your hot water for washing and cooking and your space heating demand. Whether or not you choose a non-fossil fuel heating system the priority should be to minimise the heating load as far as possible, in order to conserve fuel and optimise financial payback. Good standards of thermal insulation, glazing specification, air-tightness and ventilation should be adopted. Whilst

this may be easier to implement for new build projects the importance of upgrading existing buildings should be integral to any change or upgrade of a space heating system. Other issues relating to heating controls are also important and will depend very much on the actual system used to heat the building.

Fuel choice

The choice of fuel will be influenced by a number of considerations. All fuels need to be able to satisfy an end-users requirement in terms of environmental impact, affordable cost, availability, whether specialised equipment or facilities are needed, whether it is "user friendly" and whether it needs to meet both heating and cooking needs.

Solid fuel

Non-fossil solid fuels include hard and soft wood and timber derivatives such as processed timber bricks. Pellets and chips may also be classed as a solid fuel, although due to their own specialist development over recent years these fuels are considered separately. Basic non-fossil solid fuel is predominately derived from logs, timber processing and forestry thinnings, commonly used for small scale applications such as firewood in individual homes. The ability to burn a solid fuel like wood may be very limited if you live in an area classed as a smoke free zone. Under the Clean Air Act, you may have to apply to your local authority for an "exemption licence", to burn any type of wood fuel.

If you are lucky enough to live near to forest or woodland you may find you are close to a conveniently sourced supply of timber. Of course permission to cut trees, unless they are on your own land, cannot be assumed and even when trees are on your own property, there may be local covenants and restrictions in place preventing you from doing so. To put this into perspective, the amount of timber a typical home operating entirely on solid fuel timber for all space heating, hot water and cooking needs is likely to be in excess of three tonnes a year. If you have plenty of land the option to grow and harvest timber on a coppicing basis might be an alternative. This sort of enterprise, even on a small scale, planting densely, high-yielding varieties such as willow or poplar, is likely to require at least 1 hectare for self-sufficiency[1].

Timber fuel must be available to burn in as dry a state as possible. You should avoid burning green, damp and unseasoned wood on the grounds not only of reduced combustion efficiency but because it can also cause a harmful build up of resinous deposits in the chimney preventing it from functioning safely. Any building that incorporates solid fuel heating using timber will therefore require spatial allocation to ensure dry storage of the fuel.

Small-scale domestic solid fuel is usually combusted within wood-burners, which heat the space they are in directly and their primary means of control, is governed by manual adjustment of combustion air intake by the user. The wood burner, which could be a cooking range, located in the kitchen, or a box stove in the living room may be connected to a hot water storage vessel for domestic hot water use and can also incorporate a pumped hot water circuit to remote radiators to heat the rest of the house. Prices range from around £350 for a 3 kW box stove to well over £1000 for a solid fuel boiler. Flues may utilise existing chimneys, although depending upon their condition internal liners may be required. New flues are usually stainless steel and are required to comply with UK Building Regulations Part J (Part F in Scotland).

Wood chip

Chipped wood is commonly available from timber processing and tree surgery waste. Timber can be chipped on site using machines, where it should also be possible to dry the chippings. Until quite recently wood chip heating was predominantly restricted to large-scale non-domestic applications. In recent years smaller wood chip boilers have become commercially available down to about 25 kW output, making them suitable for large domestic or small-scale commercial use. A wood chip boiler can connect to conventional pumped hot water heating circuits and hot water storage cylinders. Modern woodchip boilers keep a small core of the fire-bed continuously alight, allowing the boiler to respond to periodic drops in heating load. Unlike conventional gas fired boilers they cannot respond instantaneously to changes in heating demand. To accommodate periods when there is no heat demand, a heat accumulator is recommended, to store the heat produced during peak burn for use later, either for space heating or domestic hot water.

A dry storage facility for the wood chip fuel is necessary and this needs to be adjacent to the boiler location so that the chips can be fed automatically to the boiler. Combustion efficiency will be dependant upon moisture content. Wood chips are typically supplied pre-dried at 20-25% moisture content. It may be possible to obtain chips with higher moisture content at a lower price than dryer fuel, but it is difficult to dry-out in bulk before use on a small-scale and the lower calorific value could make what seemed like a bargain at the time a false economy.

Wood pellet

Wood pellets are a type of reconstituted wood-fuel and originate from the by-products of the timber processing industry, utilising sawdust and shavings extruded into small cylindrical pellets. They are of consistent quality and size, have low moisture content (5 to 10%), are relatively clean to use and produce less smoke and ash compared with unrefined forms of wood fuel.

Pellets can be used in a wide range of stove and boiler equipment, making it a convenient choice for heating domestic properties and small buildings. Wood pellets are usually gravity or screw fed into the appliance automatically, at a rate that is varied, depending upon the desired heat output from the appliance. Larger wood pellet boiler models are usually installed within designated boiler rooms or utility spaces and are screw fed from covered fuel stores located outside of the building. As with all solid wood fuel the pellets must be kept dry.

Prices start at around £1000 for an 8 kW (max) pellet burner that has a combined hopper feed. Grant funding is available under the UK Government "Clear Skies" renewables initiative. As a private householder you may be eligible for a grant to cover a good proportion of an installation and if you are undertaking a community project up to 50% of capital and installation costs (up to a maximum limit) may be available. These grants are unlikely to be awarded to DIY installations, as the funding is meant to encourage development of an accredited installer network.

Although supply sources are improving, wood pellet fuel can be difficult to source and is one of the reasons why pellets can be a more expensive fuel when compared with wood chip or seasoned logs. Price will also be dependant upon whether you buy in bulk or in bags. Recent comparisons published by British Biogen place bulk purchased wood pellets as being slightly more expensive than natural gas in terms of pence per kilowatt hour, with bagged pellets about 60% more expensive and seasoned logs being slightly less than natural gas[2]. Of course natural gas prices are currently on the rise, so the comparison is heading more in favour of wood fuels.

Bio gas

Bio gas is produced primarily from anaerobic digestion, a process involving the digestion of organic wastes by bacteria in the absence of air. The process occurs in an anaerobic digester enabling the conversion of organic waste from livestock farming and food processing into methane. The waste from the digestion process is reduced to slurry and is suitable as a fertiliser. Bio gas requires cleaning before being used in conventional gas boilers. Although it is possible to operate a conventional heating boiler from bio gas it is unlikely that you will have easy access to a bio gas source due to the limited avenues currently available.

Bio gas cannot be liquefied like LPG, which means that it requires large volume storage even when pressurised and has attendant safety issues, due to its high combustibility. This coupled with the ability to produce enough fuel for self sufficiency on an individual cost effective domestic scale has limited development in the UK. Nevertheless as the technology becomes more cost effective, there is an increasing potential for small scale bio gas operations run by farmers using their own animal waste feedstock, recycling the residue as fertiliser and using the bio gas for heating farm buildings. Larger scale centralised operations have also been established that involve feedstock from multiple sources including both livestock farming and commercial food processing waste.

Bio gas can also be produced from both gasification and pyrolysis of wood and organic matter.

Although possible at small scale, gasification and pyrolysis development has tended to focus on larger scale operations that enable the use of solid bio fuel to run engines to generate electricity and heat (combined heat and power).

Solar heating

Up until now we have concentrated upon heating that involves the direct or indirect combustion of bio fuels. Using the sun's energy directly in the form of solar heat to heat buildings and hot water is a way of offsetting the fossil fuel that would have otherwise been used by conventional heating plant. Even with our UK climate, the application of passive solar design within our buildings can be worthwhile, helping to minimise space heating load and the installation of solar panels effective at contributing to reduced operation of boilers to service hot water demand. Passive solar design is discussed in detail elsewhere in this publication, so a brief look at solar hot water heating is covered here.

Solar hot water is an established technology and whilst ideally optimised when drawing up plans for a new build project, systems can also be incorporated fairly easily into existing buildings and often without the need to throw away your existing hot water installation. Solar panels are able to utilise the sun's heat even on cloudy days, with a typical system capable of providing enough heat to satisfy up to 50% of the average annual household hot water demand.

There are various types of solar panel, ranging in efficiency from fairly basic flat plate designs that are often available as DIY kits and comprise black aluminium fins fixed to a copper piping grid, enclosed in a thermally insulated box with a glazed top facing the sky. More efficient and more expensive designs consist of factory made arrays of evacuated tubes each enclosing a heat pipe, connected to a water manifold. Hot water is either circulated via thermosyphon effect or pumped through a solar panel and used to indirectly heat water in a hot water storage cylinder. Usually the solar heated water is stored separately from the hot water generated by a conventional boiler and connected so that the solar hot water preheats the conventional cylinder, reducing the need for the boiler to operate. Solar panels are usually roof mounted, although they don't have to be and thermosyphon systems require the panel to be below the hot water storage cylinder, making roof mounting impossible on some buildings. For optimum effect panels should be located on an aspect within 45° of south. A typical solar hot water system employed on a house would require spatial allocation of about 4 m² for the panel.

Domestic scale solar hot water systems currently cost in the range of £1500 to £3000 to supply and install and with typical annual savings on conventional hot water heating bills between £50 and £100, paybacks are long[3]. As mentioned earlier, it maybe that your project is eligible for funding under the UK Government Clear Skies scheme.

Renewable generated electric heating

You may wish to consider the use of electricity, generated from a renewable non fossil fuel source. The ability to plug in electric heaters anywhere within your building might appear an attractive and convenient form of heating, but how can you ensure the electricity used is fossil fuel free? One way is to ensure you generate enough electrical power on site to service all your electrical power needs for space heating and hot water. In most cases it is unlikely that you would achieve 100% self sufficiency, even when incorporating a mixed bag of renewable generation including photovoltaic and wind power, so you will need to consider import of additional electrical power from the national grid. If you have no intention of generating any of your own power at all you will of course be totally reliant on the national grid to power your heating.

The use of grid supplied electricity that is sourced solely and directly from a renewable basis is not in reality possible. This is because the National Grid is a UK wide network of power distribution taken from a number of different generation sources, of which renewables account for only a tiny proportion in comparison to contribution from gas and coal fired power generation. Your commitment to purchase electricity using a green tariff scheme may on the face of it be a way of ensuring you contribute to investment in renewable power on the basis of the amount of electrical power that you use. A green tariff makes a positive contribution to

increasing the use of renewable generation only if it increases the amount of renewable sourced power that a supply company has to buy over and above their minimum statutory obligation. There are only a limited number of green tariffs currently available that do this and these are based upon ensuring the supply company surrenders their surplus Renewable Obligation Certificates (ROC), rather than selling them on to supply companies that have not met their renewable supply. This creates a higher demand for renewable generated power than is already created by the government's legal obligation on suppliers to source a percentage of their total supply from renewables.

Conclusion

The reality is that for most domestic and small scale building projects aiming to totally avoid the use of fossil fuels for heating, a number of different solutions will need to be encompassed. Any non fossil fuel scheme should have at its foundation a thermally efficient building envelope and encompass the principles of passive solar design in order to minimise the heating requirement in the first place. Wood based fuels such as log or pellet are likely to be the most appropriate choice for many domestic scale projects, backed up with solar hot water generation and utilisation of woodchip fuelled boilers on larger projects. Other projects may rely more on a mixture of building integrated renewable power generation and purchase of green tariff electricity to achieve the fossil fuel free goal. ❖

Sources of further information

British Biogen have a very helpful website advising on all aspects of wood heating; www.britishbiogen.co.uk The government website for grant funding information for biofuel heating and building integrated renewable projects is www.clear-skies.org

References

1 Borer P, Harris C, 1998, The Whole House Book, p177, (available from The Green Shop, www.greenshop.co.uk 01452 770629)
2. 'Wood as a fuel", British Biogen web site www.britishbiogen.co.uk
3 Energy Saving Trust web site: www.est.org.uk

Heating your home with wood

So you have planned your eco-home down to the last detail. Natural insulation, ecopaint, solar panels etc.etc. But how have you chosen to heat it? I bet you have decided to use a gas or oil condensing boiler. Well think again! There are other environmental and healthier options **Keith Hall** explains ...

When my family and I first moved to our rambling farm in west Wales we made a conscious decision to avoid the use of fossil fuels in as many aspects of our lives as possible. In reality this meant some fairly costly investment in wind, solar and hydro power for electricity. But perhaps the biggest challenge was to avoid the use of fossil fuels in the heating of the farmhouse and nearby office building. One of the last things to be installed was a 50kW log-burning boiler.

Burn wood to see more trees

Less than 10% of the UK is covered in woodland and most of that is coniferous. Most native woodland in the UK is currently neglected and under-managed. Landowners with woodland or potential woodland sites have been reluctant to plant or maintain woodland because of the non existent market for the wood. Contrary to popular belief, neglected temperate woodland is not as good for wildlife as managed woodland. Historically, native UK woodland would have been managed for construction timber, firewood, coppice crafts: charcoal, fencing, hurdles etc. Many of these uses have all but died out other than as novelty craft revival interests. Most construction timber is imported. If more of us began burning wood to heat our homes, offices and factories we would offer purpose to the expansion and care of native woodland right across the UK. This would, in-turn, allow woodland owners to invest more time in growing high quality construction and joinery timbers (firewood is usually harvested from thinnings during the growth of quality timber).

Burn wood to help the environment

It is now widely agreed that, when burnt efficiently, wood gives off far lower pollution than fossil fuelled appliances. Efficiently burned wood only releases the same amount of carbon dioxide - CO_2 - as the wood had locked up during its growth (even less if the timber originates from coppice woodland as the roots remain in the ground to grow again therefore acting as a real carbon sink). Recent comparisons[1] suggest:

Fuel	kg CO_2/kWh
wood pellets	0.03
gas	0.19
oil	0.27
coal	0.27

Harvest and burn wood for your health

Almost every day we hear of new techno-gadgets promoted to make our lives easier and more satisfying. But the reality is that far from making us more satisfied with life they just separate us further from the natural environment, make us lazier, and as a result our waists expand and obesity is fast becoming the UK's biggest killer,

Most of us are very separated from the need to provide ourselves with basic food, shelter and warmth. This alienation may cause a negative imbalance in our lives. Putting in at least a little physical effort towards making our homes warm and comfortable reconnects us both mentally and physically with the natural environment, and you do not have to live in the countryside to experience it. Even with the best, most energy efficient and mechanised equipment wood burning offers a measure of laborious input. With the right aptitude from the outset, wood cutting, collection, converting, stacking and burning is one of the most satisfying, enjoyable and health promoting tasks that you could undertake. It's real satisfaction too, - every log stacked in the shed becomes an investment - not only financially, as we all tend to measure things these days, but an investment in your own personal health and well-being.

The sustainable heating fuel

Prices for oil and gas are unrealistically low at present, although they have at last begun to rise. Demand will soon outstrip supply (recent suggestions are 2020). Improvements in energy efficiency are barely keeping pace with our insatiable demand. On the other hand wood when used for heating has everything going for it - the sustainable cycle for wood is well within human life-scales.

Whenever you mention wood burning to anyone they immediately think of a focal stove in the living room. Few people know of the technically advanced systems that are now available from long established European manufacturers. Whilst the UK turned its back on wood burning decades ago, other countries, particularly Scandinavia and Denmark, pursued the technology and invested heavily into refining the technology that we have available today.

Cost

The capital cost of a woodburning boiler system will vary depending on the sophistication of the equipment chosen (for sophistication read mechanisation, not efficiency - efficiency is essential in all systems) and the fuel (logs, pellets or wood chips). As a very rough guide you could expect to pay the following + VAT costs for a fully installed system in an average sized detached home using a 15-30kW boiler:

Logs	£7-11,000
Wood-pellets and chip	£9-19,000

The Clear Skies grant scheme is now available for wood fired boilers up to a boiler size of 30kw.

As far as efficiency is concerned all of the systems compare well with the best condensing gas or oil boilers. As for running costs, the comparison between the various wood fuel option are: logs £65 -£85 delivered per tonne; pellets £246[2] per tonne. Prices include VAT and delivery. Wood chips would fall somewhere in between.

Wood fuel efficiency is highly dependant on the moisture content of the wood fuel used. Pellets have a guaranteed moisture content from the manufacturer that is below 12% . Logs, with a good storage regime, can easily be brought down to 15-20% (well within high efficiency levels) in two to three years, so a minimum of two years' storage should be allowed for. Wood-chips are

the most difficult to dry and unless mechanical turning equipment for drying and large storage areas are available, then this might not be a good choice.

Of course if you are lucky enough to own your own woodland then your ideal system choice would be logs or if you have plenty of space but want more mechanisation and less manual labour, wood-chips.

The downdraught log boiler

I chose a Baxi Solo Innova[3] log burning boiler rather than a pellet or wood-chip (even though I have a chipper) for two reasons. Firstly, the price of log burning boilers are, at present, significantly cheaper than pellet boilers due mainly to the more straightforward technology involved. Secondly, I have more than ample supplies of timber at the farm and enjoy managing my own woodlands. I might have considered a pellet boiler if machines were available to make pellets

from your own timber (a long way off yet). There is only one efficient method of burning wood. It has to be done fast and in a high temperature environment. A water jacket around the combustion zone is a definite drawback as it cools the temperature of the fire. So how have manufacturers overcome this problem? Well, in my boiler, the water jacket is behind the chamber rather than around it (see picture). It is in a pre-chimney where gasses leaving the combustion chamber are sucked by an inbuilt fan, at temperatures around 900°C, through a collection of water filled baffles (heat exchanger). This is where the heat is effectively transferred to the water without having any cooling effect on the combustion process at all. This arrangement allows the boiler to operate at an efficiency of 89-91% which in reality is probably better than most condensing gas boilers perform. The real work of the boiler takes place in a ceramic flame tunnel (ceramic is one of the only materials able to withstand such high temperatures) directly below where the wood is loaded and this combustion takes place at full output with an appropriate mixture of primary and secondary air.

Once lit the boiler needs no further adjustment and switches itself off at the end of a burn. My boiler is rated at 50kW which means that when running it will output 50kW of heat per hour. A full load of ash species timber will burn for up to 4 hours, therefore creating towards 200kW hours of heat as hot water which is stored in a well-insulated accumulator tank (large water vessel) sized appropriately for the boiler - in my instance 2,500 litres. The accumulator tank serves as a large battery which reduces firing times. In my case, depending on the weather, I usually fire up once every two days in the spring and autumn and each day during the winter.

The accumulator

Accumulator tanks are beginning to become more widely available but are still expensive. I converted an old oil tank with a view to replacing it sometime in the future when there is more choice and lower prices. Most of the suppliers of log boilers should be able to offer something but Baxi still could only offer 750 litre tanks and suggest coupling them together (this seems to be the commonly accepted practice on the conti-

nent). My 50kW boiler has a minimum tank size requirement of 2100 litres, so, to use their tanks I would need to couple three of these together. This, to me, has practical disadvantages - everything times three - three tanks to check for leaks, three sets of couplings, not to mention the vast floor-space requirement. Personally I don't think this is a very practical or economical option, with the basic tank costing about £530 + VAT and delivery.

During my research I found that Construction Resources[4] based in London offer a highly advanced heating management system suitable for my needs. Called 'The Sandler System'. It sounds fantastic - computer controlled flows and returns, mixing, intelligent, monitoring of inputs and outputs, able to cope easily with disparate demands (high and low temp circuits) special boiler monitoring etc. etc. However, at a cool starting price of £7000 for a tank and associated equipment (this price does include a couple of solar panels but no boiler), it makes the boiler look cheap in comparison (my 50kW cost £2,500). Unless you plan to convert an oil

System layout of Baxi Solo Innova wood burning boiler with accumulator tank.

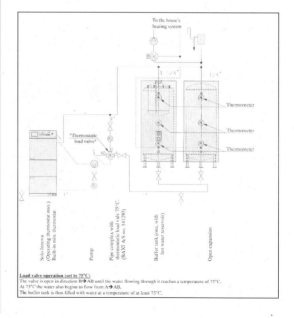

tank like I did (not recommended because of its limited lifespan) then budget on spending at least as much for the accumulator tank as the boiler.

Baxi and others, also produce log burning boilers that have advanced modulating controls which allow the boiler to be coupled with a much smaller accumulator tank. These are known as 'Lambda Controlled' but the boiler costs are far higher, the refuelling would be more frequent and the efficiency does drop, (though not by much on Baxi's offering). Pellet and woodchip boilers use a hopper and or auger systems that are automated therefore they have less need for accumulators too.

Conclusion

I really see woodburning as the future. No doubt systems will continue to become even more sophisticated. There is little doubt in my mind that pellet fuelled appliances will ultimately find the lion's share of the market as they have the potential to appeal to those users that want minimal input into the running of the system. Whatever system you choose, providing it's wood fuelled, you can rest assured that you will have chosen the most environmentally friendly system possible - whilst at the same time contributing towards the reforesting of the UK. ❖

Refs.

1. The 'John Willoughby domestic Fuel Price Guide April 04. www.johnwilloughby.co.uk
2. The price is taken from the 'John Willoughby domestic Fuel Price Guide, April 04
www.johnwilloughby.co.uk
3. Baxi Solo Innova - marketed in the UK by Foundation Firewood 01674 271271
www.fbcgroup.co.uk
4. Construction Resources 020 7450 2211

Other useful contacts

The British Pellet Club - promoting the widespread use of wood pellet heating
www.british-pellet-club.org.uk

The Logpile Project - promoting and aiding the use of wood as a source of renewable energy
www.logpile.co.uk

Good financial support for the planting and establishment of woodlands

The Forestry Commission offer a number of woodland establishment and managment grants. Their grant system is well established and has minimal bureaucracy. The basic establishment grant starts at £1380 per hectare with a better land supplement of £600 if the land is being removed from intensive or semi-intensive agriculture. At the present time, in Wales there is also a special grant available (£3500 per hectare for the extension of existing native woodlands or the creation of new woodlands - over 5 hectares in size). Anyone can apply, even tenants (with the landowners permission of course). Some areas of the UK also benefit from increased premiums (check with the Forestry Commission). There are increased supplements available for woodland that will be open to public access. Agricultural holdings may also claim Farm Woodland Premium Supplements (FWPS) of £200 per hectare for 15 years following the year of planting.

Forestry Commission www.forestry.gov.uk/

Energy saving advice for those on low incomes

In recent years there have been many schemes introduced to help you save energy, save money and keep warm at the same time. Many of the bigger schemes are outlined elsewhere in this book. But did you know that there is a mixture of discounted and subsidised goods and services, as well as government grants, available to people on a low income, to help them make their homes more energy efficient. **Ben Bamber** reports...

You can get discounts on low energy light bulbs; fridges and fridge/freezers, grants for insulating windows, lofts, walls, and hot water cylinders. There are also a few basic things you can do around your home, to keep out the draughts and keep in the warmth, saving you money on your fuel bills. Below are some details of costs, discounts and grants: how to get them, and who to contact.

Fridges and freezers

Two companies provide services for low energy fridges and freezers. They are roughly half the normal price, and this discount is largely covered by the power companies involved in the scheme. To qualify for both schemes you must be on state benefit.
- Powergen, FridgeSavers, FREEPOST NAT8431, Sheffield, S22 5ZZ Or phone Powergen on 0845 604 0045. Costs are from £50 for a basic fridge and £75 for a fridge freezer. This particular scheme is a swap for an old energy inefficient fridge, or fridge/freezer.
- NPower on 0845 330 1113. Costs are £35 for

an energy efficient fridge while stocks lost.

Low energy light bulbs.

Low energy light bulbs come in packs of two and are available from Scottish Power to anyone.
- Pack A - 2 x 20W PLET lamp (resembles toaster, lots of loops) £4.70 (RRP £17.98)
- Pack B - 2 x 16W Ambience (resembles ordinary lamp) £6.00 (RRP £15.98)
- Pack C - 2 x 18W Stick (just one loop) £5.20 (RRP £7.98)

Contact: Scottish Power, Response Centre, Unit 18, Sandbank Business Park, Dunoon, Argyll PA23 8PB. Phone 0845 602 3876 or order the light bulbs on line at **www.scottishpower.com/bulbs**

Government insulation grants.

The government is keen to make homes better insulated and energy efficient, and for this reason are providing grants to people on low incomes, for cavity wall insulation, loft insulation and other measures. However, some schemes are only discounted and others are in conjunction with landlords (if you live in rented accommodation). There should be a local contact based at your local county or district council who will respond to enquiries about grants provided by the government, or at least will know of government sponsored schemes run by private companies.

Draught excluders, insulation and secondary glazing.

Draught excluders are a cheap and effective way of making your home more energy efficient. Much of the wasted energy is lost through gaps in doors and windows, key holes, letter boxes and gaps in loft hatches. Sometimes the most obvious things can be missed, and it is these aspects of energy saving devices which are the most available, and easiest to fix. A roll of draught proofing tape for windows will cost around £6, (10 m) and is available from any good DIY shop. A letter box cover can cost as little as £4, and a draught excluder for external doors, (and internal if necessary), can be picked up at about £6 each. A hot water cylinder jacket costs about £12, depending on the size of the cylinder. It is also possible to insulate exposed hot water pipes. The basic tasks outlined above will cost about £60 in total, and could save up to £25 in fuel bills, annually.

Secondary glazing is more expensive, and as far as I know there are no government schemes to cover the costs. A basic pack for an average sized un-openable window will cost £65. Although the cheaper option, secondary glazing, can still be expensive, and may not be all that achievable if you're on a low income.

According to the Severn Wye Energy Agency, if everything you can do is being done, you can expect to save up to £165 from your yearly electric and gas bills. It never ceases to amaze me, just how much energy is being wasted from simple, and easily fixed problems. All of the above can be achieved within a budget of £500 - £800 and therefore it is possible to have repaid your investment within 3 to 5 years.

Water

If your loo flushes 9 litres (80% of houses still use this size cistern) then fit the award winning 'Interflush' retrofit kit to your your existing toilet syphon **www.interflush.co.uk** Once fitted, the averge houseold of 2.4 people could save 27,000 litres per year which equates to a saving £50 per annum and rising. ❖

www.housewarming.org.uk

S E D A
Scottish Ecological Design Association

Scotland's foremost voluntary forum for promoting ecological design:

- *regular events, large and small*
- *magazine three times a year*
- *e-mail bulletins*
- *research and projects*
- *opportunities for meeting like-minded people*

Membership is open to interested groups, companies and individuals.

Contact: **Gill Pemberton, SEDA Membership Secretary, Abbey St. Bathans House, Duns, Berwickshire TD11 3TX. Tel. 01361 840 230**

Dealing with grey water and black water

Every litre of water piped into our homes has to leave again one way or another. Most exits carrying away contaminants of waste and washing, while any clean water quickly mixes in the sewers and tanks to become contaminated itself. The management of grey water from sinks, kitchens, washing machines and baths and black water from toilets, is a very significant part of our overall environmental impact. **Féidhlim Harty** reports...

In the past decade, huge strides have been taken in wastewater awareness, technology and legislation. Generally it is considered inadequate to use a septic tank and percolation alone on anything but the most suitable of soil and subsoil conditions. A standard alternative is the domestic scale package treatment system, which uses electricity and pumps to oxygenate the wastewater within a plastic or concrete tank. While the treatment afforded the wastewater is quite acceptable, if sustainability is your aim, both the long-term energy consumption and the high embedded-energy are a downside.

Another way to reach the same, or higher, quality of wastewater treatment is to use a constructed wetland or reed bed system. Constructed wetlands usually refer to soil-based surface-flow systems, while the term reed bed is usually used to describe a gravel-based system of subsurface horizontal flow or vertical flow. If you have the space and gradient, constructed wetlands or reed beds can be used without the need for electricity for pumps or air blowers. Where sufficient wetland area is used, nitrates and phosphates can be reduced to acceptable levels without the need for chemical dosing. They are also beneficial for wildlife, attracting wetland flora and fauna such as dragonflies, butterflies and birds.

A septic tank is the usual settlement stage before a constructed wetland or reed bed, but other systems can also be used. A package treatment system can be used instead of a septic tank in conjunction with a constructed wetland to achieve a higher wastewater discharge quality where land area is limited. Where gradient permits, a vortex separator unit can be used without the need for electricity if you want to recoup the faecal matter from the black water prior to, or instead of, the septic tank. This can collect the faecal matter for composting in a chamber beneath the separator, while the flush water and urine continues to the septic tank or reed bed. The cleaner wastewater results in improved discharge quality or smaller treatment area. This type of system is very handy where you want to recoup the nutrients in the faecal matter but still wish to use a flush toilet in your home.

A further way to minimise the impact on the environment, and maximise the recovery of nutrients, is to use a urine separating toilet to take out nitrogen-rich urine before the treatment system. The urine can then be used as a liquid fertiliser. Used in combination, the urine separating toilet and vortex separator unit can remove the vast majority of polluting matter from black water in the form of useable nutrients. The final wastewater is thus much cleaner entering the local environment.

Taking a step further, a dry toilet cuts down your water consumption immediately. There are many types of composting toilets, inside the home or outside in a privy. If sustainability is your top priority, mixing clean water with nutrients to make a fairly useless and polluting mixture is not the ideal.

For grey water, a reed-bed or constructed wetland can be used, even if you do opt for a compost toilet. If you are careful of your cleaning products, and avoid common harmful ingredients, you can use the grey water for irrigation in the garden. Straightforward settlement can remove solids before use, or there are suppliers of grey water reuse equipment for pumping, plumbing and filtration. Then it can be used for toilet flushing and car washing as well as in the garden.

With very careful design of the plumbing in your house, you can plumb the waste outlet from the wash hand basin to the toilet cistern to cut down on clean water use where it is not necessary. Low-delivery taps are another way to maximise water conservation. Even simple measures like not leaving the tap running while brushing your teeth helps.

To minimise the consumption of mains or pumped well-water, roof-water can be harvested and filtered to provide clean water for the home. As a minimum, collecting water from each gutter around your house can provide water for the garden and washing the car, without using anything more costly or resource/energy heavy than an old barrel and a bucket. It doesn't have to be a fancy, all-in system to be effective.

Reusing roof water has the additional benefit of evening out flood-peaks of heavy rainfall on your roof. Since rainwater runs more quickly from impervious surfaces than from grassland, storage of flood-water for slower steady release helps to redress the changes in flow patterns caused by house construction. It may not seem to be much on an individual house scale, but Sustained Urban Drainage Systems (SUDS) do the same job in larger catchment areas, and every bit makes a difference.

In addition to the obvious environmental benefits of adequately treating your wastewater, minimising water consumption also has a number of benefits from a sustainability point of view. It minimises the energy involved in pumping the water to the council treatment plant, the energy used in treatment, the energy used in pumping it to your home and then the energy used in treatment of the waste water because of the reduced volume becoming polluted. There are also resources used at each stage, which are minimised by maximising water conservation. So, as with all areas of sustainability and environmental protection, all impacts and conservation measures are linked together.

Whatever level of wastewater treatment and conservation you choose for your home, remember that water flow into and out of your home is one area that you can make many choices for greater sustainability. ❖

A review of green building organisations in the UK

This, the second edition of the Green Building Bible, has been encouraged and supported by a number of organisations that promote green building in the United Kingdom. Here we present a brief summary of their recent work and future aims.

Low Impact Living Initiative

Lili ran some new courses in 2004. These included one on 'rammed earth building' when a rammed earth barbecue area was constructed. Lili has also produced and are working on some new manuals (available on the website) on the

following subjects; 'how to make biodiesel', 'compost toilets' and 'natural paints & lime'. A domestic biodiesel reactor is expected to be available soon via the website. During 2005, Lili will be hosting more residential weekend courses at Redfield Community in Buckinghamshire. Examples of the subjects that will becovered on the courses include straw-bale building; how to make biodiesel; self-build solar hot water; rammed earth building; self-build geodesic domes; natural paints & lime; low-impact living general course; and cob building.

More information sheets, manuals, books and products, including solar hot water kit and biodiesel reactors are planned for the future.
www.lowimpact.org
01296 714184

Sponge

Sponge is a network of young professionals with an interest in sustainability and the built environment. It received charitable status in 2004. A busy events schedule included a site visit to SEEDA's Chatham Maritime development, two special Sponge members' tours of 'the Gherkin', a Sponge trail of sustainable buildings in conjunction with London Open House, and guided tours of BedZED and Gallions Ecopark.

On top of this, Sponge volunteers have helped to build homes for low income families through Habitat for Humanity project. Sponge has been consulted and represented on government proposals including the amendments to the UK Sustainable Development strategy and the new Part L regulations. All this (and  much more!) has seen membership grow to over 800 individuals (and counting..)!

2005 promises to be another busy year, filled with fresh ideas and energy! Following on from a members' survey, the aim is to continue a theme running through the events on topics members are particularly concerned about; namely climate change, education and social inclusion. There will be a climate change event, followed up with

trips to Brighton and Nottingham to check out earthships, Hockerton and other worthwhile sites. Members will tackle the ideas of social inclusion and accessibility for all, and continue to feed back into policy and forge links with other organisations.
www.spongenet.org

Hockerton Housing Project

2004 saw significant changes to the work of the project; most notably the construction of a new 'Sustainable Resource Centre' which will enable HHP to provide better facilities and more effectively demonstrate key sustainability principles

of the project. The low profile 'eco-community building' is situated near to the houses and it also has an earth covered roof. The functional space includes a dedicated audio-visual room, seminar facilities and permanent exhibitions. The building was designed to meet the same high standards as the homes, 'zero CO_2' and 'zero heated'. It will be supplied with energy from a second on site wind turbine.

A number of new services have been developed during the year including "Sustainability in Practice", a comprehensive educational experience for young people to learn about the problems of sustainability and discover some of the solutions. HHP has also developed a new series of technical factsheets covering all the key aspects of the Project.

With HHP's new centre, they plan to run many more events, in particular longer tours and workshops for building professionals. Bespoke events can be organised.
www.hockerton.demon.co.uk/guidedtour/index.html

Sustainability Works

Sustainability Works is an online software package. It is specifically designed to help housing professionals and their partners deliver sustainable development efficiently, from policy level to project delivery. Sustainability Works was developed in conjunction with leading industry professionals and the Housing Corporation. The application has been live since May 2002 and has over 1400 registered organisations. It has become a leading industry standard for housing associations, architects and consultants, developers and local authorities.
Sustainability Works combines an extensive reference database with interactive software. This unique combination allows you to write, edit

Sustainability Works 2005
Online software

and store your own sustainable development policy and project development details with the benefit of expert research and guidance.

In 2004 over 300 professionals attended training courses all around the country on how to undertake sustainable development using Sustainability Works. The Sustainability Works team also provided customised training sessions designed to meet the individual needs of organisations such as major housebuilders and leading housing associations.

Sustainability Works 2005, an upgraded version of the software, is being launched in early 2005. Developed in conjunction with the Housing

Corporation, Building Research Establishment, Sustainable Homes, World Wild Fund for Nature and leading housing associations, Sustainability Works 2005 reflects registered users' comments.

New features will include; redesigned interface for easier navigation; latest EcoHomes stand-ards; new project sharing facility; improved document management. Also new for 2005 - an expanded nationwide programme of Sustainability Works training, including in-depth focus on the detailed aspects of sustainable development and housing design.
www.sustainabilityworks.org.uk/training

Association for Environment Conscious Building

The AECB has been carrying out effective lobbying of industry and government (informed

ASSOCIATION FOR
ENVIRONMENT-CONSCIOUS
BUILDING

by good research, such as the AECB's Energy Standards, often working with expert AECB members for sustainable design and construction and also forming lobbying alliances with other committed organisations); creating structures (such as the training initiative SussED) that make effec-tive use of members' knowledge and skills; and re-organising the AECB to prioritise and focus its resources.

The AECB is; improving the quality of member benefits and resources, including tightening membership criteria, helping differentiate its members in an increasingly busy marketplace; ensuring a high level of informed and critical debate within the developing sustainable construction industry e.g. through upgrading its web based technical discussion forum and disseminating definitive, well researched and

---

CSBT
Eden's Watering Lane
Nursery
Lobb's Shop
St Austell
PL26 6BE

Tel : 01726 68654
admin@csbt.org.uk

www.csbt.org.uk

CONTACT CSBT MEMBERS
You can search the CSBT Directory for sustainable building suppliers, services, professionals etc and send them all a message.

You will need to go to our website and register to use this service, but it is free and immediate.

To be listed on the directory you must be a member of CSBT.

To join CSBT, please go to our website and fill in the application form on the join page.

---

integrated technical guidance on key aspects of sustainable construction; helping to ensure an adequate construction skills base required to successfully implement the high levels of energy efficiency and sustainable design generally necessitated by the challenge of global warming and ecological degradation.

In 2005 the AECB aims to; continue to work with government and industry to ensure take up of the 'AECB New Build Energy Standards' within the Government's Sustainable Buildings Code and future Building Regulations and to further AECB work on energy efficient and eco' refurbishment of the existing UK building stock; deliver the first SussED 'Energy Efficient Construction' training courses with partner colleges and develop further training modules on different subjects; work with the Construction Industry Training Board (CITB) to ensure this type of training becomes mandatory; continue to lobby on all aspects of sustainable construction and to build a range of alliances to further its objectives; continue to implement changes to improve member benefits and to create a robust organisation.

www.aecb.net
0845 456 9773

Forest Stewardship Council

FSC is an independent, non-profit, non-governmental organisation. It is an association of members from environmental and social groups, the timber trade and the forestry profession, community forestry groups and other organisations from around the world. FSC runs a global forest certification system that includes two key aspects: Forest Management and Chain of Custody certification. This ensures that timber produced in certified forests has been traced from the forest to the end user.

Forests are inspected and certified against strict national or regional Forest Management Standards,

endorsed by FSC and based on the FSC Principles and Criteria for Forest Stewardship. These inspections are undertaken by independent organisations, such as the Soil Association, that are accredited by the FSC. In order to gain FSC certification a forest must be managed in an environmentally appropriate, socially beneficial and economically viable manner. Far more than just replanting trees: consideration of indigenous peoples' rights, water course protection, and biodiversity ensures that the forest and its dependent community will continue to thrive and to ensure future timber supplies.

The FSC trademark makes it possible to choose timber for construction projects with the confidence that you are not contributing to the destruction of the world's forests. By buying from certified sources an incentive is provided through market forces for good forestry practice.

Supply of FSC-certified building materials is improving all the time, during 2004 Travis Perkins, Jewson and Buildbase all began to offer FSC-certified materials.

For more information on certification or assistance in finding a particular FSC-certified product contact the FSC UK Advisory Service. We offer a full range of services, from simple product searches to training for those seeking certification and consultancy when starting a new project.

www.fsc-uk.org
01686 413 916

Scottish Ecological Design Association

The Scottish Ecological Design Association is preparing a full programme for 2005 and beyond with monthly events, ranging from the large and formal to small and local, and exploring cutting-edge aspects of ecological design.

It kicks off with a talk by Alastair Fuad-Luke, author of 'The Ecodesign Handbook', which will take place in Dundee. There will then be an evening on Humane Design and Hospitals, with James Hackett, joint winner of the Krystyna

SEDA
Scottish Ecological Design Association

Johnson Student Travel award for 2004 and a guest speaker.

In the spring of 2005 a joint SEDA/SEPA symposium on Water and Buildings has been organised – what are the issues for Scotland, and what can be regarded as best practice for the built environment? A few weeks later the completion of the first of three design advice guides: 'Design for Deconstruction' will be announced with a workshop, and in the summer of 2005 there will be a meeting in the Highlands for a day on 'Ecological Building' at Glen Coe Visitors' Centre, (jointly run with the National Trust for Scotland).
www.seda2.org
01361 840230

Sustainable Homes

Sustainable Homes is a not-for-profit project based at Hastoe Housing Association. Its aim is to promote understanding of sustainable development, and to encourage action by the housing association sector, and their partners, including architects, developers and designers. It is Housing Corporation funded, and the free service includes tailored advice, an enquiry service, updates on current activity within the sector and best practice examples. A key role is to provide easy access to the comprehensive range of tools, resources, advice and training available. This year it undertook a co-ordination role on behalf of the Housing Corporation, to ensure that the outputs and resources from the sustainability projects of the Innovation and Good Practice programme were effectively disseminated and taken up by the sector.

As well as promoting what is available, several other resources have been produced including a guide called 'Green Voices and Choices', which draws together the lessons learned from research with residents to find out what they really think about the environmental features that help to cut down energy-use, water-use, pollution and waste. There is an updated library of case studies, with an additional 15 case studies on sustainable refurbishment, available as both an electronic and printed format.

Future developments at Sustainable Homes include a follow up to the 'Guide to EcoHomes' called 'EcoHomes in Construction'. A guide will be available early 2005, aimed at all those involved in the process of building to EcoHomes, both the housing association and for-profit sector. It builds on the results of a survey and interviews with the sector, and puts forward solutions together with

Sustainable H●mes

expert advice and case studies.

In addition to this all the core work will continue, such as the provision of information and advice, and the dissemination of activity and news to the sector. Monthly e-bulletins will continue to be circulated at the end of each month, along with regular newsletters. The next phase of Sustainable Homes beyond March 2005 is being planned - so watch this space!
www.sustainablehomes.co.uk
www.greenstreet.co.uk
020 8973 0429

Walter Segal Self Build Trust

The Trust currently works from a head office in Belford, Northumberland, with a network of volunteers providing advice and information. The Trust runs a programme of self-funding regional training courses, maintains a database of projects, and provides general information on self build and environmental issues through a web-site, telephone helpline and response service by post and email. Volunteers provide limited technical assistance, and information on design and funding. In 2004 12 courses were organised around the country - in London, Cambridge,

The Walter Segal Self Build Trust

helping people to build their own homes

www.segalselfbuild.co.uk

211

Swansea, Bristol, Plymouth, Nottingham, Manchester, Belford and Leeds.

Groups were assisted through more project specific support with homeless people's housing (Tyneside Cyrenians), community centres (North Seaton Colliery, Acklington Village Hall), and with proposals for training facilities (Harehope Quarry, Northumberland Community Council, Northumberland National Parks Authority). The Trust also assisted individuals and groups seeking support to create their own environmentally-friendly housing solutions. Other activities included: delivering talks in the UK and in Italy; arranging visits to other projects (Bore Place); developing and site managing the House Race programme on Carlton TV; providing group training with housing projects in Devon and Scotland and providing practical training courses at CAT and in Frosterley.

During 2005 WSSBT will be running more introductory courses. Those scheduled so far are in Edinburgh, Norwich, Belford and Birmingham. It is hoped to expand the range and type of courses offered, including more practical courses and specialist courses in design, services, organisation etc. Introductory courses will be extended – in response to feedback from those who have attended them – to provide more project specific advice and to work with groups to create and develop their own environmentally-friendly building proposals. Funding is currently being sought to enable staff to be employed to provide information and technical assistance in the regions while also building up a volunteer base. Website information will be continually reviewed and updated. The Trust will continue to contribute articles and features on its activities as well as continuing to build on relationships with national and regional organisations in order to share information and good practice, and to ensure that groups can access the best sources of information for their particular project needs. www,segalselfbuild.co.uk 01668 213 544

BioRegional

Building on the success of BedZED, in which BioRegional are a partner, they have begun a new international programme of work with WWF called One Planet Living (OPL). The name stems from the fact that if everyone in the world consumed as much as the average UK resident we'd need 3 planets to support us. The programme aims to build a world-wide network of OPL Communities to demonstrate OPL in action.

BioRegional launched the first OPL community in May 2004. The 6,000 home Portuguese Mata de Sesimbra project will be the world's first ever integrated sustainable building, tourism, nature conservation and reforestation programme.

BioRegional has also been working with partners on Z-squared, a concept design for a 2,000 home zero waste and zero carbon OPL community for the Thames Gateway regeneration area. They hope to have a site confirmed by the end of 2004.

In 2005 BioRegional will begin

construction on the Mata de Sesimbra project. It is hoped that the Z-squared One Planet Living community project will be submitted for planning and its zero carbon, zero waste strategies will continue to be refined. It will be working with new architects and developers to show that sustainable communities do not have a prescribed appearance. It will also be looking for new OPL sites in China, South Africa, North America and Australia.

It is intended to set up a new buyers group called One Planet Products to offer discounted sustainable building products and service for new build and refurbishment.

BioRegional will continue to offer CPD training based on Egan Review recommendations and the BedZED Visitor Centre will be open for tours.
www.bioregional.com
020 8404 4881

Cornwall Sustainable Building Trust

Cornwall Sustainable Building Trust (CSBT) has had a very successful and exciting 2004. Having become a registered charity in 2003, this year saw the establishment of a trading arm known as Sustain Cornwall Ltd.

This year Bill Dunster Architects won CSBT's ANSAS competition to find 'a novel sustainable affordable solution to Cornwall's dire housing situation'.

The winning design is now known as Rural Zed and was seen at The Sky's the Limit Expo in Camborne, having been built by CSBT's Sustainable skills trainees in the redundant Comp-Air factory.

In 2005 the training will take place on a real site build and may be featured on Grand Designs. It is also hoped that Sustain Cornwall Ltd. will be marketing the Rural Zed as a combined training and kit build system.

CSBT is also delivering traditional skills training, having now run courses on building with lime, natural stonework, scantle slating, cob and traditional heavy timber framing based at Mount Pleasant Eco Park Porthtowan; all of which were featured at another Expo entitled Down to Earth.

In 2005 CSBT will be extending the range of its training courses in both traditional and sustainable skills to include renewable energy installers and more site based courses.
www.csbt.org.uk
01726 68654

Centre for Resource Management

2004 has been a period of transition for resource management at BRE, having moved away from landfill tax and government funded

work to more applied research/ consultancy with the construction industry and WRAP (Waste and Resource Action

213

Programme). This year saw the conclusion of a composting project where wood based panel board waste was successfully converted into various composts and investigations continued into the the bioremediation of creosote treated timber. Other highlights have been the registration of over 100 construction sites on the SMARTStart database (a waste benchmarking tool), pre-demolition audits to maximise demolition product recovery, window waste recycling trials, waste auditing and reduction on several construction projects, winning a high profile award for BREMAP (a resource management tool), investigating construction waste minimisation case studies and the certification of a recycled damp proof membrane. Last, but not least, was the launch of the Recycled Building Products Network.

Objectives include; publicise Recycled Building Products Network with relevant events and high level profiling of the members involved; update the SMARTWaste system to add further value to subscribers with access to cutting edge guidance, industry benchmarks, enhanced data on BREMAP and demonstration projects; and help more construction companies achieve real reductions in waste throughout the supply chain.

Future projects will include the Recycled Roads Show in 10 venues across the UK, a procurement model for specifying recycled content, partnership waste minimisation training programme and developing specifications for recycled building products for the NGS web site.
www.bre.co.uk
01923 664471

The Green Register

The Green Register (TGR) has continued to rapidly expand in the last year, both in terms of the training provided and in additional locations. In 2003, TGR introduced its one-day seminar programme, which is designed to provide specific training on a range of important sustainable building topics. The first of these seminars was "Excellent EcoHomes" and was the biggest training event provided by TGR to date. Since

then there have been 7 one-day seminars and there are plans to run a further 5 in 2005. The TGR has developed further its regional centres to include the South West and Sussex regions. Since the launch in the South West in 2004, there have been two introductory training sessions and also the first of several one-day seminars taking place at the CREATE Centre in Bristol.

The future includes some ambitious plans that will see The Green Register expand into the North of England, Scotland and Northern Ireland. This growth means that TGR will be able to offer more services to construction professionals

and local authorities, as well as providing clients with a more diverse list of professionals who can help them with their sustainable projects.

TGR is also investigating ways of providing tailored training to different professions within the industry, including builders and landscape architects, which should lead to a more diverse network of professionals on the Register. The intention is that, over time, TGR will have regional representation across the UK with local networking groups promoting sustainable building practices.
www.greenregister.org

RIAS Sustainable Building Design Accreditation

The Royal Incorporation of Architects in Scotland (RIAS) has pioneered the world's first Sustainable Design Accreditation scheme for the built environment. The sustainable design scheme offers individual designers the opportunity to register their performance in sustainable design and to thereby gain a classification.

The accreditation process is unique in that it deliberately targets practical implementation rather than relying on training and CPD based evidence. Applicants are required to submit information on a number of completed building projects and to describe their involvement

214

and achievements. The work is independently peer-assessed with higher classifications being awarded on the basis of complexity, scale, technical integration, development of interdisciplinary professional skills and integration of economic and social factors. Accreditation classifications range from one to four with an additional star rating to recognise the innovation that is needed in order to move closer to the requirements of sustainable design. The scheme was piloted in 2003/4 and thirteen awards made in total across all four levels. Only one 4-star award was achieved.

By only rewarding evidence-based achievement, it fully acknowledges the clear distinction between aspirations and the very real problems to be overcome in seeking to deliver sustainable design. It thereby rewards not what designers know, but importantly what they have been able to achieve with clients and colleagues.

The scheme is proving to be of interest to those already implementing sustainable design who wish to have this acknowledged and those designers seeking to better understand such requirements. For the latter the scheme is underpinned by a CPD course in Sustainable Design produced by Gaia Research that gives a broad indication of the achievements that are likely to be rewarded.

The scheme now sits alongside the RIAS's pioneering work into development of an accreditation scheme into conservation architecture. Subject to a current review, the RIAS will welcome applications from designers across the UK and is happy to provide further information on request. The initiators of the scheme and the project steering group are also keen to extend the project to cover other professions involved in the built environment.

Gaia Research

research@gaiagroup.org

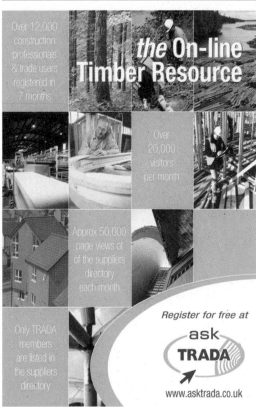
215

Design tools & resources

The Internet is a useful source of information. **Nanik Deswani, David Thorpe and Maya Karkour** have composed this section with a heavy emphasis on online resources.

The following pages aim to allow fast and easy access to a variety of on-line sustainability and eco-building resources and tools. Whether an eco-building amateur, an enthusiastic environmentally-friendly homeowner, or a professional in "green" construction, this section makes available to you a selection of pertinent web links, technical information, publications, tools, calculators, checklists, courses, and events all related to the wide topic of sustainable building. By no means was the intention to compose an exhaustive and complete list of on-line green building resources, but merely to provide stepping-stones of sources and information into an ever-expanding field of eco-building. Nonetheless, we have attempted to compile a thorough list with many of the most important links, and have checked that the websites are relevant, knowledgeable, and trustworthy.

Contents

1. Online tools for the homeowner

2. Online tools and resources for the professional

3. Practical training, courses, and events in green building

4. Advisory bodies, groups and trade associations

5. Further reading

1. Online tools for the homeowner

Green Building

www.newbuilder.co.uk

An online resource built up over the last 14 years and the main website of the Green Building Press. It includes freely downloadable back issues of Building for a Future magazine UK. It also includes GreenPro, the on-line green building products database as well as regular news and artices from leading experts in the field of sustainable building.

Green Street

www.greenstreet.org.uk

Green Street contains detailed information and advice on why and how to take action to improve your homes in the following areas: energy efficiency; water efficiency; material use; waste reduction; and health and wellbeing.

Bright ideas

www.cyberium.co.uk/bright.html

By inputting the number of light bulbs of different wattages you have and how long they are switched on, you will obtain the benefits of using compact fluorescent light bulbs compared to conventional ones. The result comes as an interest rate on your investment - and is frequently above 50%.

Building Lifecycle Carbon Calculator

www.cyberium.co.uk/carboncalculator/

How many trees should you plant to compensate for the global warming effect caused by your building and its usage? The Carbon calculator is a simple five-step interactive questionnaire, which, alternatively, can also use the output of a SAP assessment. The tool can be run several times to see the effect of different specifications.

Save Money on your Gas & Electricity

http://212.241.173.29/greenpower/domestic-input.asp

Switching to green electricity is easy. Use this calculator to see how much you can save by comparing all energy suppliers' prices for renewable electricity in your region. Enter your location and supply details, compare the results, and use the application links to switch to a green supplier.

Save Energy

www.saveenergy.co.uk

0845 1207799

This website is the place to find out how much money and energy your home and all its appliances are wasting, and as the site strongly puts it, to "discover a wealth of information designed to help your home mend its criminal ways".

Renewables

Renewable Energy Wizard

www.saveenergy.co.uk/renewables/started/wizard.cfm

The EST's very basic Renewable Energy Wizard helps you assess what renewable energy measures could be undertaken in a home.

Home Power

www.homepower.com/resources/energy_master.cfm

This Excel Spreadsheet allows you to input all the data for your electricity loads, and helps determine what PV panels, batteries, and other equipment are needed. The same information can be used for wind or water generators. The site is that of the Home Power magazine, with US expertise.

Hugh Piggott's Windpower website

www.scoraigwind.com

Hugh Pigott is a guru of the small scale wind power world. His website contains numerous links summarizing all of his knowledge.

Other power

www.otherpower.com

This website is by a group of alternative energy enthusiasts who want to spread the message that "it's easy to make your own power from scratch"... The site contains a lot of practical information about renewable energy sources for the house-builder.

Solar Electricity

www.solar-power-answers.co.uk/solar_panel.html

This great little page includes a loads calculator, an array size calculator, a battery calculator, and all the other info you need to design a basic solar electric system.

Solar Water Heating

www.thecei.org.uk/solarHeating/default.htm

This website includes benefits and costs information, descriptive diagrams, and frequently asked questions on solar water heating systems and how to install them - all on one page.

Waste & Recycling

Rethink Rubbish

www.rethinkrubbish.com

This site gives the low-down on the growing problem of household rubbish in the UK and some quick and easy steps to help solve the problem.

Scope Recycling

www.scope.org.uk/recycling/

Scope runs several recycling schemes across England and Wales to raise funds in order to provide services for disabled people. Recycling options include the recycling of toners (printer and fax laser and inkjet cartridges), phones, IT equipment, CDs and books.

Recycle More

www.recycle-more.co.uk

In the household section, you will find hints and tips for managing household rubbish, how to minimise the effects a household has on the environment, and how to make a household more environmentally friendly.

Salvo

www.salvo.co.uk

This online directory is tailored for people in search of antique, reclaimed, salvaged, and green building materials for gardens and homes.

2   Online tools and resources for the professional

Sustainable Planning and Design BedZed

www.bedzed.org.uk

A virtual tour of the BedZed development, the innovative zero (fossil) energy development by the Peabody Trust at Beddington, Sutton will certainly give you good ideas for new eco-friendly and energy-efficient house designs.

EcoLaw

www.ha-ecolaw.org.uk

EcoLaw is a web-based guide to environmental regulation for housing associations, covering environmental law, UK policy, EU directives and Housing Corporation Regulation, Inspection and Scheme Development Standards.

Design Quality Indicators (DQI)

www.dqi.org.uk

DQI Online is an interactive tool that includes a simple and non-technical questionnaire. The questionnaire helps making an assessment of the quality of a building in an interactive and participative process which enables stakeholders' involvement.

dti – Key Performance Indicators

www.dti.gov.uk/construction/kpi/

This Department of Trade & Industry web page outlines the Construction Industry Key Performance Indicators (KPIs). KPIs are national data sets against which a project or a company can benchmark its performance.

International Ecological Engineering Society

www.iees.ch

The IEES provides a common forum for anyone involved in ecological engineering projects. These include traditional engineers, marine biologists, ecological economists, development workers, and many others.

SPeAR

www.arup.com/sustainability/services/

Arup's Sustainable Project Appraisal Routine measures the sustainability of a project at all stages with optimisation of its key elements: environment, social, economic, and resource use.

The Town & Country Planning Association

www.wwf.org.uk/filelibrary/pdf/buildingsustainably.pdf

This is a link to the Sustainable Housing Forum's publication 'Building Sustainably, how to plan and construct new housing for the 21st century'. Like the WWF and other groups, the Town & Country Planning Association is calling for a fundamental review of the Building Regulations.

BRE Sustainable Construction

www.bre.co.uk/services/Sustainable_construction.html

BRE offers many tools to help assessing and reducing the environmental impacts of the built environment and its associated costs, and comply with existing and proposed legislation.

BREEAM

www.bre.co.uk/service.jsp?id=51

BREEAM (BRE Environmental Assessment Method) is a sustainability evaluation method for assessing and improving the environmental performance of office, retail, and industrial buildings, and Ecohomes is its equivalent for residential developments. BREEAM is currently the world's most widely used means of reviewing and improving the environmental performance of buildings. Some 600 major office buildings have already been BREEAM assessed in the UK.

Considerate Constructors Scheme

www.ccscheme.org.uk

The Considerate Constructors Scheme is a code of practice for improved construction sites, and promotes working practices to minimise disturbance and disruption caused by noise, dust, additional traffic and pavement congestion.

dti - Rethinking Construction

www.dti.gov.uk/construction/rethink/

Rethinking Construction is a government initiative; their report identifies targets for improvement in construction productivity, profits, defect and accident reduction. The central message of Rethinking Construction is that through the application of best practices, the industry and its clients can collectively act to improve their performance.

EcoConstruction

www.ecoconstruction.org

This site contains guidance on issues ranging from planning, choosing and specifying materials, to case studies of recycled & reclaimed material use.

EcoHomes

http://products.bre.co.uk/breeam/ecohomes.html

EcoHomes is the BREEAM-equivalent certification scheme for homes. EcoHomes provides an authoritative rating for new and converted or renovated homes, and covers houses, apartments and sheltered accommodation. The scheme assesses seven categories of best-practice criteria: energy; water; pollution; materials; transport; ecology and land use; health and well-being. EcoHomes assessments are carried out by independent assessors who are trained and licensed by the BRE. You can get a good idea of the EcoHomes credit requirements by downloading the documents available from this website, or by buying the guides 'EcoHomes: the environmental rating for homes' (£25) and 'The Green Guide to Housing Specification' (£35) from the BRE bookshop.

Envest

www.bre.co.uk/service

Envest is a software developed by BRE that simplifies the otherwise very complex process of designing environmentally-friendly buildings. The tool assesses the environmental impacts of a building at its early design stage. By inputting information about a development, such as height, number of storeys, window area, and choices of elements (external wall, roof covering, etc), Envest identifies those elements with the most influence on the building's environmental impact, showing the effects of selecting different materials. It also predicts the effects of various strategies for heating, cooling, and operating a building.

Environmental profiles

http://cig.bre.co.uk/envprofiles

A universal method of measuring the sustainability of all construction products and materials over their entire life cycle, through their extraction, processing, construction, use and maintenance, and their eventual demolition and disposal. The website also provides profiles of building elements (e.g., roofs, walls) and materials (e.g., aerated blocks, glass wool insulation, kiln dried timber and MDF).

GreenPro

www.newbuilder.co.uk/greenpro/login.asp

GreenPro is an online Internet library and archive of green building products, case studies and research information, which have been carefully selected by the Green Building Press to meet high environmental credentials. The database contains details of over 1000 green building products for the UK as well as eco-building articles.

GreenSpec

www.greenspec.co.uk

GreenSpec is a BRE website allowing constructors to design greener materials specifications for their developments.

Managing sustainable Companies (MaSC)

http://projects.bre.co.uk/masc

MaSC facilitates the introduction and development of more sustainable business practices, through a process designed to help construction companies improve their businesses' sustainability. The site includes guides and site visits. Office Scorer www.officescorer.info Refurb, or demolish and rebuild? Which is the most sustainable? The answer is often unclear... BRE's Sustainable Refurbishment / Redevelopment Decision Support Tool enables users to systematically compare and test the environmental and economic impacts of different office design concepts, using BRE's Ecopoints system.

Square One

www.squ1.com

Square One - Environmental Design Website provides free information for architects, building designers, students and anyone else interested in energy efficient and sustainable design. The site also contains on-line courses on eco-building design issues, such as natural lighting, passive systems, and acoustics.

Sustainable Homes

www.sustainablehomes.co.uk

Sustainable Homes promotes awareness of sustainable development issues and good practice, and encourages housing associations to adopt sustainable policies and practices.

Well Built!

www.wellbuilt.org.uk

Well Built! is a network site for local authorities about sustainable construction, supported by DTI Construction Industries Directorate. The aim of the site is to build up a network of local authority staff who are interested in undertaking more sustainable construction. Exchange of information on best practice, worst practice, action plans, and helpful organisations is available.

Energy Use in Buildings

Action Energy

www.energy-efficiency.gov.uk

A government-funded programme to help businesses and public sector organisations save money through energy saving. From simple tips to in-depth advice and on-site support, the site aims to show how to make a difference to both businesses and the environment.

Civil Estate Benchmarking Tool

http://projects.bre.co.uk/gpg286/

This website allows energy managers to calculate the energy performance of a building periodically, and compare it against benchmarks for similar buildings within the Government's Estate. The following data need to be inputted: - total floor area (m^2) and percentage of each type of floor area; annual electrical consumption; annual gas or oil consumption (kWh); the 'degree days' correction figure (available from a calculator on the same page); weekly occupancy figure (in hours).

DEFRA – Sustainable Energy

www.defra.gov.uk/environment/energy/index.htm

The Department for Environment, Food, and Rural Affairs, sustainable energy website provides valuable information about UK and EU regulations and initiatives regarding the energy use in buildings and construction.

Degree Days

http://vesma.com/ddd/

Degree-day figures are essential data for anyone who needs to manage significant energy consumption related to the heating or cooling of buildings. These figures indicate how much solar energy falls in different regions across the UK throughout the year.

Energy Saving Trust (EST)

www.est.org.uk/bestpractice/index.cfm

The EST website contains the EST guide, and Energy Efficiency in New Housing. The EST produces other free guides for building professionals to help construct more energy efficient homes.

Hospitality Industry Benchmarking Tool

www.hospitableclimates.org.uk/

This site allows comparisons of hospital premises with industry norms in terms of energy consumption, costs, and management, and advises on efficiency and comfort issues. An Energy Efficiency Map is also available, providing contact information for establishments currently registered to the Hospitable Climates programme.

Industrial Estate Benchmarking Tool

www.industrialbuildingsbenchmark.info/

The Industrial Building Benchmarking Tool for Heating and Lighting website can help determining heating and lighting efficiencies in a building by comparison with good practice benchmarks. A report of the possible energy saving measures, appropriate to the building, is issued.

National Institute of Standards and Technology

http://srdata.nist.gov/insulation/

This very technical US website contains a database to determine the heat transmission properties of insulating and building materials.

Office Benchmarking Tool

http://217.10.129.104/Energy_Benchmarking/Offices/
default.asp

The Office Benchmarking Tool has been developed to help assessing the energy consumption of an office building, by comparing an office consumption with national benchmark levels for UK office buildings. The program first calculates a benchmark based on the type of office space, number of workstations, and standard occupancy, and then allows it to be refined with additional variables. The website includes a checklist of all the data needed to run the program.

National Home Energy Rating (NHER)

www.nher.co.uk

The NHER is the UK's largest energy rating scheme, and is specialized in delivering energy efficiency advice, tackling fuel poverty, and developing local and regional improvement strategies. The scheme is designed to calculate energy ratings for existing, refurbished or new build stock, from on-site surveys or building plans, detailed or basic. The Government's Standard Assessment Procedure (SAP) is a simplified version of the NHER scheme.

Standard Assessment Procedure (SAP)

http://projects.bre.co.uk/sap2001/

The SAP specification may be downloaded free of charge, in PDF format. The SAP is the Government's recommended procedure for an energy rating of dwellings, with a final rating ranging between 1 to 120—from worst to best— based on the annual energy costs for space and water heating. SAP also calculates

the Carbon Index, on a scale of 0 to 10, based on the annual CO_2 emissions associated with space and water heating. A SAP rating for every new dwelling has become compulsory to fulfil the Building Regulations requirements of notifying and displaying an energy rating in new dwellings.

Solacalc

www.solacalc.freeserve.co.uk

Solacalc is a PC-based programme that has been developed to make predicting passive solar house design performance easier, and help using free heat from the sun to heat or cool buildings. The tool calculates heat losses and solar gains in residential buildings, using interlinked worksheets and UK climate data, to calculate thermal balances and financial analysis.

British Photovoltaic Association

www.pv-uk.org.uk/technology

The British Photovoltaic Association (PV-UK) is a non-profit trade association for the PV industry of Great Britain, and has strong ties with other organisations involved in sustainable development. The Association promotes photovoltaic technology by exchanging knowledge and information on its use and availability, and provides a complete guide to grid-connected solar electricity in the UK.

Database of Wind Characteristics

www.winddata.com

This database contains four different categories of wind data (time series of wind characteristics, time series of wind turbine responses, wind resource data and wind farm measurements), for wind turbine design purposes and site analysis, at 55 different locations in Europe, Egypt, Japan, Mexico and the United States.

Renewable Energy

www.dti.gov.uk/renewable/

DTI has developed a new website on renewable energy; with explanations of each type of renewable energy, how they works, and relevant case studies.

Heat Pumps

www.heatpumps.co.uk

This site contains useful basic information about heating-only applications with heat pumps. It covers environmental issues, and supports the appropriate use of this technology in high efficiency eco-friendly applications. The site also includes interactive heat source comparison charts.

Insolation Tables

www.powertech-solar.com

This website has a link to solar calculators for electric and thermal (water) panels, where insolation value tables can be used to work out how many panels are needed to satisfy specific water heating needs. The site uses NASA data with links to its original data page. Note that the solar calculators are specific to Apricus own panels.

Soltherm Europe

www.soltherm.org/tools_guidelines.asp

Soltherm is the central action network to stimulate market growth of solar thermal products. The site provides tools and calculators for planning, feasibility, simulation, financing, designing, and installing both small and large scale solar water heating projects. Registration is required, but it is free and quick.

Windpower

www.windpower.org/en/stat/units.htm

This Danish Wind Industry Association's website is excellent for understanding wind power, and its Wind Energy Reference Manual contains enough technical details to satisfy the most assiduous d-i-y-er or professional.

Water Power - British Hydropower Association

www.british-hydro.org/infopage.asp?infoid=186

The British Hydropower Association (BHA) is a trade association which represents the interests of all those involved in the hydropower industry. Its website helps determine if a site is suitable for water power, and how much energy could be obtained out of it.

BREWEB

www.breweb.org.uk

BRE's Waste & Environmental Body facilitates ongoing environmental improvement in the waste and construction industries by the use of landfill tax sponsorship in high-profile demonstration and research projects

DEFRA – Recycling & Waste

www.defra.gov.uk/environment/waste/index.htm

The Department for Environment, Food, and Rural Affairs, recycling & waste website provides valuable information about UK regulations with regards to waste, including the UK Waste Implementation Programme.

The Materials Information Exchange (MIE)

www.salvomie.co.uk

SalvoMIE is a free materials 'dating agency' for the construction and landscaping sectors; especially for waste materials.

SMARTWaste System

www.smartwaste.co.uk

BRE's SMARTWaste system has won several awards including an eWell-Being Award. The website includes a set of tools to help applying sustainable waste management. SMARTStart, a simple and easy-to-use benchmarking tool; SMARTStartLG, a monitoring and target-setting tool for local government, contractors, and managers; SMARTAudit, a detailed auditing tool to measure the source, type, quantity, cause, and cost of waste; BREMAP, a geographical information system that helps identify the best practical environmental

option for waste. BRE can be directly contacted for more information about using recycled aggregates and waste by-products in a construction project.

Timber BRE

http://projects.bre.co.uk/default.htm#Anchor-Timber-47857

This page from BRE website provides a variety of valuable links to best practice projects involving timber constructions.

Wood Detailing

www.cwc.ca/design/tools/calcs/dimension_calc/

The Canadian Wood Council website contains a tool to help estimate and account for dimensional change in new building construction. Wood shrinks when it dries and swells when it becomes wet. The tool determines wood dimensional changes due to changes in moisture contents.

Span Calculator

www.cwc.ca/design/tools/calcs/SpanCalc_2002/

The span calculator of the Canadian Wood Council determines the span for different types of timber for various purposes. This is a North American tool, but to our knowledge, there is no equivalent tool for British species.

BRE – Water

www.bre.co.uk/services/Water.html

BRE works to ensure the provision of clean, healthy water via efficient and cost effective supply systems and appliances. The establishment provides practical guidance, assessments, and testing in water systems and appliances; water management; water fittings and components; compliance with regulations and standards, and water sampling. A pdf leaflet on the Eco-Bio process for cleaning waste water can also be downloaded from this webpage.

Water Harvesting and Run-off Calculator

www.grow.arizona.edu/

The objective of this web page is to examine the concept of water harvesting, how it is used, and how it impacts on us. A tool allows inputting a catchment's area, efficiency figures, and annual rainfall, in order to determine the volume of run-off that can either be harvested, or needed to account for with storm sewers.

3 Practical training and courses

Bioregional Courses at BedZed

www.bioregional.com/programme_projects/ecohous prog/bedzed/bz_cpd.htm

"Developing practical skills - from the Communities Plan to reality", a one day seminar held at BedZED in South London, offers a practical framework for understand-

ing the components of sustainable communities and how to deliver them. Other MasterClass courses: "Green Water Treatment Plant master class"; "Combined Heat and Power"; and "Green Transport – Car Club", All CPD courses include a tour of BedZed.

Centre for Alternative Technology – Courses

www.cat.org.uk/courses/

CAT offers a substantial variety of courses from a range of popular and technical renewable energy courses to a range of relaxing and enjoyable leisure courses.

Courses in Sustainable Development

www.sd4bp.com/cours.htm

Sustainable Development for Building Professionals posts CPD courses, seminars, and events related to sustainable construction, as well as University courses with a sustainable theme.

Eco-Building Training

www.ecoconsulting.net/www/training_ecobuilding_ 04.htm

EcoConsulting (UK) Ltd. has designed an innovative CPD course, suitable for all levels, to give local authorities, planners, and housing associations a complete and methodical understanding of sustainable development and eco-building techniques.

Gaia Research

www.gaiagroup.org

CPD Modules . The series has been developed to assist practitioners in the understanding of sustainable design, and to provide the technical skills by which to implement the most up-to-date concepts. The modules cover technical issues such as ventilation, lighting & renewable technologies as well as guidance on materials, on legislation & cost. The final module on urban ecology looks at international solutions to sustainable building at an urban scale.
Module 1: Materials Selection
Module 2: Lighting and Daylighting
Module 3: Water and Sewage Management
Module 4: Heating
Module 5: Environmental Legislation and Policy
Module 6: Ventilation and Cooling Strategies
Module 7: Renewable Energy
Module 8: Sustainable Construction Drivers
Module 9: Site Issues and Construction Processes
Module 10: Low Impact Construction
Module 11: Electrical Installations
Module 12: Post Occupancy Evaluation
Module 13: Cost Issues
Module 14: Appraisal Tools & Techniques
Module 15: Urban Ecology
£10.00 each or Any 6 Modules for £50 or the Full Set for £120
0131 557 9292

Mike Wye and Associates

www.mikewye.co.uk

01409 281644

Regular lime mortar and natural paint practical courses.

Practical Help – Events & Training

www.practicalhelp.org.uk/events/

This page from Practical help for Local Authorities (an Energy Saving Trust initiative) provides a search tool to find forthcoming energy and sustainability training and events run by a range of organisations.

Sponge Events

www.spongenet.org/index.php

Sponge's website describes a variety of events and courses all related to sustainable construction.

Ty-Mawr

www.lime.org.uk

01874 658249

Regular practical courses on eco building techniques and the use of lime in building.

4. Advisory bodies, groups and trade associations

Architects and Engineers for Social Responsibility

www.sgr.org.uk/AESR/AESR

01727 836470

AESR, formed in 1991, works for peace, ethical values and a better environment, and encourages the socially responsible use of technology in ways which benefit humanity. AESR organises lectures and meetings in conjunction with the Royal Institution of British Architects and the major engineering Institutions, and tries to use its influence within the professional bodies to encourage discussion on issues of sustainability and the right use of technology.

Association for Environment Conscious Building

www.aecb.net

The AECB is the leading independent environmental building trade organisation in the UK. The Association and its network of members provide a wealth of knowledge to enable business to help the environment.

Be - Collaborating for the Built Environment

www.beonline.co.uk

Be is an independent construction reform group, with the aim of "Collaborating to create sustainable improvement in the built environment"

BioRegional Development Group

www.bioregional.com

BioRegional Development Group is an entrepreneurial, independent environmental organization that develops commercially viable products and services which meet more needs from local renewable and waste resources, to help enable one planet living – living within our fair share of the Earth's resources.

British Biogen

www.britishbiogen.co.uk

British BioGen is the Trade Association of the UK Bioenergy Industry.Its mission is to promote and co-ordinate the commercial development of biomass as a renewable fuel resource for energy production.

Building Research Establishment Ltd. (BRE)

www.bre.co.uk

BRE is the UK's leading centre of expertise on buildings, construction, energy, environment, fire and risk. The centre provides research-based consultancy, testing, and certification services. In particular, BREEAM and EcoHomes are sustainability rating and certifications developed by BRE respectively for commercial and residential buildings. The BRE website provides information about BREEAM, EcoHomes, Envest, Environmental Profiles, Green Guide, MaSC, post-occupancy evaluation, SMARTStart, SMARTWaste, whole life costing and much more.

Business in the Community (BITC)

www.bitc.org.uk

BITC is a movement of over 700 of the UK's top companies committed to improving their positive impact on society. The organization helps its members mitigating their impact on communities and the environment.

Carbon Trust

www.thecarbontrust.co.uk

The Carbon Trust is an independent company funded by the UK Government, with the role of helping the UK move to a low carbon economy by helping business and the public sector reduce carbon emissions and capture the commercial opportunities of low carbon technologies.

Centre for Alternative Technology (CAT)

www.cat.org.uk

CAT is an environmental charity aiming to "inspire, inform, and enable" people to live more sustainably. The organisation offers practical solutions to environmental problems, with key areas of work in renewable energy, environmental building, energy efficiency, organic growing and alternative sewage systems.

Centre for Earthen Architecture

www.tech.plym.ac.uk/soa/arch/earth.htm

Over the last five years the Centre for Earthen Architecture (CEA) has developed a unique focus for UK earth building activity with links to similar centres across the world.

Centre for Resource Management

www.bre.co.uk

They disseminate information regarding the wise management of new and reclaimed/recycled construction materials.

Chapter 7

www.thelandisours.org/chapter7/

01460 249204

Chapter 7, the Planning Office of The Land Is Ours campaigns for a planning system which actively encourages sustainable, low impact and affordable homes, and, drawing on experience from Tinker's Bubble, recently published the report Defining Rural Sustainability: 15 Criteria for Sustainable Developments in the Countryside.

Clay Pipe Development Association

www.cpoda.co.uk

01494 791456

The Clay Pipe Development Association provides a service for member companies, specifiers and users of vitrified clay pipes and flue linings. It represents the industry on technical matters, particularly on both British and European standards committees, and monitors relevant research.

Climate Change

www.ukcip.org.uk

The UK Climate Impacts Programme offers a number of resources to discover the potential impact of climate change in a specific area. A tool is offered to compare the likely cost of not taking preventive actions with the cost of taking them, in order to assess if such interventions are financially worthwhile.

Constructing Excellence

www.constructingexcellence.org.uk

Constructing Excellence aims to achieve a step change in construction productivity through focused programmes in Innovation, Best Practice Knowledge, Productivity, and Engagement. The organisation influences the Government in the formulation of construction policies.

Construction Industry Council (CIC)

www.cic.org.uk

The CIC is the representative forum for the industry's professional bodies, research organisations and specialist trade associations. CIC's approach and policy towards sustainability in construction and the built environment is translated through the work of its Sustainable Development Committee.

Cornwall Sustainable Building Trust

www.csbt.org.uk

CSBT is a charity that promotes sustainable building in Cornwall. It runs training courses on building related subjects.

Construction Skills

www.citb.org.uk

CITB-Construction Skills provides assistance in all aspects of recruiting, training and qualifying the construction workforce. The organisation also works with partners in industry and government to improve the competitiveness of the industry as a whole.

Council for the Protection of Rural England

www.cpre.org.uk *020 7981 2800*

CPRE campaigns for the protection of the countryside.

Energy 21

www.energy21.org.uk *01249 783415*

Energy 21 is the hub of a national network of grassroots renewable energy groups. These groups work to make a difference at a local level to reduce our reliance on fossil fuels and to promote a more sustainable future for everyone. A future with clean renewable energy driving progress.

Engineering for a Sustainable Future (IEE)

www.iee.org/OnComms/pn/sustainability/

IEE is a networking group, primarily composed of engineers, aiming at developing a sustainable society, through the promotion of new and sustainable approaches to issues such as energy generation, storage, distribution and use, design and manufacturing, consumption and production.

Environ

www.environ.org.uk *0116 222 0222*

Environ, based in Leicester, is an independent charity working to improve the environment and the communities we live in. They provide information, advice and practical help to encourage individuals and organisations to take practical steps towards a more sustainable future.

Environment Agency

www.environment-agency.gov.uk

The leading public body for protecting and improving the environment in England and Wales. It aims to make sure that air, land and water are looked after by everyone in today's society, so that tomorrow's generations inherit a cleaner, healthier world.

Envirowise

www.envirowise.gov.uk

Envirowise is a government-funded programme that offers UK businesses free, independent, confidential advice and support on practical ways to increase profits, minimise waste and reduce environmental impact. The online "Waste Minimisation Guide" can help businesses identify where waste occurs in the supply chain and audit business premises.

Eurisol – Mineral Wool Association

www.eurisol.com

Eurisol, the UK Mineral Wool Association, was formed in 1962 to represent the interests of rock and glass mineral wool manufacturers. It still remains true to it's original aims of providing an authoritative source of independent information and advice on Mineral Wool and of promoting mineral wool products in achieving improved standards of thermal and acoustic insulation and fire protection in building, industry and commerce.

Findhorn Foundation Ecovillage Project

www.ecovillagefindhorn.com *01309 690154*

The ecovillage model is a conscious response to the extremely complex problem of how to transform our human settlements, whether they be villages, towns or cities, into full-featured sustainable communities, harmlessly integrated into the natural environment. The Findhorn Foundation Ecovillage Project is a founder member of the Global Ecovillage Network (GEN), working with intergovernmental agencies in educating and developing policy guidance for sustainable development and for delivery of village-scale sustainability programmes.

Forest Stewardship Council (FSC)

www.fsc-uk.info

FSC is an international, non-governmental organisation dedicated to promoting responsible management of the world's forests. It was founded in 1993 in response to public concern about deforestation and demand for a trustworthy wood-labelling scheme. It is supported by NGOs including WWF, Greenpeace, Friends of the Earth and the Woodland Trust.

Friends of the Earth

www.foe.co.uk

Friends of the Earth aims to provide solutions to environmental problems which make life better for people.

Greenhouse Trust

www.norwichgreenhouse.fsnet.co.uk
01603 631007

A key aim of this Trust was the renovation and conversion of this building as a DIY model of what can be done to improve old and listed housing stock.

Greenpeace UK

www.greenpeace.org.uk *020 7865 8100*

Greenpeace is an independent non-profit global campaigning organization that uses non-violent, creative confrontation to expose global environmental problems and their causes. We research the solutions and alternatives to help provide a path for a green and peaceful future.

Hockerton Housing Project

www.hockerton.demon.co.uk *01636 816902*

The Hockerton Housing Project is the UK's first earth sheltered, self-sufficient ecological housing development. Project members live a holistic way of life in harmony with the environment, in which all ecological impacts have been considered and accounted for. The residents of the five houses generate their own clean energy, harvest their own water and recycle waste materials causing no pollution or carbon dioxide emissions. The houses are amongst the most energy efficient, purpose built dwellings in Europe.

House Builders Federation (HBF)

www.hbf.co.uk

HBF is the principal trade federation for private sector housebuilders and voice of the house building industry in England and Wales. The organization's mission statement is "A single voice for the industry; A strong voice for the industry; A fresh voice for the industry". The 300 member firms account for over 80% of all new houses built in England and Wales in any one yearr.

London Hazards Centre

www.lhc.org.uk *020 7794 5999*

The London Hazards Centre is a resource centre dedicated to fighting health and safety hazards in the workplace and community. This site is for union and community organisers anywhere who need health and safety information.

Midlands Renewable Energy Technology Transfer

www.mrett.co.uk/ *01509 610033*

MRETT was formed to promote renewable energy research, development and implementation. Based in Nanpantan, Leicestershire, in low-energy offices which also incorporate grid-connected PV, its growing list of members includes commercial companies and university research departments. MRETT aims to place the results of research projects with industrial partners willing to take them forward to production.

New Economics Foundation (NEF)

www.neweconomics.org *020 7820 6300*

NEF is an independent think-and-do tank that inspires and demonstrates real economic well-being. Its aim is to improve quality of life by promoting innovative solutions that challenge mainstream thinking on economic, environment and social issues.

PEX Action on Pesticide Exposure

www.pan-uk.org *020 7274 6611*

PEX is a support group for anyone whose health has been affected by exposure to pesticides. The PEX project provides information about pesticides, and puts exposure sufferers in contact with one another and with sympathetic professionals.

Scottish Ecological Design Association

www.seda2.org

SEDA promotes ecological building design and construction in Scotland. It organises a full programme of events and innitiatives throughout the region.

Sherwood Energy Village

www.sev.org.uk *01623 860222*

Sherwood Energy Village is a unique initiative that has transformed a 91-acre former colliery into an environmental enterprise. The site comprises industry, commerce, housing, education, recreation, tourism and leisure.

Soil Association (Woodmark)

www.soilassociation.org

The Woodmark programme (FSC accredited since 1996) is concerned with responsible forest management and the labelling and promotion of forest products. It is now expanding the programme to include organic certification of wood and paper products, and organic and FSC certification of non-timber forest products. Woodmark provides a full FSC-accredited certification service.

The Solar Energy Society

www.brookes.ac.uk

This is a non-profit organisation. It is a forum for all those interested in the advancement of the utilisation of the sun's energy. Members of the Society are drawn from industry, government, academic institutions, architectural and engineering practices, as well as the general public.

Solar Trade Association

www.greenenergy.org.uk

The Solar Trade Association Ltd. (STA) was formed in 1978 to serve as a focal point for organisations with business interests in the Solar Energy industry. Those interests cover thermal applications, such as the production of domestic or industrial hot water or the heating of swimming pools.

Sponge

www.spongenet.org

Sponge is a network for young professionals who share a particular interest in sustainable construction. These individuals generally work in, or are associated with the development of the built environment; from bricks and mortar through design, engineering and planning to communities and regeneration.

Straw Bale Building Association
www.strawbalebuildingassociation.org.uk
An informal, grassroots association of people who have an interest in strawbale building. Members arefrom very varied backgrounds - some are environmental enthusiasts, others are sustainable builders, some are building officials or architects, others simply believe strongly in a vision of a different world.

Sustainable Development Commission
www.sd-commission.gov.uk
The Sustainable Development Commission (SDC) is the Government's independent advisory body on sustainable development. Cutting-edge policy documents are available at their website.

Sustainable Development for Building Professionals
www.sd4bp.com
Sustainable Development for Building Professionals provides a guide to what's available in sustainable education. The organization's aim is to address the need for greater awareness of sustainability issues amongst all professionals involved within the built environment. Developed under the government's (DTI) Partners in Innovation programme, it is advised by a project consortium including leading companies involved in sustainability and the construction industry as well as both professional and academic institutes.

Sustainable Homes
www.sustainablehomes.co.uk
Sustainable Homes is a project for housing asociations and their partners. It provides training and advice.

The Green Register
www.greenregister.org
The Green Register provides training and registration for professionals who are interested in sustainable building.

Walter Segal Self Build Trust
www.segalselfbuild.co.uk
The Walter Segal Self Build Trust is a community development agency which provides a free resource service giving technical advice and general information to groups and individuals who wish to use a self build approach to solve their social housing and community building needs.

Waste Watch
www.wastewatch.org.uk
Waste Watch is the leading national organisation promoting and encouraging action on the 3Rs - waste reduction, reuse and recycling.

Welsh Timber Forum
www.welshtimberforum.co.uk
The Welsh Timber Forum was set up in September 1999 by a number of individuals working in wood-based industries in Wales. They had the vision of an organisation which could work for them and represent them inside and beyond Wales.

Women and Manual Trades
www.wamt.org
020 7251 9192
Women and Manual Trades is the national organisation for tradeswomen and women training in the trades.

Women's Environmental Network
www.wen.org.uk
Formed in 1988 WEN is a unique, vital and innovative campaigning organisation, which represents women and campaigns on issues, which link women, environment and health.

World Wildlife Fund (WWF)
www.wwf.org.uk
At the World Summit on Sustainable Development in August 2002, WWF launched its One Million Sustainable Homes (OMSH) campaign to bring sustainable homes from the fringes of the housing sector to the mainstream. WWF is working with government, industry and consumers to ensure that one million sustainable homes are developed across the UK by 2012 (refurbished as well as new homes).

5   Further reading
A vast range of books, magazines, reports, and other publications is available in the UK on green construction methods and materials. A small selection is described in this section. See also individual book reviews elsewhere in this book and titles given at the end of some articles.

BedZED Total Energy Strategy
www.bioregional.com/retail/customer/home.php
This report (£20) covers the 'zero energy' concept of meeting building and transport energy demands from on-site renewable energy sources, and includes a description of the BedZED Green Transport Plan.

Building For a Future magazine (BFF)
www.newbuilder.co.uk/bffmag/index.asp
BFF is an excellent, quarterly magazine giving an overview of the green construction industry in the UK, with a large range of articles describing experiences and case studies, technical information on building materials and technologies, as well as green building news. Free downloads of BFF recent and back issues are also available

The Construction Industry Council (CIC)

www.cic.org.uk

Useful sustainability studies are available from the CIC, including 'Constructing for Sustainability'; 'Brownfields - building on previously developed land'; and 'Water Conservation in Business'.

dti - Sustainable Construction Resources

www.dti.gov.uk/construction/sustain/

The Sustainable Construction page of the Department of Trade & Industry gives access to a broad range of documents and studies on green construction and legislation in a downloadable format.

Ethical Consumer magazine

www.ethicalconsumer.org

Promoting change by informing and empowering the consumer.

Green Construction

www.greenconstruction.co.uk

Green Construction is a collection of abstracts of newspaper and periodical articles relevant to green building in the UK.

Green Futures

www.greenfutures.org.uk

Green Futures aim is to lead the debate on sustainable development, provide a lively snapshot of the latest news and opinion, along with cutting edge examples of good practice. The monthly magazine often features interesting articles on sustainable construction.

The Green Guide to Specification

www.BREbookshop.com

A book by Jane Anderson, Building Research Establishment, David E Shiers, Oxford Brookes University, Mike Sinclair (£45) outlining the ecological rating of different building materials, following extensive research undertaken by BRE.

Renewable Energy World

www.jxj.com/magsandj/rew

REW is a monthly magazine that will allow you to catch up with renewable energy news, technologies, and case studies from around the globe.

Sustain Magazine

www.sustainmagazine.com

Sustain is a very succinct well-presented monthly magazine focusing on the sustainability of the built environment.

Sustainable Housing Schemes in the UK

www.hockerton.demon.co.uk

01636 816902

This guide (£10) is a gateway to a range of sustainable development projects from all over the UK, with a profile of over 30 schemes.

Guide to the Energy-Saving Home

www.which.net

The Which? Guide to the Energy-Saving Home (£11) offers tips and advice for ensuring households don't fall foul of the impending bad weather. As well as suggesting immediate heat-saving measures, the book advises on longer-term improvements and on energy-efficiency in household appliances, such as saving water, conservation in the garden and recycling.

WWF Reports

www.wwf.org.uk/sustainablehomes/reports.asp

WWF has a variety of interesting downloadable reports and studies related to sustainable construction, and describing their "1 Million Sustainable Homes" UK campaign. In particular, the report 'Building Towards Sustainability" helps to show strong investors support for sustainable homes. Undertaken by Insight Investment, the asset management arm of HBOS plc, it provides a benchmarking study of the sustainability performance of UK's leading house-builders.

Books

Eco - Renovation

Edward Harland 1999 Revised edition (USA)

A revised edition of this best selling book on renovating your home in an ecological way. It shows how you can improve the health and efficiency of your home in easy to follow sections covering space, energy, health, materials and more. Contains 80 informative diagrams and ends with an incredibly useful section on assessing your home, saving money and facts about products and organisations that can help. A real step by step guide to allow the 'green' homeowner to make a small but significant contribution to the well-being of the global environment.

244 pp Price: £9.95

All About Self Build

Robert Matthews

One of the very few books for selfbuilders written in the UK for the UK market. The authors own experience of self build and considerable research make it an invaluable read. >>>

All aspects you can possibly think of are covered in detail. It starts with the vital topics of the plot, design, planning permission, building contracts and finances and management of the actual build.

Information on self build, contracted out, or working with subcontractors is all explained in a no-nonsense approach. *565pp £22.00*

which need to be repaired and maintained sympathetically. All too often inappropriate modern techniques and materials are used. This book deals with traditional methods and includes walls and foundations (clay, chalk, flint, cobble, limestone, wattle and daub); facings (pargetting, mathematical tiles) and roofs (thatching, stone and shingle). This book helps preserve vital knowledge of these traditional crafts.

176 pp £19.99

Housebuilders Bible 6th Edition

Mark Brinkley

Described as an insider's guide to the construction jungle, it includes information on most aspects of construction connected with residential building projects in the UK. The author is an experienced house builder and renovator so much of the text is drawn from personal experience. There is a separate section on green issues. Ideal for the self builder or professional who seeks to build well and to budget.

400pp £19.95

Most of the above books can be purchased from the Green Shop, **www.greenshop.co.uk** *01452 770629*

Whole House Book

Borer and Harris

Whether you are renovating, extending or building from scratch, the Whole House Book guides you **through** the process in easy to **follow** sections. From foundations **to** paint finishes, this is **definitely** a book that covers **every**thing you'll need to **know**. Suitable for architects, **builders** and DIYers. A mine **of** practical information with **over** 500 beautiful photos **and** illustrations to accompany it. Sustainable technologies used with sustainable thinking, excellent!

312pp £35.00

Ecohouse 2

Sue Roaf

The general format and organisation of this second edition has changed very little from the first, however, many of the topics previously covered have been updated and expanded. It stresses the importance of building ecologically in order to avoid ruining the earth with buildings that are profligate consumers of energy and producers of more than half of all greenhouse gases. The main aim of Ecohouse 2 is to provide 'how to' information not well covered in other books and therefore, should not be seen as an all encompassing guide to energy saving or ecological construction.

£26.00 available from **www.newbuilder.co.uk**

Craft Techniques for Traditional Buildings

Adela Wright

Britain has a rich and varied **number** of vernacular buildings

Resource guide to the properties of most commonly available building insulation materials

Many people wish to understand more about the properties of insulation products. **John Garbutt**, with the assistance of members of the Thermal Insulation Manufacturers Association (TIMSA) and others have compiled the following checklist...

Cellular glass

Cellular glass is manufactured using glass, which is ground into a fine powder and mixed with carbon. It is then placed in trays and passes through a cellulating oven. The reaction of oxygen in the glass and the carbon results in an inert, mass of hermetically sealed glass cells which contain 2/3rd vacuum and 1/3rd CO_2. It is inorganic and contains no binders. It is suitable for roofs, walls and floors.

*   Manufactured from 66% post consumer recycled glass.
*   Thermal conductivity typically ranges from 0.040 to 0.050 W/m.K depending on compressive strength.
*   Relies on CO_2 and a partial vacuum in cells for its thermal properties.
*   Non-toxic, non-irritant, HFA blowing agent, formaldehyde and fibre free.
*   Non-combustible and Euroclass A1, no contribution to fire.
*   When used with combustible products it will retard the spread of fire.
*   Non-corrosive and fungus/insect resistant.
*   Impervious to water vapour diffusion and does not require a vapour barrier to protect it.
*   Impervious to liquid water.
*   Impermeable to air and manufacturers recommend that all board joints are sealed to give a completely air-tight layer.
*   Dimensionally stable, with high compressive strength - 500 to 1600 kPa.
*   Does not settle.
*   Can be recycled.
*   As an inert product it has no effect on the water table and in time it is assumed that it would return eventually to be sand from which it originated.

Cellulose fibre

Cellulose fibre insulation is typically manufactured from recycled newspaper. The addition of a non-hazardous,

inorganic salt fire retardant provides excellent protection against fire well above the building regulations' requirements. It is also protected against biological and fungal attack, treated against insects and is unattractive to vermin.

It is designed for use in timber frame walls or other constructions protected against exposure to liquid water e.g. lofts, pitched roofs, steel framed structures and floors. It is installed by registered specialist installers, employing one of three recommended installation techniques: damp spray, open blown or dry injection. Correctly installed, cellulose fibre completely fills the inner wall cavity, eliminating all gaps, which prevents convection currents. No cutting is required. It is harmless to other common building components, such as copper pipes, electric cabling and nail plate fasteners.

*   Content is over 80% by weight recycled paper; balance comprises inorganic salt fire retardant.
*   Thermal conductivity typically ranges from 0.035 to 0.036 W/m.K
*   Relies on entrapped air and the insulation properties of paper for its thermal performance.
*   Non-toxic and non-irritant, no added formaldehyde and free from VOCs.
*   Flame retardant; Class 1 flame spread rating.
*   Non-corrosive and fungus/insect/vermin resistant.
*   Its hygroscopic nature means that it absorbs water vapour at times of high humidity and releases it when conditions allow, this prevents any problems of excessive moisture build up within a wall or other insulated structure.
*   Should not be used in applications exposed to liquid water.
*   Air movement will not disturb the product in a loft because of the friction bonding between adjacent fibres.
*   Dimensional stable
*   Low compressive strength.
*   When installed in lofts and floors at densities between 25-30 kg/m3 it may settle (due to vibration or other reasons), but an allowance is made for this during installation
*   When installed in walls, at densities between 45-60 kg/m3, the installation method ensures no settlement.
*   Can be recycled or reused at end of life.
*   The paper content is biodegradable.

Mineral wool (glass wool and rock wool)

Glass wool and rock wool insulation are manufactured by spinning a molten inorganic material at high temperature to form a matrix of fibres, which are bonded with a thermosetting organic resin binder. The fibres are stable and durable and are typically available in the form of mats, rolls, slabs, pipe sections and loose wool.

UK and EU legislation confirms that mineral wool Insulation is safe to work with. Mineral wool has been cleared of any suspicion of being a possible carcinogen by IARC (the International Agency for Research on Cancer), which is part of the WHO.

*   In the UK glass wool typically contains from 50% recycled glass both from manufacturing waste and post-consumer glass (cullet).
*   Rock wool contains varying amounts of recycled material, including post-consumer waste and by-products from other industries diverted from the waste stream.

- Thermal conductivity typically ranges from 0.031 to 0.044 W/m.K depending upon product.
- Relies on entrapped air for its thermal properties.
- Non-toxic & free from pentane or other VOCs.
- Non-combustible in accordance with ISO 1182 and typically rated Euroclass A1 or A2.
- Non-corrosive and fungus/insect resistant.
- Water repellent and non-hygroscopic.
- Air and vapour permeable in unfaced forms, allowing constructions to 'breathe' and providing suitability for acoustic applications.
- Dimensionally stable.
- Compressive strength varies depending upon product. Resists settlement.
- Can be recycled at end-of-life - availability of facilities varies by manufacturer.
- Non-biodegradable but any waste sent to landfill is classified non-hazardous.

Expanded polystyrene (EPS)

Polystyrene is an organic, thermoplastic polymer. The manufacturing process of EPS uses expandable beads. The beads incorporate a hydrocarbon blowing agent (pentane) so that, when heated with steam, they expand to more than 30 times their original size. The expanded beads are subsequently fused together in a mould to produce a shaped product or a large block, which can be sliced into boards.

The tiny amount of pentane used in the product is released to atmosphere immediately on manufacture and is replaced by air. The released pentane is quickly broken down in the atmosphere but can also be recovered in processing plants.

- All waste EPS produced during the course of manufacture is recycled back into the manufacturing process.
- Waste packaging is collected and incorporated in insulation products to provide a second long term use of the raw material.
- Thermal conductivity typically 0.038 W/m.K.
- Some modified types of EPS can achieve values as low as 0.030 W/m.K.
- Relies on entrapped air for its thermal properties.
- Non-toxic and non-irritant, HFA blowing agent-free, formaldehyde and fibre free.
- Styrene monomer present in minute amounts.
- Fire performance when installed as recommended meets all the requirements of the Building Regulations.
- Non-corrosive and fungus/insect resistant.
- Water repellent - moisture has a minimal effect on thermal performance.
- Virtually impenetrable to air flow through the product.
- Dimensionally stable in use.
- A wide range of compressive strengths available up to 500 kPa / does not settle in use.
- Can be recycled by a variety of processes at end of life.
- Non-biodegradable

Extruded polystyrene (XPS)

Polystyrene is an organic, thermoplastic polymer. XPS is manufactured via a continuous extrusion process. Polystyrene granules are melted, mixed together with additives and a blowing agent, and then extruded under pressure through a die to form rigid foamed polystyrene which is then cut and trimmed to form insulation boards. The flexibility of the process allows XPS to be produced with a wide range of physical properties and board dimensions.

Blowing agents used today include HFCs, carbon dioxide and pentane. Of these, HFCs provide the best (i.e. lowest) thermal conductivity. The blowing agent migrates out of the cell structure over a very long period of time and is replaced by air thereby increasing the product's thermal conductivity. This, however, is accounted for in the 'declared' thermal conductivity values used for design.

- All waste XPS produced during the course of manufacture is recycled back into the manufacturing process, as can be customers' scrap.
- Thermal conductivity typically ranges from 0.029 to 0.038 W/m.K depending upon the blowing agent.
- Has a closed cell structure and relies on the entrapped blowing agent for its thermal properties.
- Non-toxic, non-irritant, formaldehyde and fibre free / no health risks associated with the use of XPS.
- Styrene monomer present in minute amounts.
- Fire performance: Reaction to fire - Euroclass E.
- Non-corrosive and fungus/insect resistant.
- Resistant to rain, snow, frost and water vapour / very low water absorption.
- Unaffected by air movement as it is a rigid closed cell foamed plastic.
- Excellent thermal dimensional stability - note though that maximum working service temperature is 75 deg C.
- Range of compressive strengths available including high strength products for load bearing applications / does not settle.
- Can be recycled at end of life.
- Non-biodegradable / prolonged exposure to intense sunlight will cause surface to degrade into fine dust.

Rigid urethane (PIR/PUR)

Rigid urethane is a term that covers a spectrum of products incorporating polyurethane and polyisocyanurate insulation. Rigid urethane insulation is manufactured by a continuous process in which a liquid insulation mixture is laid down between two flexible facing layers. The mixture contains two components which under the action of a catalyst creates an exothermic reaction. This heat evaporates a volatile liquid blowing agent contained in the mixture which forms a matrix of small bubbles or cells. When the reaction in the mixture stops a rigid cellular board is created which is then cut and trimmed to size.

The main blowing agent used today by far is pentane. The blowing agent will remain in the cells if they are left intact by the manufacturing process but, over time, air will diffuse into the cells diluting the blowing agent and the products thermal conductivity. This, however, takes many years and is accounted for in 'declared' thermal conductivity values. The process is much slower and much less marked in products faced with gas-tight foil based facing materials, hence these products have very low thermal conductivity values.

These products are suitable for virtually any thermal insulation application. The main exceptions are applications where extremely high compressive strength is required and inverted roofs. Rigid urethane products are even available for injection into cavity walls (NOT to be confused with UF foam).

- Some manufacturers use raw materials from recycled plastic (PET) drinks bottles and x-ray film / some facing materials contain recycled paper and glass.
- Thermal conductivity – 0.022 to 0.028 depending upon thickness and facing material.
- Relies largely on entrapped blowing agent for its thermal properties.
- Insulation is non-toxic, non-irritant, fibre-free, formaldehyde-free & styrene-free.
- Results of fire tests to BS 476: Parts 6 and 7 depend upon the product and the manufacturer but data is generally available - fire performance when installed as recommended meets all the requirements of the Building Regulations – products are available with LPCB and FM approval and half hour fire resistance certification to BS 476: Part 21 – products are available that achieve a Euroclass B in application.
- Non-corrosive and fungus/insect resistant.
- Moisture has a minimal effect on thermal performance.
- Virtually impenetrable to air flow through the product.
- Dimensionally stable in use.
- High compressive strength – up to 150 kPa / does not settle in use.
- Can be reclaimed and reused as an insulation material or in a variety of other non-original applications / if not reclaimable then incineration for useful heat is the recommended end-of-life option.
- Non-biodegradable

Phenolic (PF)

Phenolic insulation is manufactured by a continuous process in which a liquid insulation mixture is laid down between two flexible facing layers. The mixture contains two components which under the action of a catalyst create an exothermic reaction. This heat evaporates a volatile liquid blowing agent contained in the mixture which forms a matrix of small bubbles or cells. When the reaction in the mixture stops a rigid cellular board is created which is then cut and trimmed to size.

The main blowing agent used today by far is pentane though some other blowing agents are still used. The blowing agent will remain in the cells if they are left intact by the manufacturing process but, over time, air will diffuse into the cells diluting the blowing agent and the products thermal conductivity. This, however, takes many years and is accounted for in 'declared' thermal conductivity values. The cellular structure of phenolic insulation is much finer than rigid urethane. This inhibits gas diffusion and hence these products have very low thermal conductivity values regardless of facing material.

These products are suitable for virtually any thermal insulation application. The main exceptions are applications where extremely high compressive strength is required and inverted roofs. They are commonly used in applications where fire and smoke performance is critical e.g. in applications where the insulation is exposed on the inside of buildings (pipe and duct insulation / wall and ceiling lining products).

- Little or no recycled content
- Thermal conductivity – 0.021 to 0.024 depending upon thickness.
- Relies largely on entrapped blowing agent for its thermal properties.
- Insulation is non-toxic, non-irritant, fibre-free & styrene-free.

- Independent measurements on installed phenolic insulation have revealed atmospheric formaldehyde concentrations of around 0.02ppm (well within the limits of the natural background level of 0.00-0.05ppm) - exposure to levels below 0.05ppm is normally classified as unexposed.
- Results of fire tests to BS476: Parts 6 and 7 give the insulation a rating of Class O to the Building Regulations – products are available that achieve a Euroclass B rating – insulation carries a best possible smoke obscuration rating of <5% to BS 5111: Part 1 - products are available that achieve an s1 SMOGRA rating.
- Fungus/insect resistant and no more corrosive than other common insulation materials.
- Moisture has a minimal effect on thermal performance.
- Virtually impenetrable to air flow through the product.
- Dimensionally stable in use.
- High compressive strength – up to 150 kPa / does not settle in use.
- Can be reclaimed and reused as an insulation material or in a variety of other non-original applications / if not reclaimable then incineration for useful heat is the recommended end-of-life option.
- Non-biodegradableCellulose Fibre

Sheep's wool

Sheep's wool insulation can contain up to 15% polyester within its blend as a necessary lofting agent. Wool Insulation will adapt to the shape of rafters, joists and studs to provide a permanently tight fit. It is suitable for use in roofs, walls and floors and ideal for breathing wall constructions.

- No recycled content but wool is a fully renewable resource
- Thermal conductivity is typically 0.039 W/m.K.
- Relies on entrapped air for its thermal properties.
- Cost can be higher than other insulants.
- Non-toxic, non-irritant & formaldehyde free.
- Wool does not burn but rather melts away from an ignition source and extinguishes itself. It is treated with a natural fire-proofing agent to improve its intrinsic fire resistance and complies with BS 5803-4 (spread of fire) achieving results of zero for ignitability, spread of flame and heat evolved.
- Non-corrosive and fungus/insect resistant.
- Allows the migration of water vapour throughout the material – it is naturally breathable
- Will absorb up to 40% of its own weight in moisture, which will subsequently re-evaporate when conditions change - insulation will maintain its thermal performance during this process
- Any external water ingress into the product will subsequently re-evaporate out.
- Still air does not affect the product.
- Dimensionally stable.
- Compressible
- End-of-life - can be reclaimed and reused.
- Biodegradable (it is assumed that the polyester content is so negligible that biodegradation would take place).

Editor's note: other less common insulations (eg hemp flax, cork etc.) are covered in detail elsewhere in this book. See the index.

Glossary of terms

Compiled by **Robin Hillier**

ACH	Air changes per hour, stated as the volume of air changed per hour / volume of room
Air tightness	Of increasing importance within the building regulations, energy efficient building design should ensure that ventilation only occurs as desired by the occupants, and not through unwanted draughts and air leakage through or around the building elements.
Alternative energy	The use of energy produced using non-carbon resources eg. solar, wind, water, thermal etc.
Borax / boron-based preservatives/ boron compounds / inorganic borates	A family of natural mineral based products which have the ability to protect timber from rot, insect attack and fire (spread of flame) if applied and used correctly. Harmless to humans at normal concentrations.
Breathable sheathing	Many boards are now available which are sufficiently vapour permeable to allow them to be used externally on a timber frame and allow vapour generated within the building to pass through to the outside without risk of condensation within the fabric.
Breather membrane	Usually paper or a woven membrane which is used to prevent water entry to the construction, whilst allowing vapour to escape.
Breathing construction	A term used to describe vapour resistant layers within a wall or roof construction to ensure that moisture is allowed to pass safely (eg without condensing) from the interior to the exterior of a building.
BREEAM	Environmental assessment method from the Building Research Establishment (BRE)
Brown roof	A roof covering comprising rubble and earth which is designed to be bird friendly in urban environments where certain species have adapted to inner city living
Carbon index	An addendum to the SAP rating (see later in glossary) which measures the CO_2 'created' in use, expressed as a measure of the CO_2 / m^2 of floor area. One method of satisfying the building regulations re thermal properties.
Carbon neutral	The use of appropriate energy sources to ensure that the total production of CO_2 related to a building or project is zero.
Cellulose insulation	Can be manufactured from recycled newspapers (pre or post consumer waste), cellulose is shredded and treated with borax against insect and rot attack. Can be installed as loose fill, damp spray, or dry-blown to a specified density.
Closed panel system	Panels built on site with sheathing to both sides (internal and exernal) usually with insulated cavity - often using breathing wall technology and materials. An on-site (non-engineered) version of Tradis system. Differs from panels used in typical timber kit construction which are sheathed to one side only.
CO_2	Carbon dioxide - the prime 'greenhouse gas' deemed to be responsible for global warming.

Cold bridge	Term used to describe a material contained within a building element (eg. wall, roof) which has a much lower thermal resistance than the surrrounding material and is placed so as to 'bridge' the thermal resistivity of the fabric as a whole. Cold bridges can lead to condensation hotspots and high energy losses.
Draught lobby	A lobby providing a two door entry system, which can prevent much heat wasteage
Embodied energy	The energy required to produce a material, through extraction, manufacture, transport or installation.
Green roof	A description of a 'living' roof finish of some kind, usually grasses or sedum.
Heat recovery	The use of heat exchangers to extract heat from waste air or water, and transfer it into an incoming air supply.
HQis	Housing Quality indicators - a questionnaire / checklist often completed by RSLs/ housing associations and their designers to assess the performance and quality of each social housing project they build
Hygroscopic	A feature of natural insulants such as wool or cellulose, it allows vapour to be 'held' within the material without condensing, and later to release it into the atmosphere. A key principle of a breathing wall specification.
Interstitial condensation	Created where warm moisture laden air migrates through the building fabric and condenses onto a cold surface within the fabric, potentially leading to both damage to the fabric, and to an unhealthy internal environment.
Lignin	Naturally ocurring "adhesive" in wood. High levels of lignin in woods used for some compressed wood fibre boards reduces the need to use synthetic adhesives.
Low E glazing	Low E (low emittance) refers to a metallic oxide coating applied to the inner face of a double or triple glazed unit, and which reduces heat loss through the glass thereby improving the thermal performance of the unit. Can also reduce solar overheating and light levels.
Low impact	A low impact, or negative impact development (or product), aims to reduce or enhance both the overall impact of the construction process and the ongoing use of the development on the surrounding environment. This can be in terms of energy, CO_2 or even visual impact where development is proposed in a sensitive area.
Microporous finishes	Paints, stains and waxes which may be naturally produced or petrochemical based, which allow vapour to be released from the material they cover, whilst remaining impermeable to water.
Moisture content	Most natural materials will contain moisture to some extent - for example seasoned timber can still contain between 8 and 18% moisture in use, but at these levels will not rot or suffer insect or mould attack.
Natural paints, waxes and stains	A very imprecise term which is used to describe a variety of products, some of which have a petro-chemical base, but which would on the whole be manufactured from non-petrochemical ingredients.

NHER rating	An independent energy rating system which predicts cost and CO_2 outputs in use. More comprehensive alternative to SAP.
ODP (ozone depletion potential) / zero ODP	The potential for the manufacturing process of a material (usually the 'blowing' of foam based insulants) to release chemicals that are known to destroy the ozone layer around the earth. CFCs and HCFCs are the most common, and have largely been replaced by air.
Passive solar gain	Heating from sunlight entering directly into a building, usually via glazing. Can be unwanted, leading to overheating in summer, or designed to maximise the solar contribution when most useful.
Passive / stack ventilation	The use of building shape and design to produce sufficient natural ventilation without the use of electrically powered fans. Stack ventilation uses vertical ducts to stimulate natural airflow due to the 'flue' effect.
Re-cycling	The re-processing of an existing material to re-manufacture a new material for a new use - generally requires more energy than 're-use'.
Re-use	The re-use of whole or part building materials in their originally produced form
Relative humidity	This is the amount of moisture within the atmosphere, or a material, expressed as a % of the total saturation moisture content that could be contained.
Renewable resources	Materials or energy sources which can be replaced, hopefully within the lifetime of the product eg. timber can be re-grown
Renewables / non-renewables	Material from a source that is renewable (eg. wood) versus that which is not or which has a finite supply (eg. fossil fuels)
Resource depletion	The specification of certain materials, products or processes can lead to habitat damage, environmental degredation, and rarity eg. fossil fuels, peat, Welsh slates
SAP rating	An energy rating system for housing which measures the cost in £ / m^2 floor area. Now a pre-requisite for calculating the Carbon Index which is one method of satisfying the building regulations re thermal performance of housing.
Sheepswool batts	A natural, hygroscopic insulation product requiring little energy in the manufacturing process, and using a plentiful resource. Safe and pleasant to handle and install.
SIPs	Structurally insulated Panels, or prefabricated wall or roof elements produced from petro-chemical based insulation boards bonded to timber based boards.
Solar hot water systems	Alternative energy system which directly or indirectly heats water and can contribute about 25-40% of the hot water needs of a typical house.
Straw bales	An agricultural product which can be used for building walls, either non structural within a frame, or loadbearing - potentially a cheap way to obtain a high insulation value.
SUDS	Sustainable Urban Drainage System. Aims to reduce the water load on the man-made drainage systems, and to reduce flood risk, by designing the external environment to redistribute rainwater falling onto a site via porous surfaces, soakaways etc.
Tannic bleed	Staining which occurs on timber shingles and cladding when moisture migrates through the wood and which can cause discoloration on the external surface.
Thermal conductivity	Is a measure of the rate of energy or heat flow through a material, stated as W/mK
Thermal properties	The characteristics of a building material which define how heat, or energy, passes through the material eg. thermal resistance and density.
Thermal resistance	This is a measure of resistance to heat flow given a specified thickness of a material and a temperature difference each side.
U-value	A U-Value is a measure of potential heat or energy flow through a specified building fabric element given a temperature difference each side, measured as W/m^2K
Vapour barrier	Usually in sheet or brush-on form, used in 'non-breathing' construction to prevent water vapour from entering the construction. Unreliable due to difficulties in effecting a seal
Vapour permeability	Vapour permeable materials allow moisture to migrate from inside to outside of building fabric in a controlled mannner. BS5250 suggests that vapour should permeate through external sheathing materials at a rate 5 times that of the internal sheathing or lining material so as to reduce the risk of interstitial condensation.
VOCs	Volatile organic compounds are emitted as gases from certain solids or liquids. They include a variety of chemicals, many of which may have both short- and long-term adverse health effects.
VOCs / Zero VOCs	Volatile organic compounds - usually refers to any organic compound chemical emitted into the atmosphere during the use, application or drying out of a paint or other coating. Nail polish is a good example of an everyday product which gives off VOC's. VOC's are not always harmful - some natural products like citrus oils used as solvents will give off VOCs but these are claimed to dissipate quickly and safely and are not absorbed into rugs, curtains and upholstery.
Water conservation	The design of water useage and waste systems to minimise wasteage, reduce flooding and un-necessary re-processing to ensure that an essential primary resource remains readily available.

Contents -
Professionals and trades- regional

Contents -
Products and trade organisations - national

IMPORTANT INFORMATION

FOR MORE PRODUCT MANUFACTURERS, SUPPLIERS ETC. PLEASE SEE THE ADVERTISEMENT LIST AT THE BACK OF THIS BOOK

ALL BUSINESSES LISTED IN THIS BOOK WERE REQUIRED TO PROVIDE EVIDENCE OF GREEN BUILDING EXPERIENCE OR MEMBERSHIP OF A RELEVANT ORGANISATION.

DISCLAIMER

East

Cambridgeshire

ARCHITECT(S)

IAIN FREARSON
Iain Frearson
68 Cavendish Road, Cambridge
CB1 3AF
T: 01223 473997
E: iain.frearson@ntlworld.com
Specialising in all aspects of ecological building and historic/ traditional building conservation - from timber frames to earth buildings from self-build to specialist conservation and repair from low-energy design to low-impact development and advice.

MOLE ARCHITECTS LTD.
Meredith Bowles
The Black House, Prickwillow
CB7 4UL
T: 01353 688 287
E: studio@molearchitects.co.uk
www.molearchitects.co.uk
Award-winning Architects designing low energy, contemporary houses. Prime exponents of "The New Vernacular" architecture.

HEATING ENGINEER

GREEN SYSTEMS UK
Paul Elliott-Smith
43 New Road, Melbourn SG8 6BX
T: 01763 260719
E: info@greensystemsuk.com
www.greensystemsuk.com
Supply, installation, maintenance and repair of renewable energy hot water and heating systems. Flat plate and vacuum tube solar thermal systems. Biomass (wood fuel) boilers and room heaters. Ground sourced heat pumps.

Hertfordshire

ARCHITECT(S)

ANDREW GOODMAN ARCHITECTURE
Andrew Goodman
90 Ware Road, Hertford
SG13 7HN
T: 01992 501073
E: andrew@goodarchitecture. co.uk
The practice has a philosophy of developing adaptable, environmentally friendly and energy conscious designs for living and working.

CIVIL ENGINEER

BUILDING RESEARCH ESTABLISHMENT
Tim Reynolds
Bucknalls Lane, Garston, Watford
WD25 9XX
T: 01923 664832
E: reynoldst@bre.co.uk
www.bre.co.uk
The Building Research Establishment is the UK's leading centre of expertise on buildings, construction, energy, environment, fire and risk. BRE provides research-based consultancy, testing and certification services.

CONSULTING ENGINEERS

PENTANGLE CONSULTING ENGINEERS LTD.
John Smith
Target House, 257-263 High Street, St. Albans AL2 1HA
T: 01727 825580
E: consult@pcel.co.uk
www.pcel.co.uk
Building Services Engineering and Environmental Engineering, Providing Mechanical and Electrical Designs and Feasibility studies for new and existing buildings. Additional services include: Energy studies / Management, Value Engineering, Cross-Disciplinary Project Management and PPM Procurement.

HOUSE BUILDER

WILKINSON BUILDERS
Patrick Wilkinson
Westland Green, Little Hadham
SG11 2AQ
T: 07970 119107
E: pat@wilkinsonbuilders.co.uk
www.wilkinsonbuilders.co.uk
Wilkinson builders is a small family business, we design and build energy efficient buildings for clients and our own developments. We are installers of Warmcel cellulose fibre insulation and importers of Finnish timber products, windows, doors, staircases and claddings.

Lincolnshire

HEATING ENGINEER

ME MECHANICAL SERVICES
Matthew Elkin
The Cottage, 41 Cross O'Cliff Hill, Lincoln LN5 8PR
T: 01522 520146
E: matt.elkin@ntlworld.com
www.memech.co.uk
ME Mechanical Services specialises in supplying and installing solar water heating and other renewables. A small plumbing and heating company established in 1993, we have a wide range of experience - from small domestic systems to larger housing association projects.

Norfolk

ARCHITECT(S)

GREEN INC ARCHITECTURE
Ian Witcomb
Summer Cottage, Dragaway, Glandford, Holt NR25 7JS
T: 01263 741 552
E: ian@bhwarchitecture.co.uk
www.bhwarchitecture.co.uk
Green Ink Architecture is a specialised subsidiary of Barnes: Harley:Witcomb Architects. Based in North Norfolk we have recently completed an eco friendly conversion of a redundant agricultural building into luxurious eco holiday/leisure units in an area of outstanding natural beauty.

BUILDING CONTRACTOR

CREATIVE CONSTRUCTIONS (NORFOLK) LTD.
Peter Oldfield
3 Westcliffe Avenue, Cromer
NR27 9BA
T: 01263 519255
E: creativeconstruct@btopenworld.com
North Norfolk District Council's Green Build and Small Business of The Year winners. Specialising in sustainable construction projects from Household extensions through to barn conversions and commercial projects. Advising and assisting clients to make their projects "greener".

GROOVE CONSTRUCTION LTD.
Paul McAlenan
47 Clarendon Road, Norwich
NR2 2PN
T: 01603 441564
E: office@groove.uk.net
www.groove.uk.net
New build extensions and renovation, design and build, domestic and commercial. Main contractors and project management. Open - communicative - flexible - creative - can do!

ENERGY CONSULTANT

CLEAN ENERGY CONSULTANCY
Andrew Robertson
Poppylot House, Wymondham Road, Bunwell, Norwich NR16 1NB
T: 07962 111857
E: clean.energy@btinternet.com
Energy Efficiency consultancy business. Specialising in condensing boilers, high efficiency boilers, boiler flues and fuel-oil supply. Advice on oil-fired stoves and solid fuel appliances. Also complete SAP efficiency calcs and certification service for new dwellings.

PAINTING AND DECORATING

HOLKHAM LINSEED PAINTS

Natalie Barrows
The Clock Tower, Longlands,
Holkham, Wells-next-the-Sea
NR23 1RU
T: 01328 711348
E: n.barrows@holkham.co.uk
www.holkhamlinseedpaints.co.uk
Importers of traditional Swedish
Linseed Oil Paints and accesso-
ries. Our paints are Long-Lasting,
Cost-Effective, made from sustain-
able materials and are safe to use.
They are totally solvent-free.

Suffolk

ARCHITECT(S)

STUDIOMGM LLP

Ralph Carpenter
88-89 St. Johns Street, Bury St.
Edmunds IP33 1SQ
T: 0870 050 8246
E: modece@studiomgm.co.uk
www.studiomgm.co.uk
Studiomgm was formed from
three architects practices with
an extensive and award winning
East Anglian portfolio of housing
design work with particular
strengths in areas such as
ecological design, climate change
design, beauty and a sense of
place and home.

London

ARCHITECT AND BUILDER

DGA

Dil Green
206 Lyham road, Brixton
SW2 5NR
T: 020 8671 2242
E: dilgreen@dilgreenarchitect.
co.uk
www.dilgreenarchitect.co.uk
Holistic design practice, also take
on project management / design
led construction.

JOS HAAS ING., BSC

Jos Haas
27a Westdown Road, London
SE6 4RL
T: 020 8690 4453
E: joshaas@btinternet.com
Building design, construction,
consultation.

ARCHITECT(S)

ANNE THORNE ARCHITECTS PARTNERSHIP

Zana Dean
110 Elmore Street, Islington
N1 3AH
T: 020 7704 1391
E: info@annethornearchitects.
co.uk
www.annethornearchitects.co.uk
ATAP's designs for housing and
community buildings incorporate
low embodied-energy materials
and construction, organic finishes,
low water use, non chemical
timber treatments, use of native
species and FSC certified timber.
We design to high insulation
values within cost for social
housing.

ARCHIPELECO LIMITED

Lucy Pedler
27 De Laune Street, London
SE17 3UU
T: 020 7703 3322
E: lucy.archipeleco@virgin.net
www.archipeleco.co.uk
Archipeleco offers the full range
of architectural services with
particular expertise in ecological
design. The practice also offers a
consultancy service to construction professionals on selection of
ecological materials and systems
and runs seminars on sustainable
building principles. See also www.
greenregister.org

THE ARCHITECTURE ENSEMBLE

Steven Johnson
11 Cosmo Place, WC1N 3AP
T: 020 7278 7064
E: steve@archen.demon.co.uk
We focus on better woodland
management and the sustainable use of British timber by the
construction industry. We have
been involved in the promotion
of various design projects, both
urban and rural, demonstrating
good uses of local sustainably
produced materials.

ARCHITYPE

Bob Hayes
The Morocco Store, 1b
Leathermarket Street,
SE1 3JA
T: 020 7403 2889
E: bob@architype.co.uk
www.architype.co.uk
Architype, established 20 years
ago, is one of the UK's leading
sustainable architectural prac-
tices. Architype combines cutting
edge innovation with a long track
record of successful buildings.
Architype works throughout the
UK from expanding offices in
London and the West.

BENNETTS ASSOCIATES

Denise Bennetts
1 Rawstorne Place, Islington
EC1V 7NL
T: 0207 5203300
E: mail@bennettsassociates.com
www.bennettsassociates.com
Bennetts Associates have
pioneered sustainable design
through a series of seminal low
energy headquarters buildings for
the likes of PowerGen and Wessex
Water. Current commissions
include Brighton Central Library,
a sustainable public building
procured through the PFI process.

BREE DAY PARTNERSHIP ARCHITECTS AND URBAN DESIGN
Damian Bree
1 Holly Road, Twickenham
TW1 4EA
T: 020 8744 4440
E: breeday@architech.co.uk
www.architech.co.uk
Our award winning work is guided by the principles of sustainable design and we always try to innovate by learning from past exemplar projects and the latest technical advice. We recognise that the best chance of achieving successful built environment solutions comes from working in multi-disciplinary community orientated teams.

CONSTRUCTIVE INDIVIDUALS (LONDON) LTD.
Peter Smithdale
Trinity Buoy Wharf, 64 Orchard Place E14 0JW
T: 020 7515 9299
E: info@constructiveindividuals.com
www.constructiveindividuals.com
Ecological architects with expertise in insulation and airtightness, incorporating renewable energy systems, and healthy and low impact ways of building.

DLG ARCHITECTS
Anthony Walker
11-29 Fashion Street, London
E1 6PZ
T: 020 7426 3631
E: london@dlg-architects.co.uk
www.dlg-architects.co.uk
Based in London and Leeds we work in sectors including Leisure Retail, Mixed-Use, Conservation, Education, Industrial, Residential and Offices. We specialise in architectural design, construction documentation, project implementation, feasibility studies.

DAVID MORLEY ARCHITECTS
David Morley
18 Hatton Place, London
EC1N 8RU
T: 020 7430 2444
E: info@dmarch.co.uk
www.davidmorleyarchitects.co.uk
Our design approach is contemporary, without over-elaboration buildings are economical to construct and efficient to run. We prioritise sustainability issues and our analytical methodology is suited to the creation of elegant architecture that meets the most stringent energy requirements.

EGER ARCHITECTS
Selina Dix Hamilton
2 D'Eynsford Road, London
SE5 7EB
T: 020 7701 6771
E: selina.hamilton@egerarchitects.com
www.egerarchitects.com
Architects specialising in innovative technologies employed for the client's benefit. Community buildings, Educational and Health sectors and private houses.

ENGLAND ARCHITECTURE
Nick England
28A Lower Marsh, London
SE1 7RG
T: 020 7928 3456
E: nengthrop@tiscali.co.uk
www.englandarchitecture.co.uk
Architecture practice specialising in sustainable design of buildings and interiors. We are keenly involved in the whole process from inception to the completion of the building, taking care that the whole process has a minimal impact on the environment.

FEILDEN CLEGG BRADLEY ARCHITECTS LLP
Felicia Mills
Circus House, 21 Great Titchfield Street, W1W 8BA
T: 01225 852545
E: fm@feildenclegg.com
www.feildenclegg.com
We are recognised for design quality, environmental expertise and innovation. Our social and environmental principles were recognised in 2003 with the Building Awards Architectural Practice of the Year, a Queen's Award for Sustainable Development.

THE FORGE COMPANY
Jim Baker
5 Macartney House, Chesterfield Walk, Greenwich SE10 8HJ
T: 020 8858 6153
E: baker@theforgecompany.com
www.theforgecompany.co.uk
The Forge Company (UK) Ltd. is a practice focused on environmentally responsible design using light guage steel as the primary, though non-exclusive structural element. Projects are mainly housing, although we have designed environmental and arts centres using the same principles.

GMW ARCHITECTS
Terry Brown
239 Kensington High Street, London W8 6SL
T: 020 8874 4505
E: terry.brown@gmw-architects.com
www.gmw-architects.com
We are a client focused architectural and interior design practice working in the office, shopping, transportation, regeneration and urban design sectors, with a sustainable design policy, offering creative designs meeting our brief but minimizing impacts on the earth's systems and resources.

HANS HAENLEIN ARCHITECTS
Julia Erdem
3 Western Terrace, London
W6 9TX
T: 020 8748 3871
E: julia@haenlein.com
www.haenlein.com
Hans Haenlein Architects design education and community buildings based on ecological principles and are active in the field of urban regeneration.

HAVERSTOCK ASSOCIATES
Rhys Rappel
10 Cliff Road Studios, Cliff Road, London NW1 9AN
T: 020 7267 7676
E: nathalie@haverstock.com
www.haverstock.com
Haverstock Associates are committed to quality and strive to ensure that our buildings improve the lives of people who use them. We create modern sustainable buildings that are stimulating and attractive, spaces that are functional not clinical, human not institutional.

HODGSON GABB STUDIO
William Hodgson
21 Hackney Road, Shoreditch
E2 7NX
T: 020 7729 0019
E: mail@hodgsongabbstudio.co.uk
www.hodgsongabbstudio.co.uk
Hodgson Gabb Studio is an Architects Office committed to well designed housing and retail projects. We seek to minimise the environmental damage caused by the construction process through careful selection of materials.

HORACE ARCHITECTS LTD.
Robert Rimell
273 Putney Bridge Road,
SW15 2PT
T: 0870 0112 204
E: robrimell@horace-architects.co.uk
We strive to continually address concerns about the global environment, incorporating and researching energy efficient buildings. Where possible, we aim to construct low energy buildings and to regulate harmful emissions. Currently two of our five architects are listed on the Green Register and one more will shortly be trained.

**JOHN THOMPSON
AND PARTNERS**
Peter Dodds
Wren House, 43 Hatton Garden,
London EC1N 8EL
T: 020 8675 4788
E: pd@jtp.co.uk
www.jtp.co.uk
John Thompson and Partners
combine community planning,
urban design and architectural
skills to create attractive, sustainable environments with strong
sense of place, and buildings that
respond to the needs and aspirations of users whilst respecting
the environment.

LYNCH ARCHITECTS
Patrick Lynch
147a Hoxton Street N1 6QG
T: 020 7739 5760
E: lyncharchitects@btopenworld.
com
www.lyncharchitects.co.uk
Recently completed projects by
Lynch architects include a house
in Norfolk, 'Marsh View', and a
community centre in East London.
Renewable timber sources
provide the structure and finishes.
Underfloor heating and passive
solar gain ensure energy-efficient
use of natural resources.

MASS ARCHITECTURE
Charlotte Harrison
410 Hackney Road, E2 7AP
T: 020 7729 4475
E: info@massarchitecture.com
www.massarchitecture.com
Mass Architecture aims to create
buildings and urban environments
using ecologically responsible
approaches, techniques and materials. We make teamwork central
to our working process where
projects are tailored to and grow
out of a close working relationship
with our clients.

MOLYNEUX ARCHITECTS
Roger Molyneux
181 Union Street SE1 0LN
T: 020 7021 0411
E: rm@molyarch.co.uk
www.molyarch.co.uk
Chartered Architects with experience of working on historic,
existing or new buildings of varied
uses in the UK and in over 40
countries worldwide. Particular
interest in environmentally
conscious buildings which are
appropriate to place and culture.

**POLLARD THOMAS EDWARDS
ARCHITECTS**
Chris Davy
Diespeker Wharf, 38 Graham
Street, London N1 8JX
T: 020 7336 7777
E: chris.davy@ptea.co.uk
www.ptea.co.uk
PTEa works to regenerate urban
communities primarily through
the provision of new housing.

Our work is diverse and includes
community buildings, estate
refurbishment, major regeneration
projects and urban planning. We
aim to create sustainable environments through close consultation
with existing communities.

PROCTOR AND MATTHEWS
Stephen Proctor
7 Blue Lion Place, 237 Long Lane,
London SE1 4PU
T: 020 7378 6695
E: info@proctorandmatthews.com
www.proctorandmatthews.com
We have realised award-winning
work in the office, housing, educa-
tion, leisure and sports sectors.
Our work at Greenwich Millennium
Village won the RIBA Housing
Design Sustainability Award in
2001 and the WWF Sustainable
New Homes Award in 2004.

**SARAH WIGGLESWORTH
ARCHITECTS**
Sarah Wigglesworth
10 Stock Orchard Street N7 9RW
T: 020 7607 9200
E: mail@swarch.co.uk
www.swarch.co.uk
Sarah Wigglesworth Architects
are experts in low energy and
sustainable construction, and
integrative design is at the heart
of everything we do. We exploit
everyday materials in an imaginative way to produce environments

that can be created and maintained economically.

SHEPHEARD EPSTEIN HUNTER
Caroline Easterbrook
Phoenix Yard, 65 Kings Cross
Road, London WC1X 9LW
T: 020 7841 7500
E: architecture@seh.co.uk
www.seh.co.uk
Shepheard Epstein Hunter are
known for the quality of their
work in regeneration, education,
housing, master planning, mixed-
use and healthcare projects.
SEH's ongoing commitment to
the development of sustainable
architecture is now backed up by
their ISO 14001 environmental
certification.

SHEPPARD ROBSON
Robert Keenan
77 Parkway, London NW1 7PU
T: 020 7504 1700
E: bob.keenan@sheppardrobson.
com
www.sheppardrobson.com
Sheppard Robson provides
architectural, town planning and
interior design services. The
practice has an in-house group
- SR:Evolution - that promotes and
assists its designers to provide
credible, integrated and sustainable solutions to its clients. The
practice has offices in London and
Manchester.

SIDELL GIBSON ARCHITECTS
Nicholas Jay
The Canal Building, 37 Kentish
Town Road, London NW1 8NX
T: 020 7284 9005
E: enquiries@sidellgibson.co.uk
www.sidellgibson.co.uk
Our design policy is to optimise
environmental performance
achieving 'excellent' ratings,
expand our 'green' knowledge
base and experience, inform and
influence others in their thinking
on environmental issues and aim
for constant improvement in the
sustainable operation of our office.

TPS CONSULT
Anna Hutton
Centre Tower, Whitgift Centre,
Croydon CR9 0AU
T: 020 8256 4000
E: marketing@tpsconsult.co.uk
www.tpsconsult.co.uk
TPS are multi-discipline designers committed to green design.
We invest in training our people
so that sustainability and environmental considerations are
carefully interwoven into the
design of the project. From land
remediation through to energy
efficient designs, we have experts
who can advise on whole life
costs.

WICEK SOSNA
ARCHITECTS LTD.
Wicek Sosna
Unit 15, 21 Plumbers Row, E1 1EQ
T: 020 7655 4430
E: studio@sosnaarchitects.com
www.sosnaarchitects.com
WSA specialise in all aspects of
transport design, from product
design to station masterplan-
ing and urban design around
transport interchanges. We are
committed to the concept of
sustainability through the application of appropriate technology.

STUDIO 4 DESIGN
Colin Laine
1st Floor, 84 Long Lane, SE1 4AU
T: 020 7357 7738
E: lucrecia@studio4design.co.uk
Studio 4 specialises in the
planning and design of healthcare buildings. We consider
good design to be linked to an
appreciation and respect for the
environment and endeavour to
produce solutions that reflect this
understanding.

ARCHITECTURAL
SERVICES

J3 BUILDING FUTURES
Jason Hawkes
E: enquiries@j3buildingfutures.
co.uk
www.j3buildingfutures.co.uk
J3 consists of construction
professionals with a wide range
of skills associated with the
environment. We offer: Architects;
architectural technician; environmental education; assessment
(Eco-homes, EIA, etc.); domestic,
community and professional
consultancy; research; policy and
planning advice; landscaping and
permaculture.

SHEPHEARD EPSTEIN HUNTER
Caroline Easterbrook
Phoenix Yard, 65 Kings Cross
Road, London WC1X 9LW
T: 020 7841 7500
E: architecture@seh.co.uk
www.seh.co.uk
Shepheard Epstein Hunter are
known for the quality of their
work in regeneration, education,
housing, masterplanning, mixed-
use and healthcare projects.
SEH's ongoing commitment to
the development of sustainable
architecture is now backed up by
their ISO 14001 environmental
certification.

BUILDING CONTRACTOR

DOMINIC SKEAPING
Dominic Skeaping
113 Holmleigh Road, N16 5QG
T: 07951 576893 /020 8802 6536
E: d.skeaping@virgin.net
Self employed builder, working
with domestic renovation and
extension through recommendations. Solar water heating
installation and unusual specifications welcome.

IN SITU RAMMED EARTH
COMPANY LIMITED
Rowland Keable
86 Brougham Road, Hackney
E8 4PB
T: 020 7241 4684
E: rowland@rammed-earth.info
www.rammed-earth.info
We have been building with
rammed earth since 1985 here
and abroad. We contract, consult,
research, teach and workshop in
the field of rammed earth. We also
pursue a standards agenda for
the U.K. and elsewhere for unsta-
bilised rammed earth.

WHOLEWOODS
Adrian Leaman
4 Hargrave Road, London
N19 5SJ
T: 07952 759 466
E: info@wholewoods.co.uk
www.wholewoods.co.uk
Wholewoods produce furniture,
garden structures and buildings.
We run courses in natural building
crafts for children and adults. The
raw materials we use are chosen
with great care. Organic production, sustainable management,
re-cycling and local sourcing are
our main objectives.

BUILDING SURVEYOR

UK DAMP AND DECAY CONTROL
Paul Taylor
10 Barley Mow Passage, Chiswick
W4 4PH
T: 0800 028 1903
E: paul-taylor@ukdamp.fsnet.co.uk
www.ukdamp.co.uk
"Damp and decay controlled the
right way"

CONSULTING
ENGINEERS

BATTLE McCARTHY
Guy Battle
Dog and Duck Yard, Princeton
Street, London WC1R 4BH
T: 020 7440 8282
E: gbattle@battlemccarthy.com
www.battlemccarthy.com
Battle McCarthy is a multi-disciplinary practice specialising in the
design and delivery of sustainable
solutions for the built environment. Our goal is to seek solutions
that find an optimum balance
between environmental impact,
social benefit and financial return.

BUILDING DESIGN
PARTNERSHIP
Trevor Butler
16 Brewhouse Yard, London
EC1V 4LJ
T: 020 7812 8000
E: TJ-Butler@bdp.co.uk
www.bdp.co.uk
We are a team from multi-disci-
plinary backgrounds focused
on addressing the issues and
embracing the challenges
of sustainable construction:
Sustainable Infrastructure,
Passive/Active Energy Systems,
Whole Life Costing, BREEAM
Assessment, EU Energy
Performance of Buildings,
Thermal Modelling, Computational
Fluid Dynamics.

FULCRUM CONSULTING
Victoria Caesar
62-68 Rosebery Avenue,
EC1R 4RR
T: 020 7520 1300
E: victoria.caesar@fulcrumfirst.
com
www.fulcrumfirst.com
Delivering innovative high quality
environmental engineering design,
Fulcrum Consulting has won
many awards. Widely known for
their expertise in Sustainability
Masterplanning at community
level, intelligent solar building
design at all scales and expertise
in interseasonal heat transfer and
thermal energy storage.

MAX FORDHAM LLP
Christian West
42/43 Gloucester Crescent,
Camden Town NW1 7PE
T: 020 7267 5161
E: post@maxfordham.com
www.maxfordham.com
Max Fordham LLP are consulting environmental and building services engineers and winners of the 2004 Queen's Award for Enterprise in the Category of Sustainable Development. The practice has completed numerous sustainable exemplars over the course of our 40 year history.

CONSULTING STRUCTURAL ENGINEER

ALAN CONISBEE AND ASSOCIATES
Ayo Abbas
1-5 Offord Street, Islington
N1 1DH
T: 020 7700 6666
E: Ayo.Abbas@conisbee.co.uk
www.conisbee.co.uk
Alan Conisbee and Associates acknowledge that the decisions and actions we take can have a significant impact on the environment and society. We follow business practices which are sustainable and design principles which promote environmentally and socially sensitive development.

EDUCATIONAL

SUSTAINABILITY WORKS SERVICES LTD.
Lenka Warren
11-29 Fashion Street, E1 6PX
T: 020 7422 1777
E: contact@sustainabilityworks.org.uk
www.sustainabilityworks.org.uk
Sustainability works provides on line software for housing professionals for delivering projects from policy level through to detailed design. Includes an extensive reference database and EcoHomes prediction tool. We provide nationwide training courses, and bespoke advice/consultancy on sustainable development.

ENERGY CONSULTANT

FABERMAUNSELL - SUSTAINABLE DEVELOPMENT GROUP
Miles Attenborough
23 Middle Street, EC1A 7JD
T: 020 7601 1652
E: miles.attenborough@fabermaunsell.com
www.fabermaunsell.com
Working with local authorities, housing associations, developers, planners and architects,

we provide advice on sustainable strategies for buildings and communities. Services include sustainability statements, feasibility studies, analysis and auditing for energy, renewables, water and waste, BREEAM and EcoHomes assessments.

XCO2
Robert Webb
1-5 Offord Street, N1 1DH
T: 020 7700 1000
E: mail@xco2.com
www.xco2.com
Engineering and design for sustainability in the built environment - projects include low and zero carbon housing schemes (both social housing and private houses), integration of low energy heating/ventilation systems, building materials, etc.

ENVIRONMENTAL BUSINESS CONSULTANT

ECOCONSULTING (UK) LTD.
Nanik M. Daswani
28 Marshalsea Road, SE1 1HF
T: 020 7939 0989
E: info@ecoconsulting.net
www.ecoconsulting.net
- Advise architects, developers, HAs on cost-effective solutions for improving energy-efficiency, environmental-friendliness, interior health and comfort - From bioclimatic design to product specification - BREEAM and EcoHomes licensed assessor.

ENVIRONMENTAL MONITORING

PDM CONSULTANTS ENVIRONMENT
Elliot Carter
178 Ebury Street, SW1W 8UP
T: 020 7881 0901
E: breeam@pdmconsultants.co.uk
www.pdmconsultants.co.uk
PDM Consultants offers a range of sustainable construction services and is officially licensed to carry out BREEAM/EcoHomes assessments. We can provide client and project team guidance throughout the design process to optimise a BREEAM rating.

LANDSCAPE ARCHITECT

LUSZCZAK ASSOCIATES
Mike Luszczak
40-42 Scrutton Street, London
EC2A 4PP
T: 020 7539 1939
E: mike@luszczak.com
www.luszczak.com
Luszczak Associates is client-focused specialist landscape architectural practice with emphasis on urban regeneration projects. Our aim is to create high

quality designs and sustainable landscapes that provide benefits to each project as well as the environment as a whole.

PAINTING AND DECORATING

ECOARTISAN
Jamie Anderson
32 Morton House, Otto Street,
London SE17 3NW
T: 07939 973141
E: info@ecoartisan.org
www.ecoartisan.org
Specialising in the application of natural paints and clay finishes, Ecoartisan's friendly, professional service ensures your home or work environment is transformed using the best quality materials. We insist on a high level of attention to preparation.

NATURAL CERTIFIED PRODUCTS UK PVT LTD.
Andrew Given
P.O. Box 50318, Chiswick W4 5BL
T: 0870 061 3427
E: sales@naturalmaterials.co.uk
www.naturalmaterials.co.uk or try www.ncpuk.com
Suppliers of Paints and finishes, insulation materials (wool, paper, warmcel, wood fibres), FSC timber, Floor coverings (Pre-finished timber, wool carpets), construction boards and clay plasters, decorating, WCs urinals, product sourcing services and mail order facility 24hr Tel/Fax.

DESIGN AND BUILD

HOMEPOTENTIAL
Martin Leach
5 Ravensbourne Road,
Twickenham TW1 2DG
T: 020 8892 2298
E: martin@homepotential.co.uk
www.homepotential.co.uk
Homepotential offers building and design services for the home owner. We recognise the subtle relationships that exist between people and their environment. We use ecological, feng shui and life coaching tools to maximise the health and comfort of both place and user.

Midlands

Bedfordshire

ARCHITECT(S)

ACAH ARCHITECTS
Angela Cox
71 High Street, Wrestlingworth
SG19 2EN
T: 01767 631081
E: angela@acah-architects.co.uk
www.acah-architects.co.uk
Low energy/ sound environmental Design (Diploma in Energy Efficient Building) coupled with architectural services from local authority approvals to project administration. Varied experience including residential, education, urban design, industrial and commercial. Of particular interest: residential, community, arts and rural projects.

NICOLAS TYE ARCHITECTS
Nicolas Tye
The Long Barn, Limbersey Lane,
Maulden MK45 2EA
T: 01525 406677
E: info@nicolastyearchitects.co.uk
www.nicolastyearchitects.co.uk
We are architects and designers involved in a range of work from master planning, commercial office developments, retail and residential work. All of these sectors are dealt with by design which is guided by protecting both the human users and environment.

Cheshire

CONSULTING ENGINEERS

CLANCY CONSULTING LIMITED
Alan Bramwell
Dunham Court, 2 Dunham Road,
Altrincham, Manchester
WA14 4NX
T: 0161 613 6000
E: marketing@clancy.co.uk
www.clancy.co.uk
Clancy Consulting provide a multi-discipline engineering design, building surveying and advisory service across the built environment.

SOLAR THERMAL INSTALLER

SOLAR TWIN LTD.
Oliver Yeates
2nd Floor, 50 Watergate Street,
Chester CH1 2LA
T: 01244 403407
E: oliver@solartwin.com
www.solartwin.com
Innovative 100% solar pumped solar hot water systems for washing and bathing. Zero carbon solar heating technology. Most other solar water heating systems consume mains electricity. This has a negative impact on CO_2 savings. But Solartwin's solar electric pump is zero carbon!

Derbyshire

ARCHITECT(S)

ANTHONY SHORT AND PARTNERS, ARCHITECTS
Mark Parsons
34 Church Street, Ashbourne
DE6 1AE
T: 01335 340890
E: mark @asap-architects.com
www.asap-architects.com
ASAP Architects reinforce their expertise in the creative reuse and alteration of existing buildings with the use of low energy and energy producing building technologies and the specification of sustainable construction materials.

ARCHITECTURAL SERVICES

OLDFIELD DESIGN LTD.
Joe Oldfield
Lumford Mill, Bakewell DE45 1GS
T: 01629 813301
E: oldfield.design@btinternet.com
www.oldfielddesign.com
We are a small planning and architectural practice in the heart of the Peak District National Park, with a strong interest in conservation, environmental design and the use of ecologically friendly construction products wherever possible.

Herefordshire

ARCHITECT(S)

CHRIS MORTON ARCHITECT
Chris Morton
Rosemead, Colwall WR13 6DT
T: 01684 541480
E: krjz@freeuk.com
http://home.freeuk/krjz/
Every building problem is different, so the solution to yours need not follow boring fashions. It needs to face an unpredictable future with low energy use and plenty of flexibility. Between us we can make it exciting! Examples on web-site.

SOLAR THERMAL INSTALLER

GREENEARTH ENERGY
Dai Rees
16 Callowside, Ewyas Harold,
Hereford HR2 0HX
T: 01981 241399
E: info@greenearthenergy.co.uk
www.greenearthenergy.co.uk
Solar Thermal, Solar PV and Electrical installations for healthy living. Clear Skies and EST/DTI accreditied. Design, install, commission, consultancy.

Leicestershire

ARCHITECT(S)

YMD ARCHITECTURE
David Yates
141 London Road, Leicester
LE2 1EF
T: 0116 2755181
E: ymd-a@pipemedia.co.uk
The practice, whose work includes industrial, special needs, educational, residential, leisure and commercial, is dedicated to promoting environmentally aware construction. We encourage an integrated approach to design and procurement so that the ecological footprint of user and project are minimised.

ENVIRONMENTAL BUSINESS CONSULTANT

RESPONSIBLE SOLUTIONS LTD.
Ian Nicholson
87 Parklands Drive, Loughborough
LE11 2SZ
T: 01509 552545
E: ian@responsible-solutions.co.uk
www.responsible-solutions.co.uk
A business improvement consultancy specialising in environmental and social responsibility. Services offered include environmental and social impact/opportunity reviews, EMS development, training, performance measurement, project management, auditing, etc.

RESEARCHER

BUILDING AND SOCIAL HOUSING FOUNDATION
Diane Diacon
Memorial Square, Coalville
LE67 3TU
T: 01530 510444
E: bshf@bshf.org
www.bshf.org
Established in 1976, the Building and Social Housing Foundation (BSHF) is an independent research organisation that promotes sustainable development and innovation in housing through collaborative research and knowledge transfer.

Northamptonshire

DESIGN AND BUILD

HOLISTIC HOMES
Gina Yuzbasioglu
T: 07962 160 804
E: ginafran@onetel.com /
holistichomes@onetel.com
Low energy and environmental building advice and design. Extensions and sun porches. Will also design for alternative building methods. Also available - craftsman built, bespoke, low energy, timber frame homes from Germany.

DESIGNER

SQUEAKY DESIGN
Mark James
Northampton NN12 7XU
T: 07904 540583
E: squeakydesign@aol.com
Qualified designer. Twenty years living without mains services spent acquiring experience in structural solutions and interior design on land and afloat. Special interests: carvel planking, timber framing (tree to erection), 12 volt electrics, low-tech solutions, model making, disability access. Member of Federation of Small Businesses (FSB).

EDUCATIONAL

BLACKCURRENT CENTRE
Jenny Vaughan
24 St. Michaels Avenue,
Northampton NN1 4JQ
T: 01604 628956
E: blackcurrent@members.v21.
co.uk
The Centre is an example of environmentally friendly building restoration, and provides free meeting space for groups, drop-in times for individuals, environmental advice, workshops, educational films and a library. We also sell environmentally friendly materials and run an organic vegetable box scheme.

Nottinghamshire

ARCHITECT(S)

MARK STEWART ARCHITECTS
Gil Schalom
34A Musters Road, West
Bridgford, Nottingham NG2 7PL
T: 0115 945 5787
E: gil@msarch.co.uk www.msarch.
co.uk
The practice behind the award winning Nottingham Ecohome, MSA are experts in sustainable design and eco renovation, combining traditional and cutting edge solutions that sit gracefully alongside nature. Contact us and create a genuinely efficient, beautiful building.

DEVELOPER

GUSTO CONSTRUCTION LTD.
Stephen Wright
Business Centre, Rio Drive,
Collingham, Newark
NG23 7NB
T: 01636 894900
E: steff@gusto-uk.com
www.gustohomes.com
Gusto Construction is at the forefront in the UK in the development of sustainable homes. With solar heating, rainwater harvesting, super-insulation levels and whole-house air-management fitted as standard, a typical Gusto home uses around 50% less energy and mains water than a conventionally built new home.

ECOLOGICAL COMMUNITY

HOCKERTON HOUSING PROJECT
Nick White
The Watershed, Gables Drive,
Hockerton, Southwell NG25 0QU
T: 01636 816902
E: hhp@hockerton.demon.co.uk
www.hockerton.demon.co.uk
The UK's first earth-sheltered, self-sufficient ecological housing development. Members live a holistic way of life in harmony with the environment, where all ecological impacts have been considered. The houses are amongst the most energy efficient, purpose built dwellings in Europe.

HOUSE BUILDER

NOTTINGHAM COMMUNITY HOUSING ASSOCIATION (NCHA)
Andrea Griffiths-James
12/14 Pelham Road, Nottingham
NG5 1AP
T: 0115 9104444
E: andrea.griffithsjames@ncha.
org.uk
www.ncha.org.uk
Nottingham Community Housing Association provides quality housing for people in need throughout the East Midlands.

Oxfordshire

ARCHITECT AND BUILDER

PAUL VENNING LEACH
Paul Venning Leach
Radcliffe Road, Oxford OX4 4BX
T: 01865249691
E: paulvleach@hotmail.com
www.paulvenningleach.co.uk
Formerly a cabinet maker, designer and builder for 20 years, Paul re-trained as an Architect at

http://home.freeuk.com/krjz

01684 541480

Chris Morton Architect

can I help make your life greener?

Manchester and Oxford schools of Architecture, specializing in community sector practice, Bio-climatic architecture and Green Building. He now offers specialist sustainable design based on practical experience.

ARCHITECT(S)

DAVID HYAMS CONSULTING
David Hyams
19 Meadow Prospect, Oxford
OX2 8PP
T: 01865 517077
E: hyams@oxfordshire.co.uk
Since 1988 DHC has provided services in two areas: a full architectural service for small projects and, for large projects, briefing and strategic space planning. DHC is currently working on a number of projects for sustainable living space.

DENNIS COX ARCHITECT
Dennis Cox
20 Gloucester Street, Farringdon
SN7 7HY
T: 01367 241006
E: denniscoxarchitect@lineone.net
We offer an integrated design approach for buildings that use sustainable construction conserve energy and enhance life. Experienced in repair/conversion of older/listed- domestic/commercial-rural/urban-and new build including self build.

JOHN BLEACH
John Bleach
47 Rosamund Road, Oxford
OX2 8NU
T: 01865 512114
E: bleachfamily@onetel.com
Architect with 30 years experience in new and existing buildings, including housing, university buildings and hospitals. Recently acquired MSc in energy efficient building. Can provide advice for controlling energy consumption and sustainable design solutions for small building projects.

THE OXFORDSHIRE PRACTICE
Barbara Griffiths
70 High Street, Wallingford
OX10 0BX
T: 01491 826001
E: barbara.griffiths@oxfordshire-practice.co.uk
www.pinnacle-psg.com
We are a multi-disciplinary practice of architects and surveyors which actively promotes the integration of energy efficient and sustainable methods of construction and site development in all schemes - including Social Housing, Special Needs, Sports and Leisure, Healthcare and Schools.

ARCHITECTURAL SERVICES

PLANNED APPROACH ARCHITECTURAL SERVICES
Tim Howard
Larkhill Cottage, College Farm, Wendlebury, Bicester, Oxford
OX25 2PR
T: 01869 249746
E: tp.howard@farming.me.uk
Complete Planning and Design Service for green projects, newbuild, conversions and extensions. Site supervision for both domestic and commercial projects. SAP and NHER ratings (quality assured).

BREEAM ASSESSOR

ENERGY EFFICIENT DESIGN
Martyn Gamble
13 Bleache Place, Oxford OX4 2JD
T: 01865 396172
E: martyngamble@lineone.net
EcoHomes Assessor, Energy-efficiency advice, SAP ratings, etc. Worked with housing associations and architects on range of projects for last 10 years.

EDUCATION

OXFORD ECO HOUSE
Sue Roaf
26 Blandford Avenue, Oxford
OX2 8DY
T: 01865 515001
E: s.roaf@btinternet.com
Architect, author, lecturer and city councillor. Consultant and designer specialising in ecohousing, and the integration of renewable energy and issues of sustainability into buildings and communities.

LANDSCAPE ARCHITECT

MARY DALE LANDSCAPE ARCHITECTS
Mary Dale
The Leggett, Thatcher's Close, Epwell, Banbury OX15 6LJ
T: 01295 780377
E: info@mdla.com
www.mdla.com
Mary Dale Landscape Architects is a registered practice of the Landscape Institute. We specialise in landscape planning for new developments, environmental assessment and planting design and management. We work to achieve cost effective and sustainable solutions that will enhance the environment.

Shropshire

ARCHITECT(S)

BAART HARRIES NEWALL
Robert Morris
1 Wilderhope House, Pountney Gardens, Belle Vue, Shrewsbury
SY3 7LU
T: 01743 361261
E: studio@bhn.co.uk
www.bhn.co.uk
A recent project is St. Judes Primary School, Wolverhampton, new build 2300m². Commencement on site November 2004. Features include rainwater recycling, solar water heating, SUDs and 100% natural ventilation together with thermal mass to control temperature. Pilot project for new BREEAM for schools.

ENVIRONMENTAL AND ARCHITECTURAL DESIGN
David Gomersall
4 Lower Down, Lydbury north
SY7 8BB
T: 01588 680693
E: david@eadstudio4.co.uk
Small practice specialising in contemporary ecological design. Practical, innovative and energy efficient design solutions, fitting new buildings, extensions and conversions into their context whilst using environmentally sensitive techniques and materials. Domestic, community, small commercial buildings and integrated landscape design.

ARCHITECTURAL SERVICES

PHILIP POOL BUILDING DESIGN
Philip Pool
32 Mount Street, Shrewsbury
SY3 8QH
T: 01743 367968
E: poolmuris32@btinternet.com
Advice and design. Experienced in extension, repair and conversion of existing buildings as well as new build, using a range of environmentally-sensitive solutions, including locally sourced materials, low energy buildings, straw-bale construction, and renewable energy systems.

ENVIRONMENTAL BUSINESS CONSULTANT

ENVIROS
Robert Baylis
Enviros House, Shrewsbury
SY2 6LG
T: 01743 284852
E: r.baylis@enviros.com
www.enviros.com
Through eight UK offices, Enviros services cover resource/energy/water efficiency, renewable energy, environmental management,

materials, drainage, contaminated land, ecology, planning, impact assessment, landscape, health and safety, supply chain management, stakeholder engagement, corporate communications, design for sustainability and BREEAM assessments.

EID
Fiona Gomersall
4 Lower Down, Lydbury North
SY7 8BB
T: 01588 680693
E: fiona@eadstudio4.co.uk
Botanical surveys carried out for environmental impact assessment. Advice on grassland and other habitat management and solutions for site restoration. Writing on ecological building subjects and environmental interpretation.

INTERIOR DESIGNER

PRECIOUS EARTH LTD.
Paul Williams
22 Corve Street, Ludlow SY8 1DA
T: 01584 878633
E: info@preciousearth.co.uk
www.preciousearth.co.uk
Natural materials suppliers and interior designers. A wealth of experience designing rooms that use traditional and innovative sustainable materials. We create and enhance living spaces through thoughtful design and carefully selected products. Ecologically low impact "green-kitchens", flooring and building materials.

SOLAR THERMAL INSTALLER

SOLAR DAWN
David Luckhurst
16, Brockton, Lydbury North
SY7 8BA
T: 01588 680469
E: solardawn@care4free.net
www.solardawn.co.uk
Solar Dawn installs solar thermal systems in the Shropshire and Welsh Borders area. Flat panels to evacuated tubes free surveys independent advice. Fully Registered Clear Skies Installer. Solar Trade Association and AECB member. Comprehensive environmental policy.

Warwickshire

HEATING ENGINEER

CALOR GAS LTD.
Andrea Price
Athena House, Athena Drive,
Tachbrook Park, Warwick
CV34 6RL
T: 0800 626 626
E: telemarketing@calor.co.uk
www.calor.co.uk

Calor, UK's largest supplier of LPG. Heat from LPG is instantly available and temperature is controllable. Uses same type of appliances and fittings as natural gas. Metered installations served from central tank above / underground tank to individual buildings cylinders.

West Midlands

ARCHITECT(S)

AXIS DESIGN COLLECTIVE
Michael Menzies
Crosby Court, 28 George Street,
Birmingham B3 1QG
T: 0121 236 1726
E: mail@axisdesigncollective.com
www.axisdesigncollective.com
Architects & Urban Designers - established in 1980. Our experience, commitment and enthusiasm enables us to give personal attention to a wide range of commissions. Whatever the project, we believe good design should enrich the lives and activities of its users.

ARCHITECTURAL SERVICES

E2S@BCS ASSOCIATES LTD.
Richard Baines
134 High Street, Blackheath
B65 0EE
T: 0121 561 1969
E: bainesr@bcha.co.uk
www.bcha.co.uk/bryce2.htm
Our e2S service: Guides development of sustainability policy, Facilitates consultation, provides information on alternative technologies, Predicts performance (SAP to dynamic computer simulations), Assesses sustainability (EcoHomes to Environmental Impact Assessments) and Monitors environmental performance.

CONSULTING ENGINEERS

TENBY CONSULTANCY GROUP
Trevor Floyd
248 Rocky Lane, Great Barr,
Birmingham B42 1QX
T: 0121 250 5455
E: trevorfloyd@aol.com
www.tenby.org.uk
TENBY has worked for 15 years in areas of Energy Auditing, Design, Awareness raising and Staff training with most of its activities delivered via 'Carbon Trust' and 'Energy Institute'. It has started to specialise in advising on renewable options.

PROJECT MANAGEMENT

ENCRAFT
Matthew Rhodes
46 Northumberland Road,
Leamington Spa CV32 6HB
T: 01926 771465
E: matthew.rhodes@encraft.co.uk
www.encraft.co.uk
We offer independent personalised specifications for homeowners looking to improve the environmental and energy performance of existing or new properties. Unique software simulates adding micro-generation and energy efficiency technologies to you.

Worcestershire

ARCHITECT(S)

HOWL ASSOCIATES LTD.
Phil Howl
Shrubbery House, 21 Birmingham Road, Kidderminster DY10 2BX
T: 01562 820022
E: design@howl.co.uk
www.howl.co.uk
We are architects committed to contemporary design of high quality and work with our clients to seek cost effective and sustainable solutions. We have experience of natural ventilation principles, light tubes, passive solar control, active environmental systems and ecological specification.

ENVIRONMENTAL BUSINESS CONSULTANT

GREEN BY DESIGN ENVIRONMENTAL CONSULTANCY
Karen Harris
1 Eastwood Drive, Kidderminster
DY10 3AW
T: 01562 748404
E: karen.harris@whsmithnet.co.uk
An environmental consultant offering: Independent and impartial advice on sustainable construction materials, products and techniques. Advice and setting up of Environmental Management Systems, e.g. ISO14001 for businesses.

OFF MAINS DRAINAGE

CRESS WATER LTD.
Rick Hudson
61 Woodstock Road, Worcester
WR2 5ND
T: 01905 422707
E: info@cresswater.co.uk
www.cresswater.co.uk
We specialise in the design and installation of reed-beds, ponds and wetlands for sewage and wastewater treatment, recycling treated effluent, water conserva-

tion, rainwater harvesting and water management, and the creation of attractive aquatic garden features. We provide a nation-wide service.

SELF BUILD

WALTER SEGAL SELF BUILD TRUST AND DIY
Geoff Stow
1 Fitcher Close, Worcester
WR2 6DP
T: 01905 749665
E: geoff@segalselfbuild.co.uk
www.segalselfbuild.co.uk
Advice, training and consultancy on self build housing and community buildings. Principle interest is in timber construction using an environmental aspect to design and materials as well as community and individual involvement in the design and construction process.

STRUCTURAL ENGINEER

QUERCUS
Deb Turnbull
1 Spa Cottages, Beacon Road, Malvern WR14 4EH
T: 01684 567196
E: deb.turnbull@tiscali.co.uk
I specialise in the engineering design of timber structures and have experience of traditional and newer forms of timber framing including pole buildings, barn conversion, straw bale, SIPs. I bring personal experience of building with these methods to the design.

Northern

Cumbria

ARCHITECT(S)

DAY CUMMINS LTD.
Stuart Woodall
Lakeland Business Park, Lamplugh Road, Cockermouth CA13 0QT
T: 01900 820700
E: stuart.woodall@day-cummins. co.uk
www.day-cummins.co.uk
We are architect's working with clients interested in a ''green'' approach to design, developing from concept to completion. We have constructed our first eco-barn conversion during 2004 with a host of environmental features including heat pumps and sedum roofs.

JOHN BODGER CHARTERED ARCHITECT LTD.
John Bodger
13B Angel Lane, Penrith CA11 7BP
T: 01768 864224
E: bodger-architect@btconnect.

com
Chartered architect and interior designer specialising in environmental design. Designed the underground house at Appleby as featured on Grand Designs in 2003. Architect for the Brompton Ecohouse. Currently working on a range of eco building projects.

PROJECT MANAGEMENT

BARCO DEVELOPMENTS LTD.
John Trengrove
Barco, Carleton Road, Penrith
CA11 8LR
T: 01768 867338
E: john@edenframe.com
www.barcodevelopments.com
Specialising in Management Contracting to manage a project from inception to completion utilising the JCT Form of Management Contract.

Lancashire

ENERGY CONSULTANT

ENERGY COUNCIL
Jeff/ Matthew Gibson
Rhodes House, 16 Cartmel Close, Bury BL9 8JA
T: 0161 766 7067
E: energycouncil@aol.com
www.energycouncil.co.uk
Energy Council are specialist energy consultants providing comprehensive technical expertise including: M and E Design, Advice and Implementation of Green Buildings, EcoHomes and BREEAM Assessments, SAP/NHER Energy Assessments.

Lincolnshire

ARCHITECT(S)

HODSON ARCHITECTS
Mark Hodson
28 Chantry Lane, Grimsby
DN31 2LJ
T: 01472 327991
E: info@hodsonarchitects.com
www.hodsonarchitects.com
The practice aims to provide poetic solutions through detailed pragmatic study. Emphasis is placed on successfully reconciling the demands of brief, site, context and sustainability. Our design for the Ecology Building Society was awarded the 2004 Building of the Year Award by BDDA.

Manchester

ARCHITECTURE: M
Mark Percival
57 Hilton Street, Manchester
M1 2EJ
T: 0161 237 3324
E: markpercival@mac.com

www.architecturem.co.uk
We look to bring ''surprise and delight'' to our clients on their projects. We believe in developing schemes that answer the clients brief, and surpass their expectations, combining good design, and rational thinking.

CTAC
Neil Allen
Green Fish Resource Centre, 1st Floor, 46-50 Oldham Street, Manchester M4 1LE
T: 0161 234 2950
E: nallen@ctac.co.uk
www.ctac.co.uk
CTAC is an Architectural and Landscape Design Consultancy assisting voluntary organisations, regeneration agencies developing community initiatives throughout the North West. Specialisms include: Ecological Design, Energy efficiency, Accessibility Issues, Feasibility Studies, Project Management, Community Consultation, Project Development, Resourcing & Funding Advice.

Merseyside

ALUKO BROOKS ARCHITECTS
Tayo Aluko
59 Seel Street, Liverpool L15 3LA
T: 0151 707 8187
E: office@alukobrooks.co.uk
www.alukobrooks.co.uk
Due to a scarcity of sufficiently ''green'' clients, we formed a sister development company to purchase sites to design and build green on. Our first two projects start in Spring 2005, totalling 19 eco-friendly flats intended for shared ownership sale.

North Yorkshire

ECO ARC
Andrew Yeats
Old Village School, Harton
YO60 7NP
T: 01904 468 752
E: ecoarc@ecoarc.co.uk
www.ecoarc.co.uk
Andrew particularly enjoys designing beautiful and healthy buildings built to the highest technical and spatial standards incorporating best practice in low energy, passive and active solar design, utilising low embodied energy materials, renewable wind and solar technologies, biological sewage treatments, water recycling systems all within a holistic framework.

WILSON KENNETT PARTNERSHIP
Mark Kennett
College House, 2 College Street, Harrogate HG2 0AH
T: 01423 531183

E: wkp@wkpartnership.co.uk
www.wkpartnership.co.uk
A small friendly practice offering a personal professional service tailored to your needs. We work with you to achieve an imaginative well-designed ecological and environmental solution. New houses, alterations, extensions, grant aided, barn conversions and listed building works.

South Yorkshire

ARCHITECT(S)

NEIL PRITCHARD ASSOCIATES
Neil Pritchard
Lynthorpe House, 86 Charlotte Road, Sheffield S1 4TL
T: 0114 276 8422
E: neilpritchard@clara.co.uk
Specialising in domestic architecture and community architecture with sustainable design as an active component of the design decision making process.

ECOLOGICAL COMMUNITY

RECYCLING MATTERS!
Nicola Freeman
127 Spital Hill, Sheffield S4 7LF
T: 0114 275 8985
E: nicola@recyclingmatters.org.uk
www.recyclingmatters.org.uk
Recycling Matters! is a Sheffield

Community Recycling Action Programme (SCRAP) project promoting waste avoidance, re-use recycling and sustainable living. The Recycling Matters! Information Bureau is an eco built resource centre created from a derelict building using reclaimed and recycled materials.

SOLAR THERMAL INSTALLER

ENVIROPLUMB
Phil Hurley
30 Rushley Drive, Sheffield S17 3EN
T: 0114 236 3910
E: info@enviroplumb.co.uk
www.enviroplumb.co.uk
Enviroplumb specialise in underfloor heating, renewable energy systems and water conservation. Enviroplumb is committed to supplying and installing the most energy efficient systems in your home. We can design, supply and install solar water systems.

Tyne and Wear

ARCHITECT AND BUILDER

GLASS ARC LIMITED
Henry Amos
Studio 6, Tynemouth Metro Station, North Shields NE30 4RE

T: 0191 257 4454
E: info@glassarc.com
www.glassarc.com
Glass Arc Limited develops and researches projects that are hybrids of Innovative Architecture and Art using appropriate technologies and materials. Projects include a wide range of buildings of different scales, interior and lit projects, as well as inter-active and public installations.

ARCHITECT(S)

JANE DARBYSHIRE AND DAVID KENDALL LIMITED
Kevin Turnbull
Millmount, Ponteland Road, Newcastle upon Tyne NE5 3AL
T: 0191 2860811
E: AngieC@jddk.co.uk
www.jddk.co.uk
Chartered Architect and Landscape Architects

West Yorkshire

ALLEN TOD ARCHITECTURE
Andrew May
The Studio, 32 The Calls, Leeds LS2 7EW
T: 0113 244 9973
E: amay@allentod.co.uk
www.allentod.co.uk
Allen Tod Architecture is an award-winning practice with projects throughout the country.

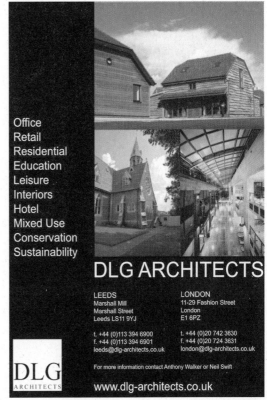

We offer a unique combination of skills to deliver new or better buildings and places and encourage a sustainable approach to the design and delivery of our projects.

JOHN YARD ARCHITECTS
John Yard
10, Allergill Park, Upperthong, Holmfirth HD9 3XH
T: 01484 687412
E: johnyard.architect@btopenworld.com
Full range of architectural services with a particular expertise in ecological design. Design work ranges from sustainable principles and conceptual layouts right through to the selection of environmentally sound building materials.

LEEDS ENVIRONMENTAL DESIGN ASSOCIATES LTD.
Jonathan Lindh
Micklethwaite House, 70 Cross Green lane, Leeds
LS9 0DG
T: 0113 200 9380
E: office@leda.org.uk
www.leda.org.uk
LEDA integrates architectural and environmental design to create sustainable buildings.

SENSE OF SPACE ARCHITECTS AND BUILDING SURVEYORS
Richard Addenbrook
35 The Grove, Ilkley LS29 9NJ
T: 01943 816489
E: enquiries@senseofspace.net
www.senseofspace.net
We take great care to ensure our projects satisfy our Clients' needs in terms of functionality, economics and environmental performance. We design for the future by taking a flexible approach, allowing for new developments in technology and changes in legislation.

ECOLOGICAL COMMUNITY

ECOLOGY BUILDING SOCIETY
Mortgage Team
7 Belton Road, Silsden, Keighley
BD20 0EE
T: 0845 674 5566
E: loans@ecology.co.uk
www.ecology.co.uk
Specialists in mortgages for the renovation or conversion of run down and derelict property, from humble terraces to listed buildings. We also provide mortgages for energy and resource efficient self build homes, organic farmers, ecological businesses, housing co-operatives and small scale eco development finance.

ENVIRONMENTAL BUSINESS CONSULTANT

CONSULTING WITH A PURPOSE
Gideon Richards
25 Sunnydale Park, Ossett
WF5 0RJ
T: 01924 261341
E: gideon@cwap.co.uk
www.cwap.co.uk
Consulting With A Purpose work with people to make the environment safe and energy effective. We do this by advising organisations and individuals on their environmental obligations and how to capitalise on the latest environmental developments.

South East

Berkshire

ARCHITECT(S)

CA SUSTAINABLE ARCHITECTURE
Isabel Carmona Andreu
83 Old Newtown Road, Newbury
RG14 7DE
T: 01635 48363
E: isabelcarmona@ca-sa.co.uk
www.ca-sa.co.uk
CA sustainable architecture aims to provide lasting comfortable buildings.

ENERGY CONSULTANT

ECONOPOWER CEL
Paul Mills
268 Bath Road, Slough SL1 4DX
T: 01753 708881
E: pmills@econopower.co.uk
www.econopower.co.uk
EconoPower provides bespoke eco-design services for clients to help achieve their dream buildings. From energy strategies to detailed design, from test performance to commissioning, both commercial and domestic sectors, either refurbishment or new build. Government vetted consultants established since 1996.

Buckinghamshire

BREEAM ASSESSOR

NHBC SERVICES LTD.
Mike Priaulx
Energy and Environment, Ash House, Breckland, Linford Wood, Milton Keynes MK14 6ET
T: 0870 241 4310
E: energyadmin@nhbc.co.uk
www.nhbc.co.uk
NHBC Services have licensed EcoHomes, BREEAM for Offices and bespoke BREEAM assessors based in Milton Keynes, London

and Edinburgh. We are also the largest provider of energy ratings in the UK - our service is independently monitored for quality.

ENERGY CONSULTANT

OPEN UNIVERSITY
David Elliott
OU, Walton Hall, Milton Keynes
MK7 6AA
T: 01908 653197
E: D.A.Elliott@open.ac.uk
http://eeru.open.ac.uk
Prof. David Elliott is Director of the Open University Energy and Environment Research Unit, and has been producing courses on sustainable energy and researching renewable energy development and deployment policy issues. He is editor of EERU's journal NATTA.

RICKABY THOMPSON ASSOCIATES LTD.
Peter Rickaby
Witan Court, 296 Witan Gate West, Central Milton Keynes
MK9 1EJ
T: 01908 679520
E: peter.rickaby@rickabythompson.co.uk
www.rickabythompson.co.uk
Rickaby Thompson Associates is an energy and environmental consultancy. Our core skills include: assessment of the energy efficiency of buildings, design and specification of energy efficient buildings and improvements, developing energy strategies.

ENVIRONMENTAL MONITORING

ENVIRONMENTAL BUILDING SOLUTIONS LTD.
Huw Lloyd
Galley Cottage, Milton Keynes
MK17 9AA
T: 01525 261922
E: ebs@ebssurvey.co.uk
www.ebssurvey.co.uk
EBS provides independent scientific advice and analysis on fungal, insect pest and damp problems in buildings. EBS aims to improve customers' home and work environments by identifying and curing building problems without the use of chemicals.

RESEARCHER

AYLESBURY VALE DISTRICT COUNCIL
Robert Smart
Environmental Health, 66 High Street, Aylesbury HP20 1SD
T: 01280 815507
E: rsmart@aylesburyvaledc.gov.uk
www.aylesburyvaledc.gov.uk
Local Government.

East Sussex

ARCHITECT(S)

DRP ARCHITECTS
Giles Ings
87-88 Upper Lewes Road,
Brighton BN2 3FF
T: 01273 888080
E: info@drparchitects.co.uk
www.drparchitects.co.uk
DRP are engaged on a wide range
of domestic, community and
medical projects from one-off
houses to multi-flat developments.

KORU DESIGN - SUSTAINABLE ARCHITECTURE
Mark Pellant
4a Burton Villas, Hove BN3 6FN
T: 01273 204065
E: info@korudesign.co.uk
www.korudesign.co.uk
Architects specialising in high
quality, contemporary design
guided by sustainable principles.
We undertake residential and
small commercial projects including new build, extensions and
refurbishments.

NICOLAS POPLE ARCHITECT
Nicolas Pople
6 Highfields, Forest Row RH18 5AJ
T: 01342 822240
E: poplenj@dircon.co.uk
Specialist in sustainable architecture and the conservation of
historic buildings with emphasis
on community and residen-
tial projects. Senior lecturer
in Environmental Design at
Southbank University, London.
Author of "Experimental Houses"
(2000) and "Small Houses" (2003)
published by Laurence King.

BUILDING CONTRACTOR

DOUCH PARTNERS LTD.
Toby Douch
Court Mead, Forest RH18 5HS
T: 01342 825766
E: enquiries@douchpartners.co.uk
www.douchpartners.co.uk
A long established family business
with extensive experience in
traditional building methods. We
have broad experience in the use
of modern materials and design
techniques in creating both environmentally sensitive and quality
conventional buildings.

ECOLOGISE LTD.
Dan England
49 Newmarket Road, Brighton
BN2 3QG
T: 01273 885458
E: info@ecologise.co.uk
General eco-building firm.
Plumbing, carpentry, masonry,
plastering, decorating. Specialists
in energy and water efficiency,
condensing boilers, solar thermal
systems, insulation, reclaimed
timber, eco-paint, lime plaster. Our
main focus is eco-refurbishment
of old buildings. Happy to take on
any work, big or small. Free quotes
and advice.

THOMPSON CONSTRUCTION ENGINEERING LTD.
Steve Thompson
Upper Lodge, Cinder Hill,
Chailey East Sussex BN8 4HR
T: 01825 7234556
E: s.thompson@btconnect.com
www.thomstruct.co.uk
Contractors carrying out conventional and sustainable projects
such as extensions, alterations,
refurbishment and all types of
conversion including listed buildings. We specialise in specific
elements of construction which
covers groundworks, drainage,
foundations, underpinning,
substructures, structural alterations and hard landscaping. Our
motto is the Four R's.

CONSULTING ENGINEERS

PJR DESIGN SERVICES
Jeff Fuller
Suite 29 New England House, New
England Street, Brighton BN1 4GH
T: 01273 626247
E: PJRServices@BTInternet.com
Mechanical and electrical engi-
neering consultancy, and building
surveyors with special interest in
implementing sustainable and low
energy solutions.

DEVELOPER

CREATING1OFFS
Paul Talbot
3 Belgrave Place, Brighton
BN2 1EL
T: 0127 367 5433
E: creating1offs@yahoo.co.uk
Using and manipulating ecological materials is a passion of mine.
As an artist I use a conceptual
approach in my work to express to
the viewer / consumer, how buying
material objects will never satisfy
the hole we try to fill.

GREENERLIVING HOMES
Paul Mustard
PO Box 83, Lewes BN7 2YD
T: 01273 488588
E: info@greenerlivinghomes.co.uk
www.greenerlivinghomes.co.uk
GreenerLiving Homes create
stylish, modern homes with very
low environmental impact. By the
process of renovation or new
build, our sustainable homes are
designed to enable the occupants to significantly reduce their
environmental footprint without
having to change their lifestyle.

Hampshire

ARCHITECT(S)

THE GENESIS DESIGN STUDIO
David Barnes
Mead Mill, 77 Mill Lane, Romsey
SO51 8EQ
T: 01794 519333
E: d.barnes@thegenesisdesignst
udio.com
www.thegenesisdesignstudio.com
We are an enthusiastic company
of Architects who provide innovative and cost effective design to a
wide range of projects of varying
size. We promote sustainable
and energy efficient solutions
wherever possible.

HADDOW PARTNERSHIP
Robin Haddow
Market Place House, 2/4 Market
Place, Basingstoke
T: 01256 335000
E: info@haddowpartnership.co.uk
www.haddowpartnership.co.uk
Haddow partnership is known
for high quality work in designing
buildings across the community,
commercial and domestic sectors,
producing interesting and sensitive traditional contemporary
architecture.

TIMBER FRAMER, TRADITIONAL

THE GREEN OAK CARPENTRY CO LTD.
Andrew Holloway
Langley Farm, Rake, Liss
GU33 7JW
T: 01730 892049
E: enquiries@greenoakcarpentry.
co.uk
www.greenoakcarpentry.co.uk
Design, fabrication and engineering of high quality traditional and
modern structures such as halls,
houses, trussed roofs, outbuildings, bridges, etc. Also specialising
in round pole structures, grid-
shells, lamellar and other types of
structure.

Isle of Wight

LANDSCAPE ARCHITECT

NEWLEAF GARDENING
Rowan Adams
29 Lowtherville Road, Ventnor
PO38 1AP
T: 01983 856936
E: rowan@quickbeam.plus.com
I design gardens for modern
peasants, cottage gardens for a
future - inspiring spaces where
useful and beautiful plants grow
happily together, and wildlife flour-
ishes. Clients get easy pickings of
mostly perennial plants for food,
fuel, craft, healing, and cut flowers.

www.forevergreen.org.uk

Kent

ARCHITECT(S)

CHRISTOPHER RAYNER ARCHITECTS
Christopher Rayner
Applecross House, 52 The Rise,
Sevenoaks TN13 1RN
T: 01732 461806
E: christopherraynerarchitects@yahoo.com
We specialise in ecological and traditional design, historic building conservation, housing/community projects, and have a concern for context and the timeless quality of buildings. Background at Berkeley, California includes design using 'Pattern Languages'.

FOREVER GREEN PROJECTS LTD.
Robin Hillier
3 Onslow House, Castle Road, Tunbridge Wells TN4 8BY
T: 01892 511652
E: robin@fgp.demon.co.uk
www.forevergreen.org.uk
Architects specialising in timber framed low energy buildings, with a particular interest in community self build, user involvement in design, environmentally friendly specification and non-traditional procurement methods.

BRICKLAYER

ASH DESIGN CONSULTANTS LTD.
Gary Waugh
Riverside Offices, Block A, Littlebrook Business Park, Dartford DA1 5PZ
T: 01322 627800
E: g.waugh@tribalps.co.uk
www.tribal.co.uk
We are architects committed to producing buildings which are environmental responsive. We work with clients and consultants to design best solutions, minimising energy usage in construction and running costs through a building's life within budgetary constraints.

BUILDING CONTRACTOR

ECO-LIBRIUM SOLUTIONS LTD.
Andrew Bassant
3 Standen Terrace, Alkham Valley Road, Folkestone CT18 7EW
T: 01303 891576
E: info@eco-libriumsolutions.co.uk
www.eco-libriumsolutions.co.uk
Eco-librium Solutions Ltd. is dedicated to providing environmentally responsible construction services which are healthy, sustainable, innovative and of high quality. Projects include refurbishment, renovation, new build, extensions and alterations, design and build, specific product installations e.g. sunpipes, rainwater harvesting.

BUILDING SURVEYOR

JHAI LTD.
Mark Saich
27 Nunnery Fields, Canterbury CT1 3JT
T: 01227 450464
E: marks@approvedinspector.com
www.approvedinspector.com
jhai Ltd. - approved inspectors provide building control services (as an alternative to your local authority), fire consultancy, DDA advice and more. For information on how jhai Ltd. can help you with your project call us.

MURRAY BIRRELL
Andrew Hall
207-215 High Street, Orpington BR6 0PF
T: 01689 898288
E: andrew@murraybirrell.co.uk
We undertake EcoHomes assessments for social housing providers and private developers. We are able to apply our practical knowledge to assist in the detailed design of schemes to maximise your score whilst keeping costs to a minimum.

DEVELOPER

BEACON PROPERTY
Richard Barwick
Coombe Valley Road, Dover
CT17 0UJ
T: 01304 248400
E: info@rjbarwick.co.uk
www.barwickconstruction.co.uk
Barwick has been trading as a
family business for over 150
years, currently managed by the
fifth generation. The culture and
philosophy are based around
traditional family values. Currently
Barwick employs over 150 person-
nel. Turnover is over £20 million.
Beacon Property is a new addition
to the organisation.

Middlesex

ARCHITECT(S)

DEREK PLUMMER CHARTERED ARCHITECT
Derek Plummer
28 Abbott Close, Hampton
TW12 3XR
T: 020 8979 7443
E: lizcrisp@btopenworld.com
www.lizcrisp.co.uk
Liz Crisp and Derek Plummer
have been practicing for 45
years between them. We offer
a full range of architectural
services. Specializing in conserva-
tion/restoration of historic/old
buildings, community/domestic
projects, and are committed to
the mainstream implementation of
sustainable practices.

PCKO ARCHITECTS
Peter Chlapowski
130 College Road, Harrow
HA1 1BQ
T: 020 8861 1444
E: mail@pcko.co.uk
www.pcko.co.uk
PCKO Architects is a competition
and award winning architectural
practice, with experience and
track record in creating attractive buildings. By working with
the natural environment, PCKO
creates environmentally friendly
buildings and sustainable communities. Our buildings tread lightly
on the earth.

BUILDING SURVEYOR

PANTRACO LTD.
Alex Serridge
7 Fieldend, Twickenham TW1 4TF
T: 020 8892 3963
E: aserridge@blueyonder.co.uk
Sustainable Design and Build
contractors for South East Region
Incorporated in the Chartered
Institute of Building. 25 Years
experience of all aspects of
building. Completed Ecological
Building Design Course. Building

Consultant on Earthdome Project
in Norbury 2004.

DESIGN AND BUILD

HOMEPOTENTIAL
Martin Leach
5 Ravensbourne Road,
Twickenham TW1 2DG
T: 0208 892 2298
E: martin@homepotential.co.uk
www.homepotential.co.uk
Homepotential offers building
and design services for the home
owner. We recognise the subtle
relationships that exist between
people and their environment. We
use ecological, feng shui and life
coaching tools to maximise the
health and comfort of both place
and user.

To book a listing in
the next edition of
the Green Building
Bible call Jerry now
on 01208 895103
jerry@newbuilder.
co.uk

Surrey

ARCHITECT(S)

BILL DUNSTER ARCHITECTS / ZEDFACTORY LTD.
Bill Dunster
The BedZED Centre, 24 Helios
Road, Wallington, Surrey SM6 7BZ
T: 020 8404 1380
E: bill@zedfactory.com
www.zedfactory.com
Zedfactory offer architectural services and development
appraisal services for step change
zero fossil energy communities
- ranging from a detached house
to an urban block - including
ranges of standard house types
with integrated supply chains and
volume discounts - in addition to
site specific designs.

PRP ARCHITECTS
David Housego
Ferry Works, Summer Road,
Thames Ditton KT7 0QJ
T: 020 8339 3600
E: prp@prparchitects.co.uk
www.prparchitects.co.uk
PRP Architects has been
established for over 40 years,
specialising in residential design.
The practice is committed to the

sustainable design and specification of its buildings, and seeks to
promote the use of environmentally-friendly materials and adoption
of energy-efficient design.

PW ARCHITECTS
Paulina Wojciechowska
18 The Willows, Byfleet KT14 7QY
T: 01932 352129
E: enquiries@EarthHandsAndHo
uses.org
www.EarthHandsAndHouses.org
Specialising in ecological design
and application of natural building
materials such as earth, straw
bale, stone, sandbags, etc.
Sculpting buildings out of earthen
materials with earthen finishes.

BREEAM ASSESSOR

TPS SCHAL
Chris Gee
Centre Tower, Whitgift Centre,
Croydon CR9 0AU
T: 020 8256 4364
E: gee.chris@schal.co.uk
www.tpsschal.com
TPS Schal are licensed BREEAM,
EcoHomes and Bespoke asses-
sors and are experienced in
assessments and conducting team
workshops to achieve ratings
set in project briefs/Planning
Conditions. We are trained in "The
Natural Step" Sustainability model
and ISO 14001 Certified.

ENVIRONMENTAL BUSINESS CONSULTANT

NATURAL DISCOVERY
James Brittain
2 The Hatch, The Street, Thursley,
Guildford GU8 6QG
T: 0845 458 2799
E: JamesBrittain@naturaldiscove
ry.co.uk
www.NaturalDiscovery.co.uk
Interested in experiencing
green building technologies
and products before you buy?
Discover and live with green
ideas whilst on a UK short break.
See www.naturaldiscovery.co.uk
for latest breaks, environmental
products we sell and for advice on
developing green tourism accommodation.

SUSTAINABLE DEVELOPMENT CONSULTANT

BUILT FOR LIFE LTD.
Mary Gledhill
125 Norbiton Hall, Birkenhead
Avenue, Kingston upon Thames
KT2 6RS
T: 020 8241 9048
E: marygledhill@builtforlife.co.uk
www.builtforlife.co.uk
Built for Life provides advice and
project management services to

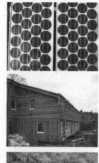

developers and companies who want to benefit from good design, professional management techniques and a sustainable approach to construction. Current clients include Neal's Yard Remedies and Westmark Development Ltd.

Sussex

ARCHITECT(S)

BBM SUSTAINABLE DESIGN
Duncan Baker-Brown
Star Brewery, Castle Ditch Lane, Lewes BNY 1YJ
T: 01273 480533
E: duncan@bbm-architects.co.uk
www.bbm-architects.co.uk
BBM were formed around a deeply felt agenda to pursue a more environmentally benign architecture, and is well known for effecting considerable influence towards sustainable development within the industry. The practice portfolio includes private and social housing, schools and community buildings and commercial work.

West Sussex

NICOLA THOMAS ARCHITECTS
Nicola Thomas
9, Cumberland Lodge, Brighton BN1 6ST
T: 01273 267184
E: nt@nicolathomas.co.uk
www.nicolathomas.co.uk
Nicola Thomas Architects is committed to creating architecture that is sustainable, environmentally friendly, socially responsible and sensitive as well as cost effective and excellently designed: Buildings which create healthy, efficient and pleasant spaces and enhance our environment.

ARCHITECTURAL SERVICES

R. E. OSBORNE BUILDING CONSULTANT
Ted Osborne
11 Danefield Road, Selsey, Chichester PO20 9DA
T: 01243 605122
E: reo@selseypc.net
New houses, extensions, conversions, alterations, remodelling (rethinking/reorienting spaces in older properties) - even the simplest project can use eco-design principles and site-specific opportunities to benefit clients and minimize impact on the environment.

CONSULTING ENGINEERS

JOHN PACKER ASSOCIATES LTD.
John Packer
5 Kingfisher Court Brambleside Bellbrook Business Park, Uckfield TN22 1QQ
T: 01825 769880
E: peter.taylor@jpa.uk.com
www.jpa,uk.com
John Packer Associates specialise in designing low energy and sustainable engineering services, aiming to "design out" energy consuming systems wherever possible by early involvement in the design process. Action Energy "Design Advice" consultant

SUSTAINABLE DEVELOPMENT CONSULTANT

IMPETUS CONSULTING LTD.
Kate Millbank
Suite 4, 39 Aldwick Road, Bognor Regis PO21 2LN
T: 01243 869 834
E: kate@impetusconsult.co.uk
www.impetusconsult.co.uk

TIMBER FRAMER

THOMLINSON'S SAWMILL
Richard Thomlinson
Slugwash Lane, Wivelsfield Green RH17 7RQ
T: 01444 454554
E: Thomlinsons-sawmill@telinco.co.uk
Thomlinson's Sawmill specialises in producing high-quality post and beam frames. We enjoy meeting the challenges of traditional and contemporary designs using carpentry techniques developed over centuries. We make furniture and joinery.

South West

Avon

DEVELOPER

URBANE
Terry Rogers
PO Box 619, Bristol BS99 3XS
T: 01179 557224
E: urbane@btopenworld.com
www.urban-e.com
Award winning company providing contemporary eco-friendly, low-energy homes of good quality with efficient speed and cost. We welcome any challenge and our system is immensely adaptable to any style. We have great experience in design cost control and construction.

Bath and NE Somerset

ARCHITECT(S)

DAVID HAYHOW ASSOCIATES
David Hayhow
Cedar High, Madam's Paddock, Chew Magna, Bristol BS40 8PN
T: 01275 333109
E: hayhow@btinternet.com
www.hayhow.btinternet.co.uk
Working with individual clients and public bodies in the Health, Education, Residential and Commercial fields, we aim for sustainability and inclusion and for quality design on modest budgets.

FEILDEN CLEGG BRADLEY ARCHITECTS LLP
Felicia Mills
Bath Brewery, Toll Bridge Road,
Bath BA1 7DE
T: 01225 852545
E: fm@feildenclegg.com
www.feildenclegg.com
We are recognised for design quality, environmental expertise and innovation. Our social and environmental principles were recognised in 2003 with the Building Awards Architectural Practice of the Year, a Queen's Award for Sustainable Development.

HETREED ROSS ARCHITECTS
Jonathan Hetreed
Bath Brewery, Toll Bridge Road,
Bath BA1 7DE
T: 01225 851860
E: jh@hetreedross.com
www.hetreedross.com
Widely experienced architects in environmental, housing, community, education, commercial and mixed use projects, from sensitive planning to detailed construction for new, existing and historic buildings.

EARTH BUILDING

UNIVERSITY OF BATH
Pete Walker
Dept. Architecture & Civil Eng.,
Bath BA2 7AY
T: 01225 386646

E: p.walker@bath.ac.uk
www.bath.ac.uk/~abspw/index.html
Able to undertake testing and evaluation of materials and offer advice on a variety of natural building methods, including rammed earth, pressed earth block, cob, limecrete, timber and straw bale.

PAINTING AND DECORATING

NATURAL PAINT STORE
Anton Saxton
Green Park Station, Bath BA1 1JB
T: 0845 330 3934
E: info@naturalpaintstore.co.uk
www.naturalpaintstore.co.uk
We supply a full range of beautiful paints and decorating products with lower emissions for healthier living. Additionally we offer simple cleaning products (lemon juice, borax, etc) in economy sizes, with refill facilities, for a less polluted home and also full Ecover range.

PAINT AND FINISHES CONSULTANT

THE NATURAL DECORATING CO.
Pam MacDonald
4 Maynard Terrace Clutton, Bristol
BS39 5PL
T: 01761 451351
E: naturaldecorating@phonecoop.coop

Natural Paints and Finishes-consultancy and specification for paints, fabrics and flooring for sustainable interiors. Design and decoration service available.

Bristol

ARCHITECT AND BUILDER

GREENHEART SUSTAINABLE DESIGN AND BUILD
Bill Flinn
79 Effingham Road, Bristol
BS6 5AY
T: 0117 9429717 E: greenheartuk.com
www.greenheartuk.com
Greenheart is a design and build partnership practising and promoting environmentally responsible building. We particularly enjoy challenging and innovative projects.

ARCHITECT(S)

ASCENT ARCHITECTURE
Steve Mardall
1 Denbigh Street, Bristol BS2 8XG
T: 0117 942 9515
E: sm@ascentarchitecture.com
www.ascentarchitecture.com
A small architectural practice offering innovative and practical designs which address the issues

HETREED ROSS ARCHITECTS

New Town Council Offices in Bradford on Avon

New 6th Form Centre for Kingswood CTC, Bristol

FRIENDLY ENVIRONMENTAL PRACTICE DESIGNING COMMUNITY, COMMERCIAL & DOMESTIC PROJECTS FOR A BETTER LIFE AND MORE SUSTAINABLE WORLD.

t: 01225 851860 f: 01225 851884
e: jh@hetreedross.com w: www.hetreedross.com

DO NOT BELIEVE WHAT YOU HEAR, WE CAN BUILD YOU A BEAUTIFUL ECO-FRIENDLY HOME AT THE SAME PRICE AS A TRADITIONALLY BUILT ONE! CONTACT US TO TALK

Urbane Sustainable Homes
PO BOX 619 Bristol BS99 3XS
tel: 01179557224
www.urban-e.com
e: urbane@btopenworld.com

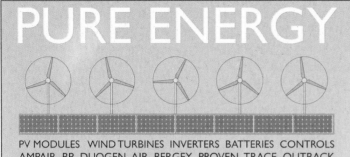
of environmental impact. Energy conservation in both the use of the building and the manufacture of materials will be considered. Materials from renewable sources specified where appropriate.

CHRIS GROSE ARCHITECTS LTD.
Christopher Grose
125 Whiteladies Road, Clifton, Bristol BS8 2PL
T: 0117 973 6606
E: chrisgrosearchitectsltd@tinyworld.co.uk
A full architectural service for clients requiring environmentally conscious solutions primarily in the residential field: one-off houses, small residential developments, major domestic refurbishment, eco-retrofit, conversion and extension, using passive solar energy, ecologically sound materials and renewable energy technology.

HALLETT POLLARD HILLIAR LTD.
Keith Hallett
The Wool Hall, 12 St. Thomas Street, Bristol BS1 6JJ
T: 0117 910 5200
E: hallett.pollard@woolhall.co.uk
Buildings count as "Green" when they meet ecological, community and economic criteria. We are strong on Eco-design. We lead the field in urban and rural regeneration through community-driven initiatives. We only work on projects which support the local economy.

QUATTRO DESIGN ARCHITECTS
Hugh Nettelfield
1 Great George Street, Bristol BS1 5RR
T: 0117 929 9672
E: hugh@quattro-bristol.co.uk
www.quattrodesign.co.uk
Quattro is a talented architectural practice committed to designing buildings which enhance the local environment both physically and socially we have built a reputation for creating innovative designs through close collaboration with users and clients within tight financial guidelines.

SOUTHPOINT
Jerry Evans
45 The Dell, Westbury-on-Trym BS9 3UF
T: 0845 644 6639
E: mail@southpoint.co.uk
www.southpoint.co.uk
Sound, practical advice is backed up by a track record in designing environmentally conscious new buildings, alterations and extensions. Our flexible service can vary from a few hours of consultation, to taking your first idea through to a completed project.

ARCHITECTURAL SERVICES

WHITE DESIGN
Linda Farrow
The Proving House, 101 Sevier St., Bristol BS2 9LB
T: 0117 954 7333
E: linda@white-design.co.uk
www.white-design.co.uk
We design beautiful, affordable spaces that help people live and work more healthily and sustainably. Our consultancy helps clients integrate this ethos within their daily practice.

BUILDING CONTRACTOR

CUBIT CONSTRUCTION
Jim Smith
20 Oakdene Avenue, Bristol BS5 6QQ
T: 0117 958 5139 / 07968 331805
E: jim.smith@cubitconstruction.co.uk
www.cubitconstruction.co.uk
As a small, general construction company with 30 years experience, we undertake projects which are environmentally friendly. This might include, solar heating and rain water collection units. We seek to source local, sustainable materials wherever possible.

FABRICK LTD.
Simon Reid
198 Cheltenham Road, Bristol BS6 5QZ
T: 0117 904 1868
E: fabrick@ukonline.co.uk
www.fabrick.co.uk
A strong team of 18 people and excellent reputation. General building works, with emphasis on recycling and use of ecologically sound practices and materials. Able to advise clients on an ecological approach. Clients: schools hotels shops many homes some new build and some development.

CONSULTING STRUCTURAL ENGINEER

STRUCTURES ONE LTD.
Ian Duncan
7 Barossa Place, Bristol BS1 6SU
T: 0117 945 9225
E: ian.duncan@structures1.com
www.structures1.com
We are a design office which has earned a good reputation over the last fifteen years for designing sustainable building structures and drainage systems. An increasing volume of our work uses timber, both traditional and contemporary, with projects large and small.

EDUCATIONAL

ECOHOME AT CREATE
Hannah Durrant
Smeaton Road, Bristol BS1 6XN
T: 0117 925 0505
E: hannah_durrant@bristol-city.gov.uk
www.bristol-city.gov.uk/create
The Ecohome is a demonstration project open to the general public and professionals, 12—3pm on weekdays. It showcases efficient and sustainable design and materials. Trails on building, DIY and eco-living, video and resource library. School groups by arrangement.

PUBLISHER/ BOOKSELLER

ECO-LOGIC BOOKS
Peter Andrews
10 Picton Street, Bristol BS6 5QA
T: 0117 942 0165
E: info@eco-logicbooks.com
www.eco-logicbooks.com
Eco-Logic specialises in books and other materials that promote practical solutions to environmental issues. We have a large section on "green building" and alternative energy. Our latest publication is on the practical use of natural paints and finishes (ISBN 189923313X).

QUANTITY SURVEYOR

GLEEDS
Terry Langdon
1400 Bristol Parkway North,
Bristol BS34 8YU
T: 0117 317 3200
E: terry.langdon@gleeds.co.uk
www.gleeds.com
International Management and
Construction Consultants,
28 offices world-wide, over
1000 staff. Services: Project
Management Cost Engineering
Cost Management, Building
Surveying, Dispute Services,
Financial Services, Funders
Representative, Health and
Safety, IT Services, PFI/PPP/Prime
Consultants, Planned Maintenance
Consultancy, Development
Management.

SOLAR POWER INSTALLER

IMAGINATION SOLAR
Jon Walker
10-12 Pictón Street, Bristol
BS6 5QA
T: 0845 458 3168
E: enquiries@imaginationsolar.com
www.imaginationsolar.com
Simple, effective, affordable
solar water heating systems for
domestic, commercial, industrial,
community sectors. Supplied and
installed via an extensive, national
network of agents. Accredited
under Governments 'Clear Skies'
grant programme.

SOLAR THERMAL INSTALLER

SOUTHERN SOLAR LTD.
Luke Hutchison
48 Yeomeads, Long Ashton,
Bristol BS41 9BQ
T: 0845 456 1706
E: luke@southernsolar.co.uk
www.southernsolar.co.uk
Covering the SW and SE,
Southern Solar design and install
renewable energy systems for
domestic, commercial and social
housing clients. These include
solar thermal, solar electric, solar
heated swimming pools, rainwater harvesting, ground source
heat pumps and small-scale wind
systems.

TIMBER FRAMER

WESTWIND OAK BUILDINGS LTD.
Rupert Newman
Unit 1, Laurel Farm, Nr. Bristol
BS49 4PZ
T: 01934 877317
E: judy@westwindoak.com
www.westwindoak.com
Westwind Oak Buildings specialise
in the design of unique hand-
crafted construction of green oak
frames.

Cornwall

ARCHITECT(S)

ARCO₂ ARCHITECTURE LTD.
Ian Armstrong
Ke-lyn, Marshall Road, Nanstallon,
Bodmin PL30 5LD
T: 01208 832990
E: info@arco2.co.uk
www.arco2.co.uk
ARCO₂ is an award winning RIBA
registered, Cornish based limited
company and honorary members
of the Cornwall Sustainable
Building Trust (CSBT).

INNES ARCHITECTS
Mark Innes
Sunny Bank, Bossiney Lane,
Tintagel PL34 0AU
T: 01840 770242 / 770099
E: mark.innes@which.net
Specialising in Cultural and
Community architecture. Well
researched green design and
energy solutions tailored to client
and site.

ARCHITECTURAL SERVICES

CHARLES GREEN DESIGN
Charles Green
The Studio, Gethsemane, Church
Lane, Redruth TR15 2SH
T: 01209 216964
E: charles@greendsgn.freeserve.
co.uk
Architectural practice committed
to DESIGN-LED energy efficient
and sustainable solutions for small
scale projects. Experience of
designing and building with straw-
bales. Familiar with green oak /
larch structural frames, the use of
reclaimed and recycled materials.

SOLAR DESIGN ASSOCIATES (CORNWALL)
Mike Grigg
29 Gardeners Way, St. Issey
PL27 7RN
T: 01841 540823
E: solatec@aol.com
www.hometown.aol.co.uk/
mikegrigg
Solar Design associates evolved
from a general architectural
practice to promote the use of
renewable energy in buildings. We
can advise on the installation of
passive and active solar heating
systems, heat recovery ventilation
systems, wind generators, etc.

EARTH BUILDERS

COB IN CORNWALL
Adam Weismann Katy Bryce
Higher Boden, Manaccan
TR12 6EN

T: 01326 231 773 /
0778 978 0391
E: info@cobincornwall.com
www.cobincornwall.com
We are ecological builders
specialising in cob building and
associated materials such as
lime renders, washes and earth
plasters. We create and build
new cob houses, cob educational
buildings, garden rooms, garden
courtyards and walls, "Rumford"
earth fireplaces, etc. We also
sensitively restore ancient and
listed bulidings with appropriate
materials.

EDUCATIONAL

CSBT
Paul Bright
Watering Lane Nursery, St. Austell
PL26 6BE
T: 01726 68654
E: paul@csbt.org.uk
www.csbt.org.uk
Cornwall Sustainable Building
Trust gives advice and training
on sustainable building methods.
We aim to raise awareness and so
minimise the effects of construc-
tion on the Cornish and Global
environments and to demon-
strate the benefits of a new
ecological approach to design,
materials, systems and planning.
BRE EcoHomes Assessors.

LANDSCAPE ARCHITECT

GARDEN DESIGN
Barbara Tremain
Penbaron, Nancledra, Penzance
TR20 8NB
T: 01736 740547
E: barbaratremain40@hotmail.com
Garden Design- Horticulture-
Permaculture- Eco-Village
Design-Eco Journalist and
Photographer-Consultation,
Design, Planting and Management

TIMBER FRAMER

PIONEER ENVIRONMENTAL BUILDERS
Tim Stirrup
Mount Pleasant Ecological,
Porthtowan Park, Truro TR4 8HL
T: 01209 891500
E: enquiries@pioneercabins.co.uk
www.pioneercabins.co.uk
Sustainable, energy efficient
construction. Mainly timber homes
and barns and commissions.

Devon

ARCHITECT(S)

BEDFORD AND JOBSON ARCHITECTS
Barry Jobson
Studio A, Foxhole, Dartington
TQ9 6EB
T: 01803 840240
E: barryjobsonriba@btopenworld.com
www.architecturedevon.co.uk
A RIBA registered practice with particular expertise in conservation work and the use of sustainable materials such as cob, lime, green oak and thatch, as well as new build and conversion work focusing on high levels of insulation.

TOM FOSTER ARCHITECTURE
Tom Foster
Holeland Farm, Dunsford, Exeter
EX6 7DJ
T: 01647 24436
E: fostertom@clara.co.uk
www.space-and-light.co.uk
My mission is to create space and light for modern living and working, whether in new build or within enjoyed, respected and transformed old buildings, all in the greenest and most geomantic possible way, anywhere in the West Country.

ARCHITECTURAL SERVICES

CLIVE JONES
Clive Jones
141 Irsha Street, Appledore,
Bideford EX39 1RY
T: 01237 421262
E: clive.jones@which.net
Environmentally friendly energy conscious healthy design.

FRANK RUSSELL MBIAT
Frank Russell
3 Rose Cottages, Lydford,
Okehampton EX20 4AW
T: 01822 820467
E: russell_frank@hotmail.com
Architectural Technologist with experience of many forms of building types, specialising in Conservation of Historic and Listed Buildings.

PCA
Phil Collins
Langapark, Dunsford, Exeter
EX6 7HE
T: 01647 253084
E: philco@globalnet.co.uk
An environmental design practice specialising in small and medium scale building design, building conservation, ecological and landscape design projects. Special expertise in environmentally sensitive building and landscape design, alternative technologies and the conservation of vernacular buildings.

BUILDING CONTRACTOR

JACK-IN-THE-GREEN
David Tyler
Church Cottage, Puddington,
Tiverton EX16 8LW
T: 01884 861095
Specialising in lime rendering and plastering, cob, stonework, and roofing in the Devon area. We undertake newbuild and repair work to old buildings. Recent projects include barn conversions and repair of cob buildings.

EARTH BUILDERS

ABEY SMALLCOMBE
Jill Smallcombe
West Ford Farm, Cheriton Bishop,
Exeter EX6 6HP
T: 01647 24145
E: jackie@abeysmallcombe.com
www.abeysmallcombe.com
We design and create traditional and contemporary cob buildings and sculptures, including the cob shelter at the Eden Project and art for the Met Office. We run practical courses on cob construction in both repairs and new build.

EDUCATIONAL

UNIVERSITY OF PLYMOUTH
Steve Goodhew
Drake Circus, Plymouth PL4 8AA
T: 01752 233664
E: sgoodhew@plymouth.ac.uk
www.plymouth.ac.uk/
The Environmental Building Group at Plymouth run three environmentally themed construction degrees. BSc (Hons) Building Surveying and the Environment, Construction Management and Environmental Surveying degrees. Our new Sustainable Construction Masters course (available both full and part-time) will be starting in September 2005 *(subject to approval).

PROJECT MANAGEMENT

WORKING WOODLANDS HOLDINGS LIMITED
Caroline Harrison
Barton Farmhouse, Dartington Hall, Totnes TQ9 6ED
T: 01803 867891
E: workingwoodlands@btconnect.com
Providing a "one-stop shop" for those looking for timber/wood products sourced from South West woodlands and local growers, harvesting contractors, hauliers, processors, manufacturers, craftspeople or retailers. Also offering seedcorn grants and field delivered support for the Cornish forestry and timber industry.

SOLAR POWER (PV) INSTALLER

BECOSOLAR
Rob Adams
8-10 Speedwell Units, Dartmouth
TQ6 9SZ
T: 01803 833636
E: radams@becosolar.com
www.becosolar.com
BECOSOLAR are BP Solar Project Partners and Distributors in UK and Ireland. We specialise in PV systems, manufacturing our own range of controllers and building custom power supplies for industrial, commercial and domestic uses. Beco are DTI / EST and ISO9001:2000 accredited.

TIMBER FRAMER, TRADITIONAL

CARPENTER OAK LTD.
Adam Milton
The Framing Yard, East Cornworthy TQ9 7HF
T: 01803 732900
E: admin@carpenteroak.com
www.carpenteroak.com
Carpenter Oak Ltd. specialises in the construction of new oak frames for any building where those who demand quality can appreciate the traditional values of durability and craftsmanship combined with energy-saving potential and integration with modern.

Dorset

ARCHITECT(S)

ECOPRIZE!
Philip Jordan
116 Monmouth Road, Dorchester
DT1 2DG
T: 01305 268583
E: philip.jordan@member.riba.org
Aims to sustainably develop accessible, elegant, equitable, enduring & economic environments through discussion, models, IT/other media and resources including: Community LA21, Architecture/surveying and asset reviews, theatre design, services and film work.

ARCHITECTURAL SERVICES

ARCHITECTURAL DESIGNS
Stuart Waite
Station Road, Stalbridge
DT10 2RQ
T: 01963 364364
E: stuart.waite@btconnect.com
www.architecturaldesigns.co.uk

Architectural Designs is a small practise which aims to assist clients in providing designs that have as low an impact on the surroundings as possible and detailing to lower the heat use within the structure.

DEVELOPER

CLIPPER ESTATES LTD.
Stuart Black
Old Fire Station, Ludbourne Road, Sherborne
DT9 3NJ
T: 01935 817220
E: clipper.estates@virgin.net
Specialist in development of genuinely sustainable buildings and groups of buildings including Co-housing (urban and rural) and rural regeneration in S.W. England.

THE RURAL RENEWAL COMPANY
Alan Heeks
Cole Street Farm, Cole Street Lane, Gillingham SP8 5JQ
T: 07976 602787
E: data@workingvision.com
www.ruralrenewal.co.uk
RRC is creating a sustainable education centre and eco-village in North Dorset. It will include a visitor centre, eco-hotel, social enterprises, co-housing for 200+ people and community facilities. Partner organisations, investors and potential residents are welcome to contact us.

SOLAR POWER INSTALLER

ACE-ECO LTD.
Alan Seviour
14A High Street, Shaftesbury
SP7 8JG
T: 01747 858852
E: alan@aceplumb.co.uk
www.ace-eco.co.uk
Ace-Eco Ltd., design and install solar heating and rainwater harvesting systems. We provide a full consultancy service for eco-friendly plumbing and heating projects including biomass, ceramic stoves and underfloor heating.

SOLAR THERMAL INSTALLER

SOLEX ENERGY LTD.
Peter Broatch
The Cartshed, Church Lane, Osmington, Dorset, Weymouth
DT3 6EW
T: 01305 837223
E: info@solexenergy.co.uk
www.solexenergy.co.uk
Solex Energy has developed, and manufactures, a new type of visually attractive solar thermal system - solar roof tiles and slates. These products enable whole roof faces to act as solar collectors, with large usable heat outputs.

SUSTAINABLE DEVELOPMENT CONSULTANT

FUTURE CREATE
Jon Dowty
2nd Floor, 107 Bournemouth Road, Poole BH14 9HR
T: 01202 747110
E: info@futurecreate.org.uk
www.futurecreate.org.uk
A sustainable development practice committed to sustainable design, construction and living. From project inception to post project appraisal, we provide an integrated package of services with expertise in stakeholder engagement, planning and design assessment, renewable energy, EcoHomes Assessment and more.

Gloucestershire

ARCHITECT(S)

ANDREW BEARD ARCHITECTS
Andrew Beard
The Bakery, Cowle Road, Stroud
GL5 2JR
T: 01453 757485
E: a.beard@virgin.net
Working with ecological principles of design and construction, we place special emphasis on an organic relationship between the form of a building, its environment and the human activities it encloses, thus enriching the lives of those who use it.

ARCHITYPE
Jonathan Hines
The Studio, Belle Vue Centre, Cinderford GL14 2AB
T: 01594 825775
E: jono@architype.co.uk
www.architype.co.uk
Architype, established 20 years ago, is one of the UK's leading sustainable architectural practices. Architype combines cutting edge innovation with a long track record of successful buildings. Architype works throughout the UK from expanding offices in London and the West.

D. STAINER-HUTCHINS ARCHITECTS LTD.
Dan Stainer-Hutchins
5 Bridge Street, Nailsworth
GL6 0AA
T: 01453 839121
E: info@dstainer-hutchinsarchitects.co.uk
www.dstainer-hutchinsarchitects.co.uk
Chartered Architects offering a full range of services, specialising in ecological design, historic conservation and community architecture.

FDH LIMITED
Rob Johnson
43 High Street, Lydney GL15 5DD
T: 01594 843154
E: rob@fdharchitecture.com
www.fdharchitecture.com
FDH actively promotes a participative approach to design to produce sustainable buildings with a minimised impact on the natural environment. We encourage the use of natural, low-energy materials, the recycling of resources and simple practical solutions to environmental design.

HEATH AVERY ARCHITECTS
David Heath
3 Bath Mews, Bath Parade,
Cheltenham GL53 0EX
T: 01242 529169
E: architects@heath-avery.co.uk
www.heath-avery.co.uk
Established in 1980, we are
architects committed to environmentally and socially responsible
design with expertise in education, housing and Brownfield sites.
Our experience also encom-
passes complex Conservation and
Planning issues.

QUATTRO DESIGN ARCHITECTS
Pauline Dewhirst
Bearland Lodge, Gloucester
GL1 2HT
T: 01452 424234
E: pauline@quattro-glos.co.uk
www.quattrodesign.co.uk
Quattro is a talented architectural
practice committed to designing
buildings which enhance the local
environment both physically and
socially we have built a reputation
for creating innovative designs
through close collaboration with
users and clients within tight
financial guidelines.

ARCHITECTURAL SERVICES

EDWARD MOSS
Edward Moss
Conifers, Long Newnton, Tetbury
GL8 8RH
T: 07969 641037
E: emoss456@yahoo.co.uk
Involved with a community field
project which is being developed
into community space, incorporat-
ing organic farming, permaculture,
and natural sustainable building
and an open air theatre.

STONEHEALTH LIMITED
Julia Fairchild
Bowers Court, Broadwell, Dursley
GL11 4JE
T: 01453 540600
E: info@stonehealth.com
www.stonehealth.com
Stonehealth, is a leading supplier
to the conservation/restoration
trades, best recognised for the
supply of the Jos/TORC and DOFF
systems. Systems frequently
specified as "the methods" for
use on all calibre and scales of
projects, along with many others
from the range of products that
they alone supply.

BUILDING CONTRACTOR

THE SUSTAINABLE BUILDING COMPANY LTD.
Stephen Rush
12 Folly Rise, Stroud GL5 1UX
T: 01453 762185 / 07976 737410
E: ecowarrior@ukonline.co.uk
www.thesustainablebuildingco.
co.uk
The Sustainable Building
Company is an environmentally
and client friendly design and
building service. We create
healthy living spaces with care
for the environment using environ
friendly, natural, sustainable and
locally produced or recycled
materials and renewable energy
systems.

HEATING ENGINEER

PETER ELY PLUMBING AND HEATING
Peter Ely
Woodland Cottage, Jacks Green ,
Sheepscombe, Stroud GL6 7RA
T: 07779 099320
E: peter.ely@talk21.com
Domestic heating engineer Corgi
and Oftec registered. Also Solar
and woodfueled heating systems.

LANDSCAPE ARCHITECT

CLASSIC LANDSCAPES
John Connell
The Ridings, Wick Lane,
Stinchcombe, Dursley GL11 6BD
T: 01453 548058
E: classic@netcomuk.co.uk
www.classic-landscapes.co.uk
We are general landscapers,
our range of work includes:
groundworks, fencing, regular
maintenance, hedgelaying, soft
and hard landscaping.

MARKETING AND MEDIA

GRAHAM BOND VISUAL COMMUNICATIONS
Graham Bond
85 Barrowfield Road, Stroud
GL5 4DG
T: 01453 758279
E: studio@gbvisual.com
www.gbvisual.com
Services specialising in the
promotion of environmen-
tally sustainable projects and
products, including: Design for
print: brochures, product data,
catalogues; Web site design:
marketing, and maintenance;
Creative graphics: corporate
ID, logos, illustrations, digital
imaging.

PAINTING AND DECORATING

AURO UK
Bryan Roe
Holbrook Garage, Bisley GL6 7BX
T: 01452 772020
E: sales@auroorganic.co.uk
www.auroorganic.co.uk
Auro paints, made exclusively
from wood resins, plant chemicals
and earth pigments, promoting a
healthy atmosphere in the home.
With 100% compostibilty of our
process waste, we demonstrate a
total commitment to the environment.

SOLAR THERMAL INSTALLER

GREENSHOP SOLAR LTD.
Eddie Tottle
Bisley, Stroud GL6 7BX
T: 01452 770629
E: solar@greenshop.co.uk
www.greenshop.co.uk
Local installer of solar thermal
hot water systems. UK Distributor
of Consolar Solar Thermal Stores
and Evacuated tube collectors.
Supplier of insulation materials, Sunpipes and other energy
conservation products.

SUSTAINABLE DEVELOPMENT CONSULTANT

THE GREEN SHOP
Bryan Roe
Cheltenham Road, Bisley GL6 7BX
T: 01452 770629
E: enquiries@greenshop.co.uk
www.greenshop.co.uk
We offer sales and advice on
products for a more sustainable future. Including a host of
different environmentally friendly
paints and wood finishes, sheeps
wool and cellulose based insulation, sunpipes and solar and wind
systems.

Somerset

ARCHITECT(S)

BH ASSOCIATES
Bob Hardcastle
The Studio, 15C Alexandra Road,
Clevedon BS21 7QH
T: 01275 871633
E: bob@bhassocs.co.uk
www.bhassocs.co.uk
Specialising in industrial and
commercial projects in the Bristol
and Somerset area.

ECOLOGIC DESIGN
John Shore
5 Riverside, Wellington TA21 8LG
T: 01823 666177
Architectural design consultants

for low-cost, self-sufficient, timber frame, self build and renovation. Passive solar space and water heating, water conservation, aerobic compost toilet design, wind and solar energy, education and training. Over 30 year's experience with ecological building and wind energy.

MARK ORME ARCHITECTS LTD.
Mark Orme
10 St. John's Square, Glastonbury
BA6 9LJ
T: 01458 830334
E: info@markormearchitects.co.uk
www.markormearchitects.co.uk
Established in 1995 we offer personal, innovative and practical design solutions for new houses, conversions, renovations, community, educational and commercial buildings. We have specialist knowledge in energy efficiency, timber frame construction, sustainable building materials and renewable energy installations.

BUILDING CONTRACTOR

ABLE BUILDERS
Tom Reed
44 Rosehill, Bath BA1 6TH
T: 01225 334172
E: tomablebuilders@btinternet.com
We are a small family firm with over twenty years experience. It is our priority to use reclaimed environmentally sensitive materials and traditional methods. From general maintenance and complete construction projects, to chlorine free, swimming pools, all completed to a high standard.

DESIGN & BUILD

SOUTH WEST ECO-HOMES
Nigel Griffiths
Old Town Hall, Bow Street,
Langport TA10 9PR
T: 01458 259400
E: admin@sustainablehousing.org.uk
www.swecohomes.co.ok
SWEH is the sister company of the Somerset Trust for Sustainable Development. Its purpose is to build real life examples of sustainable housing in the South West to show how sustainable building can work in the private sector without subsidy.

ENVIRONMENTAL BUSINESS CONSULTANT

SUSTAIN LTD.
Tobias Parker
4 High Street, Wrington, Bristol
BS40 5QA
T: 01934 863650
E: tobias@Sustain-energy.co.uk
www.sustain-environment.co.uk

Sustain Ltd. is a multi-disciplinary Sustainability Consultancy providing cost effective solutions for public- and private-sector clients in the built environment. We have expertise in areas such as Life Cycle Assessment of Products, Sustainable Energy Technologies and EcoHomes Assessments.

HEATING ENGINEER

SOMERSET COUNTY COUNCIL
Mike Fackrell
County Hall, Taunton TA1 5AX
T: 01823 355310
E: mjfackrell@somerset.gov.uk
www.somerset.gov.uk
The Sustainable Development Group at Somerset County Council is active in developing Green Buildings. This year we completed an accommodation block at Charterhouse which is timber framed, cedar clad, with a sedum roof, wind turbine and wood chip boiler.

LANDSCAPE DESIGNER

MICHAEL LITTLEWOOD
Michael Littlewood
PO Box 25, South Petherton
TA13 5WZ
T: 01460 240168
E: michael@ecodesignscape.co.uk
www.ecodesignscape.co.uk
Bio-engineering, water harvesting, natural waste treatment, bio-energy systems, organic edible production, nature conservation, natural swimming pools. International experience and expertise, Michael can demonstrate how 'Designing in Harmony with Nature' can be used to the advantage of people and the environment, as well as producing considerable financial savings and benefits.

PROJECT MANAGEMENT

JULIAN BROOKS ASSOCIATES
Julian Brooks
1 Townsend, North Perrott
TA18 7SR
T: 01460 77155
E: jb@julianbrooks.com
www.julianbrooks.com
5 years of experience specialising in projects related to sustainable construction (SC). Registered BRE EcoHomes Assessor. Research and written reports on SC. Marketing strategies and PR for SC projects. Project Management. SC workshops and training.

TIMBER FRAMER, TRADITIONAL

GREEN OAK STRUCTURES
James Godden
20 Bushy Coombe Gardens,
Glastonbury BA6 8JT
T: 01458 833420
E: timberframes@greenoakstructures.co.uk
www.greenoakstructures.co.uk
Green Oak Structures specialises in the design and construction of oak and douglas fir timber frames. We build houses, extensions and roofs. Timber is sustainably sourced and frames traditionally jointed off site, then delivered to site, pegged and raised.

THE TIMBER FRAME CO LTD.
Graham Lucas
The Framing Yard, 7 Broadway,
Charlton Adam, Somerton
TA11 7BB
T: 01458 224463
E: admin@thetimberframe.co.uk
www.thetimberframe.co.uk
We design and build traditional and modern quality timber frames using traditional joinery techniques. Our design and build service has catered for frames from large Oak barns to simple low-cost softwood self-build homes, from large corporate clients to private individuals.

Wiltshire

ARCHITECT(S)

MARK ELLERBY ARCHITECT
Mark Ellerby
The Studio, Rookery Cottage,
Uphill, Urchfont, Devizes
SN10 4SB
T: 01380 840800
E: mark.ellerby@virgin.net
Mark Ellerby is an award winning
architect specialising in the
creation of imaginative buildings
and designs that are ecologically
sustainable and cost effective. The
practice has a wide experience
of many project types, espe-
cially Community, Housing and
Education.

STUART RICHMOND ARCHITECTS
Stuart Richmond
13 Bristol Street, Malmesbury
SN16 0AY
T: 01666 826682
E: stuart@fish.co.uk
Extensive research undertaken
using sustainable techniques.
Practicing sustainable living in
the 1970's, working with CAT.
About to embark on a sustainable
project in Wiltshire associated
with a listed building.

BUILDING CONTRACTOR

BAC CONSTRUCTION
Waller Bachler
2 The Cottage, Stockley, Calne
SN11 ONT
T: 01380 850 839
E: info@BACconstruction.co.uk
www.BACconstruction.co.uk
Creative understanding and
professional approach. All aspects
of building work including: New
builds - Extensions - Conversions
- Renovations - Kitchen/bathroom
installations - Loft conversions
- Conservatories - Decking and
pergolas - Roofing ...20 years
experience ... for a competitive
quotation call 07976 422 332 or
01380 850 839

CONSULTING STRUCTURAL ENGINEER

MARK LOVELL DESIGN ENGINEERS
Mark Lovell
6 High Street, Devizes SN10 1AT
T: 01380 724213
E: team@mlde.co.uk
www.mlde.co.uk
MLDE is a structural design
consultancy which specialises
in environmentally friendly and
sustainable projects. MLDE is
experienced in the use of recycled
and low grade material for the
creative re-use within new developments to produce innovative

and inspiring forms.

EDUCATIONAL

ENERGY 21
Jackie Carpenter
The Energy Store, Estate Yard,
Castle Combe, Chippenham
SN14 7HU
T: 01249 782000
E: info@energy21.org.uk
www.energy21.org.uk
Energy 21 is the national network
of grassroots renewable energy
groups.

PROJECT MANAGEMENT

DEGREES OF GREEN
Stephen Parker
Glencairn, 17, South Street,
Corsham SN13 9HB
T: 07785 980 500
E: degreesofgreen@dsl.pipex.com
www.degreesofgreen.co.uk
Sustainable Development
Consultancy Services for housing
new build and refurbishment
projects including EcoHomes,
energy efficiency, renewable
energy and cost advice. Sole
proprietor with over 30 years
construction experience including
successful Clear Skies, PV grant
funding and 1NTEGER project
delivery.

TIMBER FRAMER

CARPENTER OAK AND WOODLAND CO LTD.
Charley Brentnall
Hall Farm, Thickwood Lane,
Colerne, Chippenham SN14 8BE
T: 01225 743089
E: head.office@cowco.biz
www.cowco.biz
From specialist conservation work
on Stirling and Windsor Castle,
to new complete frames for
dwellings, barns, extensions and
outbuildings. The award winning
designers and manufacturers of
bespoke traditional and contemporary timber framed buildings.

Ireland

Dublin

ARCHITECT(S)

SOLEARTH ECOLOGICAL ARCHITECTURE
Mike Haslam
68 Dame Street, Dublin 2
T: 01677 1766
E: info@solearth.com
www.solearth.com
Dublin based architectural
practice working in both the
Republic and in the UK. We
specialise in ecological master-

planning and in healthy, low and
zero energy buildings. Projects
include wetland masterplanning,
housing, visitor centres and work
places.

Mayo

ENERGY CONSULTANT

ANDY WILSON
Andy Wilson
Corrig Sandyhill, Westport
T: 00353 9826281
E: swellos@eircom.net
Welcome to the post fossil fuel
era! I provide a comprehensive
energy evaluation service looking
at all aspects of house design,
domestic energy requirements,
building materials, passive solar,
biomass and geothermal heating
systems. For solutions that don't
cost the earth!

Scotland

Angus

ARCHITECT(S)

WELLWOOD LESLIE ARCHITECTS
Steve Mathewson
Fort Street House, Broughty
Ferry, Dundee DD5 2AB
T: 01382 778829
E: admin@wellwoodleslie.com
www.wellwoodleslie.com
The Practice has experience
across a range of market sectors
through public and private
housing to industrial, health,
educational and commercial
commissions. Our philosophy is
to provide creative, sustainable
design, sound construction detailing and careful cost control to all
clients.

CARPENTER/JOINER

BESPOKE TIMBERWORK
Dave Saville
Dalkilry, Kilry, Blairgowrie
PH11 8HX
T: 01575 560755
E: mail@bespoketimber.co.uk
Timber framing - contemporary
and traditional. Frame design and
consultation.

TIMBER FRAMER

CARPENTER OAK AND WOODLAND CO LTD.
Scott Fotheringham
The Framing Yard, Loch of
Lintrathen, Kirriemuir DD8 5JA
T: 01575 560393
E: enquiries@cowcoscotland.co.uk
www.cowco.biz

From specialist conservation work on Stirling and Windsor Castle, to new complete frames for dwellings, barns, extensions and outbuildings.

Argyll and Bute

ARCHITECT(S)

DAVID SUMSION, ARCHITECT
David Sumsion
East Lodge, Cairndow PA26 8BE
T: 01499 600380
E: david.sumsion@btinternet.com
West Coast architectural practice with long-standing experience in all areas of ecological design. Commitment to high standards within modest budgets. Completed projects include public, commercial and residential buildings. Every project given personal attention by sole practitioner.

Edinburgh

GAIA ARCHITECTS
Howard Liddell
The Monastery, 2 Hart Street Lane, Edinburgh EH1 3RG
T: 0131 557 9191
E: architects@gaiagroup.org
www.gaiagroup.org
Gaia Architects are the oldest ecological design practice in the UK, and have received many design awards over the past two decades. Our experience includes housing, community development, commercial, sports and leisure buildings, project management, feasibility, training and specialist advice.

LOCATE ARCHITECTS
Chris Morgan
30 High Street, Portobello, Edinburgh EH15 1DD
T: 0131 620 0530
E: mail@chrismorgan.fsnet.co.uk
www.locatearchitects.co.uk
Locate Architects is an innovative young practice specialising in contemporary ecological design, tailored to circumstance and budget. Our services range from architectural commissions to technical research, masterplanning, consultancy in construction and sustainable development and lecturing.

MICHAEL LAIRD ARCHITECTS
Roy Milne
5 Forres Street, EH3 6DE
T: 0131 226 6991
E: r.milne@michaellaird.co.uk
www.michaellaird.co.uk
The practice has been committed for many years to sustainable design principles in building design, energy efficiency, responsible material specification and

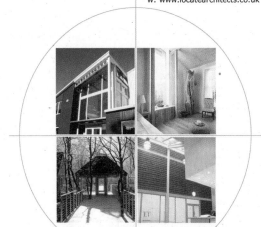

Lo-cate architects
30 high street portobello
edinburgh eh15 1dd

tel: 0131 620 0530
fax: 0131 620 0697
e: mail@chrismorgan.fsnet.co.uk
w: www.locatearchitects.co.uk

Specialists in Contemporary Ecological Design and Sustainable Development

very low energy – renewable supply – passive design
healthy interiors – chemical free - natural materials
low impact construction - local sourcing – site specific solutions
commercial – domestic - community - £50k to £5m

environmental responsibility. Many of the practice's projects demonstrate an innovative approach, recognised by numerous awards for environmentally responsible design.

RICHARD SHORTER ARCHITECT
Richard Shorter
86 Constitution Street, EH6 6RP
T: 0131 625 9100
E: richard.shorter.architect@blueyonder.co.uk
We specialise in environmentally conscious building and conservation work to historic buildings. We have experience in the use of a wide range of natural materials such as green oak and native timbers, clay, lime mortars, stone and wool.

SIMPSON AND BROWN ARCHITECTS
Jenny Humphreys
St. Ninian's Manse, Quayside Street, Edinburgh
EH6 6EJ
T: 0131 555 4678
E: admin@simpsonandbrown.co.uk
www.simpsonandbrown.co.uk
Simpson and Brown aim to create healthy and life enhancing environments, to minimise pollution and resource depletion, and to preserve biodiversity. We understand sustainable construction

methods and systems and specify natural, unprocessed, locally sourced materials.

Fife

EDUCATIONAL

SUSTAINABLE COMMUNITIES INITIATIVES
Paula Cowie
Kinghorn Loch, Fife KY3 9YG
T: 01592 891 884
E: inquiry@sci-scotland.org.uk
www.sci-scotland.org.uk
Sustainable Communities Initiatives works towards building zero waste zero energy communities and have built the first UK Earthship. A fully autonomous self-build eco-building made from car tyres and drinks cans, providing its own heating, electricity, water and sewage treatment.

Glasgow

ARCHITECT(S)

DALLMAN JOHNSTONE ARCHITECTS
Lillian Johnstone
The Studio 24 New Kirk Road,
Bearsden G61 3SL
T: 0141 942 3025
E: dallman-johnstone@dial.pipex.com
Twice chosen to represent Scottish/British architecture globally, for exemplar design, sustainability and energy efficiency. We use natural materials, avoid toxic materials, watch energy life costs and maintenance. (Our office heating and hot water bill for 14 weeks was £1.88).

HLM ARCHITECTS
Dan Hobbs
Riverside House, 260 Clyde Street, Glasgow G1 4JH
T: 0141 2217241
E: dhobbs@hlm.co.uk
www.hlm.co.uk
HLM have developed a dedicated, in-house studio resource to simulate studies that facilitate the impact of design and specification decisions on live projects at all stages with regard to building/environmental performance, facilities design and the associated costs over the life of the building.

JOHN GILBERT ARCHITECTS
John Gilbert
4C1 Templeton Business Centre, Glasgow G40 1DA
T: 0141 551 8383
E: enquiries@johngilbert.co.uk
www.johngilbert.co.uk
We have experience of integrating renewable energy systems (solar, biomass and Geothermal) into new and refurbished housing projects recycling and re-use of materials sustainable urban drainage systems and community projects.

DEVELOPER

JD CONSTRUCTION SERVICES LTD.
William Dunn
44 Ritchie Street, West Kilbride KA23 9HF
T: 01294 823252
E: billy@jdconstruction.co.uk
www.jdconstruction.co.uk
JD construction is aware of the environment around us and work towards sustainable building, components and their impact on our environment are considered during the selection process.

Highland

ARCHITECT AND BUILDER

NEIL SUTHERLAND ARCHITECTS
Neil Sutherland Clachandreggy, Torbreck, Inverness IV2 6DJ
T: 01463 709993
E: neil@organicbuildings.com
www.organicbuildings.com
We actively and consistently deliver a sustainable construction approach. This is primarily through the use of large section home grown timber and a system of building, tied to realistic construction costs, which we have used successfully in our principal projects.

ARCHITECT(S)

FRANK BURSTOW ARCHITECT
Frank Burstow
Old School, Kyle of Lochalsh IV40 8DA
T: 01599 534040
E: frank@burstow.f9.co.uk
Architect based in the Highlands and Islands since 1978. Wide range of projects including private and public housing, leisure and recreational buildings. Design ethos is to fit buildings into landscape using low energy and sustainable solutions within budget and timescale.

Lothian

DICK PEDDIE AND McKAY
Mike Henderson
The Stable Block WCWS, Society Place, West Calder EH55 8EA
T: 01056 873851
E: peddie@globalnet.co.uk
Dick Peddie and McKay is a long established Scottish Practice, which takes a pragmatic approach to the incorporation of ecological principles in its current projects, which range from the conversion of an underground Water Service tank to heather roofs in the Highlands.

Midlothian

ENVIRONMENTAL BUSINESS CONSULTANT

GAIA RESEARCH
Sandy Halliday
The Monastery, Hart Street Lane, Edinburgh EH1 3RG
T: 0131 558 7227
E: research@gaiagroup.org
www.gaiagroup.org
gaia Research provide specialist advice on sustainable design to clients and design teams. This ranges from policy development, brief writing, feasibility studies and design critique to a hand-holding service from inception to handover and beyond. Recent commissions include a new campus development in Scotland, housing, office and school projects.

Moray

ARCHITECT(S)

EDGE ARCHITECTURE AND DESIGN
Nicole Edmonds
Hillview, 167 Findhorn, Forres IV36 3YL
T: 01309 691408
E: edgearch@freenet.co.uk
Innovation and beauty flow from a passionate commitment to efficiency and quality of design with ecological integrity. "Feeling out" the client's real needs, within an agreed budget, and thorough groundwork results in spaces that really work for my clients.

SIMON RICHARDS ASSOCIATES
Simon Richards
Burnbrae, Burgie, Forres IV36 2RN
T: 01309 675766 and 690154
E: simon@ecovillagefindhorn.com
Architect and Development Consultant."Green" residential (houses/studio units) Architect, Co-developer and Architect for the Field of Dreams Project at Findhorn in Scotland, business/finance planning, strategic planning/infrastructure design, procurement and construction management. Timber frame/breathing wall specialist.

BUILDING CONTRACTOR

BUILD ONE LTD.
Mary Fielding
The Park, Findhorn Bay, Forres IV36 3TZ
T: 01309 690123
E: buildone@ukonline.co.uk
We have built over 20 houses to an ecological specification within the eco-village at Findhorn. We have constructed individually designed homes, terraced housing and holiday chalets, using conventional timber frame, exposed post and beam and straw bale techniques.

Ross-shire

ARCHITECT AND BUILDER

NORTH WOODS CONSTRUCTION LTD.
Bernard Planterose
Leckmelm Wood, Ullapool

IV23 2RH
T: 01854 613040
E: northwoods@leckmelm.demon.co.uk
Specialists in bolted post and beam construction utilizing Scottish grown Douglas fir structure and European larch cladding. Complete planning, design and build service for houses, studios, workshops. Partner in Northern European 'Brettstapel' (massive timber) research project with Gaia Architects.

THATCHER

WILDLAND SERVICES
Brian Wilson
Achlunachan, Inverbroom, Ullapool, by Garve, Inverness
IV23 2SA
T: 01854 655243
E: brian@wildlandservices.fsnet.co.uk
Twenty years' experience in building with traditional natural materials in vernacular and modern styles. Specialist in highland dry-stone building, and thatching in traditional materials such as heather, bent and bracken. (also Training Courses).

Wales

Cardiff

EDUCATIONAL

ROUNDED DEVELOPMENTS
Peter Draper
32 Splott Road, Cardiff CF24 2DA
T: 029 2040 3399
E: info@rounded-developments.org.uk
www.rounded-developments.org.uk
Rounded Developments is a not-for-profit organisation dedicated to raising community awareness of sustainable development principles in design and construction. Its Information centre / shop allows community groups and the public to access architects.

RESEARCHER

DAVIUS INCORPORATES
Paulus "Jory" Thurlbeck
9 Cranbrook Street, Cathays
CF24 4AL
T: 029 2041 2866 / 07715 106623
E: Jory@davius.co.uk, Jory@davius.co.uk
www.davius.co.uk
Davius researches and networks smaller Sustainable Development projects together. This entails small scale Eco-builds, education for all, community regeneration and social research, informal/

social economy and small scale renewables. Another arm of company deals with Environmental Policies for SME's.

Carmarthenshire

BUILDING CONSULTANT

M.V. QUARTERMAINE
M.V. Quartermaine
1 Clos Pant-y-Celyn, Llandovery
SA20 0AG
T: 01550 720835
Sustainable building consultant with 30 year's experience in the protection and repair of our local vernacular traditions.

CARPENTER/JOINER

ZAVOSKY
Tim Wade
Gorof Melyn, Rhandirmwyn
SA20 0NN
T: 01550 760386
E: tim@aeron.demon.co.uk
www.zavosky.co.uk
A small woodworking business, building hand made wooden buildings- garden offices, Barns, chapels, tree houses,rustic retreats, using locally sourced timber. Providing architectural joinery, Box sash windows specialist. Furniture for the house and garden, Wood carving and turning.

PUBLISHER/ BOOKSELLER

GREEN BUILDING PRESS
Keith Hall
PO Box 32, Llandysul SA44 5ZA
T: 01559 370798
E: info@newbuilder.co.uk
www.newbuilder.co.uk
The Green Building Press are publishers of The Green Building Bible and Building for a Future magazine.

Ceredigion

ARCHITECT(S)

HESS-KINCAID ASSOCIATES
Chris Hess
Glanrhyd, Lampeter SA48 8LJ
T: 01570 493408
E: info@hess-kincaid.co.uk
www.hess-kincaid.co.uk
SERVICES OFFERED: CAD Services, Competition Entries, Design Services and Full Architectural Service, Energy / Environmental Expertise, Feasibility Studies, Furniture Design, Graphic Design and Illustration, Interior Design, Listed Building Advice, Model Making, Party Wall Advice, Project

Management, Quantity Surveying, Refurbishment, Self Build, Valuations.

Gwynedd

ADAM AND FRANCES VOELCKER ARCHITECTS
Frances Voelcker
Pant Glas Uchaf, Pant Glas, Garndolbenmaen
LL51 9DQ
T: 01766 530657
E: frances@voelckerarchitects.co.uk
www.voelckerarchitects.co.uk
All buildings have an effect on our environment. We try to persuade clients to be responsible in this respect, and to work with them to do our part, little as it may be, in conserving the Earth's resources and minimising our harmful effects.

CARPENTER/JOINER

ENVIRO-BUILD
Kenneth Dodd
Joiners Workshop, The Green, Bala LL23 7NH
T: 01678 520 035
E: ken@enviro-build.co.uk
www.enviro-build.co.uk
Diverse carpentry and joinery / building activities with emphasis on recycling, and pollution reduced materials and methodologies. Restoration specialists. Design and build. Shopfitting. Bespoke and Architectural Joinery.

Mid Glamorgan

BUILDING CONTRACTOR

NATURAL BUILD
Caz Phillips
T: 07813 685027
E: treemajik@wildmail.com
Through natural building techniques (cob, straw, timber etc.), we empower people to realise creative abundance in our natural environment and within ourselves. We work with individuals, groups, schools building artistic and practical structures to encourage trust, co-operation and respect. Also contact Mike Pattinson 07931 598675
mikepattinson@wildmail.com

Monmouthshire

BUILDING SURVEYOR

ADRIAN BIRCH ASSOCIATES
Adrian Birch
Ridgeway, Mill Hill, Brockweir, Chepstow NP16 7NF
T: 01291 689812
E: Adrian.Birch@uwe.ac.uk

263

Reports on all types of property for purchase, conversion or refurbishment. Energy/access audits. Experienced environmental designer. Feasibility studies, drawings, specifications, for new-build and refurbishment. Project management and cost consultancy. Planning applications, appeals. Planning Supervisor. Feng shui, dowsing reports.

North Wales

BUILDING CONTRACTOR

G AND J HADDOW LTD.
Julie Haddow
The Coach House, Llanfwrog,
Ruthin LL15 2AN
T: 0798 960 0525
E: jhaddow@callnetuk.com
Conservation and Restoration of Traditional Buildings. Specialists in the use of lime for both the repair of historic buildings and ecological new builds.

Pembrokeshire

ARCHITECT(S)

JULIAN BISHOP - ARCHITECT
Julian Bishop
Danygarn, Mountain West,
Newport SA42 0QX
T: 01239 821150
E: mail@julianbishop-architect.co.uk
www.julianbishop-architect.co.uk
Dedicated to Sustainable Architecture, building design, consultancy and lecturing since 1982. Private domestic, full service or self build, community, health, commercial and industrial work undertaken, to either new or existing, and listed buildings. Fusing sustainability with traditional techniques.

SOLAR THERMAL INSTALLER

ALTERNATIVES WALES LTD.
Colin Luker
Geulan Goch, Eglwyswrw
SA41 3SE
T: 0845 4580335
E: alternatives.solar@virgin.net
www.solarenergywales.co.uk
Installed or DIY solar hot water. Evacuated Tube (Thermomax and Schott) or Flat Plate (FILSOL) collector systems. Low cost

swimming pool systems by SunStar available. Clear-Skies fully approved installer.

Powys

ARCHITECT(S)

MILSOM ARCHITECTS
Jan Milsom
1 Riverside, Crickhowell NP8 1AY
T: 01873 811291
E: jan@milsom-architects.co.uk
www.milsom-architects.co.uk
Milsom Architects are a medium size projects that works on residential and commercial schemes. These include new builds, conversions and restorations. We provide a full service from design, through construction to completion and will utilise any sustainable methods possible.

NICHOLAS SALT
20 Bethel Street
Llanidloes SY18 6BS
T: 01686 412 417
E: nicksalt@midwales.com
Nicholas Salt is an architectural design specialist.

ARCHITECTURAL SERVICES

T/A NATURAL SOLUTIONS
Andrew Warren
20 Bethel Street, Llanidloes SY18 6BS
T: 01686 412653
E: andy@natsol.co.uk
www.natsol.co.uk
Design of environmentally sound buildings, particularly timber frame using naturally durable and sustainably sourced timber. Design, manufacture and installation of urine separating, single and twin vault toilets.

EDUCATIONAL

CENTRE FOR ALTERNATIVE TECHNOLOGY
Jacinta Macdermot
Pantperthog, Machynlleth SY20 9AZ
T: 0845 3308373 and 01654 705989
E: info@cat.org.uk
www.cat.org.uk
Europe's leading eco-centre, with information on renewable energy, environmental building, energy efficiency, organic growing and alternative sewage systems.

Visitor centre, publications, mailorder, education, consultancy, residential courses, membership and free information service.

HEATING ENGINEER

JOHN CANTOR HEAT PUMPS LTD.
John Cantor
Pendraw'r Llan, Llanwrin, Machynlleth SY20 8QH
T: 01650 511575
E: johncantor@heatpumps.co.uk
www.heatpumps.co.uk
We have been involved with the design and installation of a variety of heat pump systems since 1980. We currently provide ground source installations in mid Wales, troubleshooting and modifications. We also supply very high efficiency heat recovery ventilation units.

THE VERY EFFICIENT HEATING CO.
Chris Laughton
Old Station, Machynlleth SY20 8BL
T: 01654 700324
E: enquiries@effco.co.uk
www.effco.co.uk
Independent Heating Engineers specialising in solar water heating, wood log boilers and wood pellets boilers. Also qualified in gas and solid fuel. On-site contracting, design, consultancy, technical author, training and expert witness work always considered.

INTERIOR DESIGNER

R.E.D INTERIOR ARCHITECTURE
Yonnie Kwok-Pickles
Ty-Joyo, Graig Fach, Machynlleth SY20 8BD
T: 01654 703622
E: yonnie@onetel.com
(website under construction)
Innovative and contemporary. Our design process is environment, aesthetic, health and feng shui conscious. We strive to create, through forms, space, colours and materials, functional interior architecture that brings senses to the spirit and delights to the soul. Award-winning (Asia Pacific) portfolio.

MARKETING AND MEDIA

CYBERIUM
David Thorpe
Glanydon, Corris SY20 9SH
T: 01654 761570
E: david@cyberium.co.uk
Communication is our game. We use our long experience of environmental affairs to render them engaging and absorbing for multiple audiences. We create environmental calculators, animation, video, and software and we

design accessible and attractive web sites. We also produce environmental journalism.

TIMBER FRAMER, TRADITIONAL

FRAMEWORKS
Paul Thomas
Trewalter farm Trefeinon, Brecon
LD3 0PS
T: 01874 658586
E: paul.thomas99@btinternet.com
www.oak-frameworks.co.uk
Frameworks is a company based in the Brecon Beacons national park specialising in the manufacture of Traditional Timber-framed buildings and structures using time honoured methods. Frames are designed, constructed and repaired using sustainably sourced Green Oak and other Timbers.

Swansea

BUILDING CONTRACTOR

JADE CONSTRUCTION AND RESTORATION
Dave Owen
9 Furzeland Park, Swansea
SA2 8HP
T: 0785 561 9942
E: jaderes123@aol.com

Many year's experience of working with traditional and natural materials such as lime. Comprehensive, reliable and trustworthy building service specialising in the sympathetic repair and restoration of period/vernacular buildings and structures in South and West Wales. Manufacturers of quality, bespoke joinery incorporating period detailing. Lime work consultants. Renewable energy advice and installation.

West Glamorgan

ARCHITECT AND BUILDER

GILLARD ASSOCIATES
Alan Gillard
7 Kemps Covert St. Donats,
Llantwit Major CF61 1YZ
T: 01446 794082
E: alangillard@hotmail.com
www.gillardassociates.co.uk
Architectural practice specialising in an holistic approach to environmental design using passive solar and heat storage techniques.

Applied to new and existing buildings these concepts reduce energy use, enhance comfort, and promote healthy lifestyles.

ARCHITECT(S)

AIR ARCHITECTURE
Robin Campbell
1 Brynmill Terrace, Swansea
SA2 0BA
T: 01792 465584
E: robin.campbell@ntlworld.com
www.airarchitecture.co.uk
Innovative design for environmentally-sensitive buildings with site assessment, orientation and maximisation of space the main aims, utilising renewable energies, local / recycled materials where possible. Current projects include arts, leisure and new low energy dwellings.

Products and Trade Organisations

AIR LEAKAGE SPECIALISTS

CPC RETROTEC
Paul Jennings
Units 7-8, Simmonds Buildings,
Bristol Road, Hambrook, Bristol
BS16 1RY
T: 0117 957 0670
E: paul.jennings@retroteceurope.
co.uk
www.cpcretrotec.co.uk
CPC Retrotec helps builders
deliver airtight, effectively ventilated buildings. Design reviews
and on-site inspections identify
essential modifications and
remedial works. Acceptance air
leakage testing to TM23 or other
standards is then undertaken.
Training and equipment hire also
provided.

BUILDERS MERCHANT

EBC UK LTD
Tony Bell
Unit 16 Old Brewery Yard,
Worksop, Nottinghamshire
S80 2DE
T: 01909 479276
E: Rob@ebcuk.f9.co.uk
www.e-b-c-uk.com
Suppliers of recycled roofing and
cladding products.

EARTH AND REED LTD
Christopher North
48-50 High Street, Needham
Market, Suffolk IP6 8AP
T: 01449 722255
E: info@earth-and-reed.co.uk
www.earth-and-reed.co.uk
Environmentally responsible
building / decorating materials.
Distributor for Natural Building
Technologies, Thermafleece,
Holkham Linseed Oil paints and
EarthBorn clay paints. Wide
range of Earth and Reed mineral
pigments.

LINCOLNSHIRE LIME
Shaun Evans
Northfield Farm, Dam Lane,
Thornton Curtis, Lincolnshire
DN39 6XN
T: 01469 531227
E: limelincs@btinternet.com
www.lincolnshirelime.co.uk
Manufacturers and distributors of
quality lime products. Suppliers of
environmentally friendly building
and decorating products.

NATURAL CERTIFIED PRODUCTS UK PVT LTD
Andrew Given
P.O. BOX 50318, Chiswick, London
W4 5BL
T: 0870 061 3427
E: sales@naturalmaterials.co.uk
www.naturalmaterials.co.uk or try
www.ncpuk.com
Suppliers of paints and finishes,
insulation materials (wool, paper,
Warmcel, wood fibres), FSC
timber, Floor coverings (Pre-
finished timber, wool carpets),
construction boards and clay
plasters, decorating, WC's urinals,
product sourcing services and
mail order facility 24hr Tel/Fax.

OLD HOUSE STORE
Kate Dukes
Hampstead Farm, Binfield Heath,
Henley-on-Thames, Oxfordshire
RG9 4LG
T: 0118 969 7711
E: kate@ijp.co.uk
www.oldhousestore.co.uk
Old House Store is one of the
UK's largest Builders Merchants
specialising in traditional and
ecological products. Their extensive range includes lime mortars
and plasters, earth plasters and
plaster backgrounds, natural
insulations, hand-forged ironmongery and environmentally-friendly
paints and waxes.

SAFEGUARD
Hudson Lambert
Redkiln Close, Horsham, West
Sussex RH13 5QL
T: 01403 210204
E: info@safeguardchem.com
www.safeguardchem.com
Safeguard supply the ProBor
range of boron-based timber
treatments and the Oldroyd Xv
waterproofing system for green
roofs and basements. Full details
of these products including
application instructions and CAD
drawings can be found on the
company's website.

TY-MAWR LIME LTD
Nigel Gervis
Ty-Mawr, Llangasty, Brecon,
Powys, LD3 7PJ
T: 01874 658000
E: tymawr@lime.org.uk
www.lime.org.uk
Manufacturer and supplier of
traditional and ecological building
materials including lime plasters,
mortars, paints, insulation,
building boards, oils and waxes.
Also run training courses, accred-
ited by the University of Wales, on
Lime In Building, Lime Plastering,
Natural Paints, Ecological Building
Technologies, Earth Building,
Thatching, Welsh Building Stones
and Styles.

BUILDING BOARDS AND INSULATION SUPPLIER

SKANDA (UK) LTD
Tony Carroll
64/65 Clywedog Road North,
Wrexham Industrial Estate,
Wrexham LL13 9XN
T: 01978 664255
E: info@skanda-uk.com
www.skanda-uk.com
Skanda are the exclusive sole
distributors for Heraklith materials
for the UK and Ireland. Heraklith
manufacture woodwool boards
for external and internal cladding
of timber frame structures
which allows direct application of
renders and plasters. Laminated
insulation boards and Acoustic
Ceiling panels. Heraklith also
manufacture flax insulation.

DECORATING SUPPLIES

F. W. METCALFE AND SONS
David Metcalfe
51/52 High Street, Tring,
Hertfordshire
HP23 5AG
T: 01442 827444
E: sales@tringhardware.co.uk
www.tringhardware.co.uk
Retail traditional hardware shop.
Stockists of Auro organic paints
and Osmo coverings. We have
many organic products for the
garden and a vast array of

products sold loose, including nails, screws, ironmongery, etc.

NATURAL BUILDING AND DECORATING

Kate MacDonald
Leac na Ban, Tayvallich, Lochgilphead, Argyll and Bute PA31 8PF
T: 01546 886341
E: Kate@Natural-Building-Decorating.co.uk
www.Natural-Building-Decorating. co.uk
Consultant and distributor of environmentally friendly building and decorating products, supplying the widest range of ecological materials in Scotland.

NATURAL CERTIFIED PRODUCTS UK PVT LTD

Andrew Given
P.O. Box 50318, Chiswick, London W4 5BL
T: 0870 061 3427
E: sales@naturalmaterials.co.uk
www.naturalmaterials.co.uk or try www.ncpuk.com
Suppliers of Paints and finishes, insulation materials (wool, paper, Warmcel, wood fibres), FSC timber, Floor coverings (Pre-finished timber, wool carpets) , construction boards and clay plasters, decorating, WC's urinals, product sourcing services and mail order facility 24hr Tel/Fax.

OSMO UK LTD

Steve Grimwood
Unit 2 Pembroke Road, Aylesbury, Buckinghamshire HP20 1DB
T: 01296 481220
E: steve@osmouk.com
www.osmouk.com
OSMO UK supplies a range of natural oil based wood finishes for exterior and interior use. We also supply a range of flooring and Garden Buildings, Carports and timber garden products.

FLOORING

FREUDENBERG BUILDING SYSTEMS UK LTD.

Mark Beach
Unit 6 Wycliffe Industrial Park, Leicester Road, Lutterworth LE17 4HG
T: 01455 204 483
E: norauk@freudenberg.com
www.nora.com
Manufacturer of nora rubber floor coverings. The result of experience, competence and a unique material. All floorcoverings produced by Freudenberg are subjected to a strict, regular quality inspection and as such Freudenberg Building Systems is certified to DIN EN ISO 14001 (environmental management).

HEATING APPLIANCES

BEACON STOVES

Ben Graham
Parc Gwair, Capel Iwan, Newcastle Emlyn, Carmarthenshire SA38 9LT
T: 01559 371058
E: info@beaconstoves.co.uk
www.beaconstoves.co.uk
Heart Wood Heating (Part of Beacon Stoves) Design, supply and installation of automated and traditional wood fired heating systems at domestic and small community scale. Appliances include: Log stoves metal and ceramic (retained heat).

ECONERGY LTD

Robert Rippengal
69 Hampton Park, Bristol, BS6 6LQ
T: 0870 054 5554
E: heat@econergy.ltd.uk
www.econergy.ltd.uk
Econergy is a wood energy company. We specify, design and install state-of-the-art wood heating / CHP systems on a turnkey basis and also offer comprehensive operation and maintenance services (including fuel supply).

FOUNDATION FIREWOOD

Heather Jackson
39B Park Farm Industrial Estate, Buntingford, Hertfordshire SG9 9AZ
T: 01763 271271
E: info@fbcgroup.co.uk
www.fbcgroup.co.uk
UK distributors of high efficiency (up to 90%) Baxi wood boilers for log, wood chip and wood pellets. Manufacturers of the ZedFIRE for 24 hour central heating from woodburning stoves.

IESI (UK)

Mark Boocock
PO Box 5035, Cardiff, CF5 1ZB
T: 07976 374403
E: mark.boocock@tekwin.co.uk
www.iesiusa.com
iESi heat pipe under floor heating systems maximise heat transfer and minimise energy consumption in all under floor heating installations. At its core is patented heat pipe technology that reduces manufacturing cost and increases durability relative to other heat pipes.

INSULATION SUPPLIER

ENERGY WAYS

Rob Street
Lordship Cottage, Barwick Road, Standon, Hertfordshire SG11 1PR
T: 01920 821069
E: enquiries@naturalinsulations. co.uk
We sell non-toxic, non-irritant natural insulation at competitive prices. "Warmcel 100" from

recycled paper. "Natalin" flax insulation in rolls. Pure wool insulation in rolls. Information and prices from Energyways.

HUNTON FIBER UK LTD

Jeremy Groom
Rockleigh Court, Rock Road, Finedon, Northamptonshire NN9 5EL
T: 01933 682683
E: admin@huntonfiber.co.uk
www.hunton.no
Made from reclaimed and recycled materials such as sawdust, wood-chips and newspapers, Bitroc and sarket-bitumen impregnated fibreboard provide sheathing and sarking for timber frame structure giving water resistance, breathability and warmth to any building.

JOULESAVE EMES LTD

Thomas Cook
27 Water Lane, South Witham, Grantham, Lincolnshire NG33 5PH
T: 01572 768362
E: sales@joulesave.co.uk
www.ochrewool.com
New sustainable insulation product made from sheep's wool meets/exceeds all best practices for thermal and sound insulation. Absorbs and de-absorbs moisture which helps your house warm up and cool down faster. Ideal for new, refurbished and wood built houses.

KINGSPAN INSULATION LTD

Rachael Morris
Pembridge, Leominster, Herefordshire HR6 9LA
T: 01544 387209
E: rachael.morris@insulation. kingspan.com
www.insulation.kingspan.com
Kingspan Insulation is Europe's largest manufacturer of flexible faced polyurethane and phenolic insulation. As a responsible manufacturer, Kingspan Insulation was the first insulation manufacturer to carry out an LCA on its sustainable Thermal zero ODP insulation.

NATURAL CERTIFIED PRODUCTS UK PVT LTD

Andrew Given
P.O. Box 50318, Chiswick, London W4 5BL
T: 0870 061 3427
E: sales@naturalmaterials.co.uk
www.naturalmaterials.co.uk or try www.ncpuk.com
Suppliers of Paints and finishes, insulation materials (wool, paper, Warmcel, wood fibres), FSC timber, Floor coverings (Pre-finished timber, wool carpets), construction boards and clay plasters, decorating, WC's urinals, product sourcing services and mail order facility 24hr Tel/Fax.

ROCKWOOL LIMITED
Vanessa Hatton
Wern Tarw, Pencoed, Bridgend
CF35 6NY
T: 01656 862621
E: vanessa.hatton@rockwool.co.uk
Rockwool mineral wool is amongst the most environmentally friendly insulation products available. Is supported by recently updated life cycle analysis, critically reviewed by Price Waterhouse Cooper. Our environment-award winning process is efficient and ideally suited to recycling products.

SECOND NATURE UK LTD
Penny Randell
Soulands Gate, Dacre, Penrith, Cumbria CA11 0JF
T: 01768 486285
E: info@secondnatureuk.com
www.secondnatureuk.com
Thermafleece uses wool from British hill sheep to create an exceptionally efficient insulation material in new build and refurbishment projects. Completely safe to handle, breathable, remains effective for the life of the building in which it is installed. BBA certified.

SHEEP WOOL INSULATION LTD.
David Pierce
The Square, Rathdrum, Wicklow
T: +353-404-46100
E: info@sheepwoolinsulation.ie
www.sheepwoolinsulation.ie

Sheep Wool Insulation supplies a range of natural thermal and acoustic insulation products for a variety of building projects. Our products are made from pure new wool, organic pest control and natural rubber preservatives. Our products are certified by EOTA with the CE mark, and approved for use throughout Europe.

JOINERY AND FURNITURE

ECO INTERIORS
Stephen Edwards
39d Effra Road, Brixton, London SW2 1BZ
T: 020 7737 8110
E: stephenedwards61@hotmail.com
www.ecointeriors-uk.com
Eco Interiors offers consultancy, design and construction for domestic and commercial spaces. Furniture, kitchens, retail displays, office work stations and other interior projects produced with expert knowledge and experience of eco-materials and eco-design.

OVATION WINDOWS LIMITED
David Coupe
Unit 14 Tripontium Business Centre, Newton Lane, Rugby, Warwickshire CV23 0TB
T: 01788 860032
E: mail@ovationwindows.co.uk
www.ovationwindows.co.uk

Suppliers of the WindovationSystem, an innovative frame in frame, preglazed and pre-finished solution for house builders and renovators requiring thermally efficient timber windows, doors and conservatories incorporating advanced energy efficient sealed units and environmentally sympathetic preservative treatment and finishing systems.

TAYLOR GARDNER FINE KITCHENS LTD
Jeff Taylor
Stobswood, Bannerdown Road, Batheaston, Bath BA1 7PJ
T: 01225 743975
E: taylor_gardner@dsl.pipex.com
www.taylorgardner.co.uk
Design, construction and installation of bespoke interior domestic cabinetwork, especially kitchens.

MORTGAGES

ECOLOGY BUILDING SOCIETY
Mortgage Team
7 Belton Road, Silsden
Nr Keighley BD20 0EE
T: 0845 6745566
E: loans@ecology.co.uk
Specialists in mortgages for the renovation or conversion of run down and derelict property, from humble terraces to listed buildings. We also provide mortgages for energy and resource efficient

self build homes, organic farmers, ecological businesses, housing co-operatives and small scale eco development finance.

RAINWATER HANDLING

GUSTO CONSTRUCTION LTD
Stephen Wright
Business Centre, Rio Drive, Collingham, Newark, Nottinghamshire NG23 7NB
T: 01636 894900
E: steff@gusto-uk.com
www.freerain.co.uk
Freerain is one of the UK's top performing rainwater harvesting systems for both domestic and commercial applications. Simple to install and reliable in its use. Freerain is independently shown to provide around 50% of typical household water requirements for toilets and other non-potable uses from collected rainwater.

RAINHARVESTING SYSTEMS LTD
Derek Hunt
Holbrook Garage, Cheltenham Road, Bisley, Stroud, Gloucestershire GL6 7BX
T: 01452 772000
E: sales@rainharvesting.co.uk
www.rainharvesting.co.uk
Specialist suppliers of rain-water harvesting equipment for domestic, commercial and industrial applications. UK agents for Wisy rainwater products. Also suppliers of Ifo sanitary ware and Lindab steel guttering.

RENEWABLE POWER

AERODYN SHOREPOWER
John Shore
5 Riverside, Wellington, Somerset TA21 8LG
T: 01823 666177
Wind and Solar energy systems, including lights, controls and inverters. AIR, WHISPER, BERGEY and PROVEN wind turbines, TRACE, BP and ELECSOL systems. Independent servicing consultants and designers - education and training. Over 30 years experience with wind energy and ecological building.

ECO SOLUTIONS UK LTD
Phil Owen
Tynycoed, Heol Waterloo, Penygroes, Llanelli, Carmarthenshire SA14 7RB
T: 01269 844369
E: philowen@ntlworld.com
Independent advice from environ-mental specialists.

NORTH ENERGY ASSOCIATES LTD
Nicola Smith
Old Queen's Head Yard, 7B Oldgate, Morpeth, Northumberland NE61 1PY

T: 01670 516949
E: enquiries@northenergy.co.uk
www.northenergy.co.uk
Renewable energy consultancy. Advice on use of wind, biomass and solar energy for business and community projects. Feasibility studies, architectural services, project management, registered consultants for Clear Skies, the Carbon Trust's energy efficiency programme and Countryside Renewables Initiative. Member of AECB, RIBA, British Biogen.

SUNDANCE RENEWABLES
Jan Cliff
Excal House, Capel Hendre Ind. Est., Ammanford, Carmarthenshire SA18 3SJ
T: 01269 842401
E: info@sundancerenewables. org.uk
www.sundancerenewables.org.uk
We install renewable energy systems and supply gasifying log boilers. We offer consultancy and educational services. We also collect used vegetable oil to process into bio-diesel at our manufacturing plant and run training courses for others to replicate this work.

SPECIFICATION SOFTWARE

NBS
Michael Smith
The Old Post Office, St. Nicholas Street, Newcastle upon Tyne NE1 1RH
T: 0191 2445619
E: michael.smith@theNBS.com
www.theNBS.com
NBS produces the National Building Specification and other related software products for construction industry specifiers. NBS offers a library of clauses for selection and editing that allow green issues to be integrated within project specifications users may also add their own clauses. Clauses are accompanied by extensive guidance.

TIMBER FRAME KITS

BENFIELD ATT
Paul Tappin
Castle Way, Caldicot, Monmouthshire NP26 5PR
T: 01291 437050
E: info@benfieldatt.co.uk
www.benfieldatt.co.uk
A leading Timber Frame Design and Build company, Benfield ATT offer Architectural, Engineering, Manufacture and Erection services all over the UK. All projects undertaken - Home

Extensions, Self-Build, Schools, Hospitals, Developments and Flats. Free Estimates. MD: Timber-Frame Sustainability expert, Dr Michael Benfield.

EDEN FRAME
Trevor Lowis
Mid-Town Barn, Colby, Appleby, Cumbria CA16 6BD
T: 01768 353866
E: trevor@edenframe.com
www.edenframe.com
Design, Manufacture, Supply and Erection of Tradis Masonite.

TIMBER MERCHANTS

CARPENTER OAK AND WOODLAND CO LTD
Elliot Atkinson
Hall Farm, Thickwood Lane, Colerne, Chippenham, Wiltshire SN14 8BE
T: 01225 743089
E: enquiries@cowco.biz
www.cowco.biz
Producer and retailer of traditional hand-made building products, including laths, shingles, pegs, and nails. Also a supplier of square and curved timbers to the timber framing industry and conservation bodies.

HATFIELD HOUSE OAK
Gary Bolton
Hatfield House Estate Office, Hatfield, Hertfordshire AL9 5NQ
T: 01707 287004
E: g.bolton@hatfield-house.co.uk
www.hatfield-house.co.uk
We supply FSC registered English Oak from sustainable sources and European oak. Green oak beams up to 30 foot long. Kiln dried flooring, skirting, architrave, doors, fireplace beams and joinery grade kiln dried oak.

NATURAL CERTIFIED PRODUCTS UK PVT LTD
Andrew Given
P.O. Box 50318, Chiswick, W4 5BL
T: 0870 061 3427
E: sales@naturalmaterials.co.uk
www.naturalmaterials.co.uk or try www.ncpuk.com
Suppliers of Paints and finishes, insulation materials (wool, paper, Warmcel, wood fibres), FSC timber, Floor coverings (Pre-finished timber, wool carpets), construction boards and clay plasters, decorating, WC's urinals, product sourcing services and mail order facility 24hr Tel/Fax.

NORTH HEIGHAM SAWMILLS LTD
Julie Champeney
26 Paddock Street, Norwich, Norfolk NR2 4TW
T: 01603 622978
E: dandjchampeney@freeola.com

www.northheighamsawmills.co.uk
Tongue and groove flooring in local East Anglian and other timbers. Oak beams for house/church/fireplace repairs. Untreated woods for external joinery e.g. larch, oak, chestnut, cedar. 52 species for internal joinery, furniture. Fine quality and service, established 1960.

TRADE ORGANISATIONS

EURISOL
Crispin Dunn-Meynell
PO Box 35084, Camden NW1 4XE
T: 020 7935 8532
E: office@eurisol.com
www.eurisol.com
Eurisol is the trade association representing UK manufacturers of mineral wool insulation.

SOMERSET TRUST FOR SUSTAINABLE DEVELOPMENT
Old Town Hall, Bow Street, Langport TA10 9PR
T: 01458 259400
E: admin@sustainablehousing.org.uk
wwwsustainablehomes.org.uk
STSD offers advice, consultancy, research, exhibitions, conferences and seminars on all aspects of sustainable building. Our mission is to make sustainable building normal rather than exceptional in Somerset by 2010. The Trust has its own programme of development projects undertaken by its sister company South West Eco-Homes.

SUSTAINABLE HOMES
Sarah Butler
Hastoe Housing Association, 7 High Street, Teddington TW11 8EE
T: 020 8973 0429
E: info@sustainablehomes.co.uk
www.sustainablehomes.co.uk
Sustainable Homes provides a wealth of information through websites, training and research to promote sustainable development issues to the social housing sector. Sustainable Homes also co-ordinates all sustainability projects funded by the Housing Corporation's Innovation and Good Practice Programme.

WATER AND WASTE APPLIANCES

CHI-Q
Ryokan Potier
27a Caen Street, Braunton, Devon EX33 1AA
T: 01271 817584
E: ryokan.potier@chi-q.demon.co.uk
www.chi-q.com
All-in-one water Ioniser / Purifier / Deoxidiser for main water pipes.

Maintenance free. 30 years life. Water powered. Reduce power needed for heating by 30%. Protects the system from Legionella, E-Coli, rust, mould, scale, etc. Up to 90% detergent.

WATERCOURSE SYSTEMS LTD
Chris Weedon
Will's Barn, Chipstable, Taunton, Somerset TA4 2PX
T: 01984 629 070
E: weedon@compuserve.com
Wastewater treatment consultant, specialising in reed bed treatment. 13 years designing, installing and maintaining reed bed wastewater treatment systems. Recent innovations include the compact vertical flow reed bed. Over 40 systems installed to date, from single household to 2,000 population.

WOOD BASED PANEL PRODUCTS

WEYERHAEUSER PRODUCTS LTD
Julie Peek
10th Floor Maitland House, Warrior Square, Southend on Sea, Essex SS1 2JY
T: 01702 6190044
E: euinfo@weyerhaeuser.com
www.weyerhaeuser-europe.com
Within Europe Weyerhaeuser manufactures a growing range of wood based panel products including Medite MDF, Mediland MDF and Darbo Particle board.

FOR MORE PRODUCT MANUFACTURERS, SUPPLIERS ETC. PLEASE SEE THE ADVERTISEMENT LIST AT THE BACK OF THIS BOOK

Index

Author profiles

Listed in alphabetical order by first name.

Adrian Birch BA, BSc, MSc(Arch), Dip.Proj.Man., FRICS

Adrian originally trained as a chartered building surveyor and for over 15 years worked in various architects and building surveying firms in London and Bristol, managing new-build and refurbishment projects in all property sectors. He now heads the Building Surveying courses at the University of the West of England. In addition to teaching and research in the field of sustainable design and construction he also provides consultancy advice to individuals and organisations seeking to design, construct or refurbish buildings in a sustainable way. Current projects include a village shop/cafe/business centre in Brockweir, Glos and a nursery school in Llandogo, Monmouthshire.
Adrian.Birch@uwe.ac.uk

Anita Bradley

Anita has an architecture degree from Liverpool University. She regularly reviews books for 'Building for a Future' magazine. Her particular interests are electro-pollution and geopathic stress. She is currently investigating sustainability issues regarding the built environment.

Professor Anthony Walker Dip Arch (Dist) Dip Grad (Consv) AA RIBA ACArch AABC

Currently a partner in DLG Architects and a founding member in 1972 of Damond Lock Grabowski + Partners, Anthony has proven experience which covers differing types and sizes of building, including town planning, exhibition space, urban design, interior design and space planning. He is actively involved in a wide range of leisure projects and is a founder member of the Leisure Property Forum. He has recently completed the refurbishment of Windsor Royal Station, and 109 Harley Street which required detailed negotiation with English Heritage. Amongst his current responsibilities are new premises for the Order of St John, a series of Grade 1 buildings for The Bedford Estate and a major leisure development at Camberley, Surrey. As part of the practice policy of professional development, he as completed a post graduate course in building conservation. His dissertation focused on the effects of listing modern building and the research involved has led to further studies which are currently in hand. He lectures in building conservation, prepares assessments of listed buildings and character statements for conservation areas. He is on the Register of Architects Accredited in Building Conservation (now run by the RIBA) and is an assessor to CARE, the Accreditation Body for Structural Engineers.
london@dlg-architects.co.uk

Dr Barbara Grantham

Barbara originally trained as a scientist and is currently company secretary for Dragonfly Solutions Ltd., a computer training and software development company. She is a member of LLES -Llanidloes Energy Solutions, an organisation who promote energy conservation and renewable energy to combat climate change.

She is interested in all aspects of sustainable living and has had a number of articles published on renewable enegy and cycling.
dragonfly@clara.co.uk

Barbara Tremain

Barbara lives in West Cornwall. She works as a garden designer specialising in wildlife and wildflower gardens, wetland and woodland planting and garden restorations. Qualified in advanced horticulture, garden design, permaculture, eco-village design and complementary therapies. Barbara also writes about and photographs permaculture, eco- building and related subjects in Britain and abroad.
barbaratremain40@hotmail.com

Ben Bamber

Ben is an author who specialises in both clinical psychology and architectural literature, which reflect his interests in a wide variety of other subjects, including politics and religion as well as works of fiction. He also has an interest in graphic design and computer generated art.
dedicate@blueyonder.co.uk

Bill Dunster MA Hons Edin RIBA qual 1984

Bill worked for Michael Hopkins and Partners for over 14 years specialising in low energy and sustainable development. He undertook 4 years of research in the European Union collaborating with the leading environmental consultants in Europe. He has taught at the Architectural Association and Kingston University and spoken at a number of seminars and conferences. He has recently received an Honorary Doctorate from Oxford Brookes University. Following years of research and development into high-density zero fossil fuel urban regeneration, working with a local environmental business charity, the BioRegional Development Group - his BedZED scheme was presented to the Peabody Trust. In early 1999 the disused water treatment site was purchased from the local authority and both the BedZED project and Bill Dunster architects began. The practice has transformed itself into the 'ZEDfactory' – synthesising low environmental impact product development, architecture, masterplanning and financial appraisals. In 1995 Bill Dunster built his own house, Hope House which is a prototype low energy live/work unit in which he and his family live, and from where the office operated before moving to BedZED. BedZed has won a range of awards.
bill@zedfactory.com

Chris Morgan

Chris gained 2 first class degrees in architecture at Newcastle University before working both as a builder and architect. He gained experience with Christopher Day in Wales; Malcolm Newton in Northumberland working on the Earth Balance project, across New Zealand and; from 1997 to the end of last year, with Gaia Architects in Edinburgh. At Gaia, Chris was responsible for a number of projects including the Glencoe Visitor Centre, along with other buildings featured in Building for a Future magazine. In 2004, Chris set up Locate Architects to continue work on ecological design projects and sustainable development related consultancy, research and teaching. The practice aims always for innovative and contemporary design, with particular expertise in healthy specification, timber and other low impact material based construction, low energy solutions and a desire to 'locate' buildings more fully into their surround-

ings. Chris has qualifications in permaculture and building biology and was recently accredited by the RIAS to a 3* level in sustainable design.
mail@chrismorgan.fsnet.co.uk

Chris Morton M.Arch (Liverpool)

Chris graduated in 1964. He worked in the public sector including the Government of Kenya (1967-1969) and Lewisham (1975-1977) during a brief reign of green, radical chief architect. He personally rebuilt the burnt-out remains of a timber framed cottage, using mostly recycled materials. He has been self employed since 1979 undertaking mostly domestic and restoration work - going as green as clients are prepared to.
evendine@mac.com

Damien Bree

Damian was born on the west coast of Ireland. After qualifying in Architectural Technology at Bolton Street in Dublin he went on to briefly study Architecture. After completing his studies he came to London in 1984 and worked with several practices, he worked briefly in the middle east before forming Bree Day Partnership Chartered Architects in 1995. He's been interested in how technology can be integrated within residential buildings since the late 80's and, with the formation of Bree Day Partnership Chartered Architects, has been able to concentrate on promoting sustainable environmental design through their work. The practice has undertaken several award winning environmental developments in the UK and is a founding partner of INTEGER, Intelligent & Green Ltd. Their work has been featured on television, in magazines and several books.
damian@architech.co.uk

Dave Barton

Dave is a director and co-founder of Impetus Consulting, an energy and environmental consultancy with 15 staff split between offices in London and West Sussex. Dave has 15 year's experience of working in the energy field.
info@impetusconsult.co.uk

Dave Elliott

Dave Elliott has written extensively on renewable energy issues over the years. His most recent book, 'Energy, Society and Environment', now in its second edition, combines an analytical overview of the policy issues with assessments of the practical deployment opportunities and problems. In his contributions to Building for a Future magazine he has focused on the latter, looking at examples of successful initiatives and programmes in the domestic housing and built environment field. He is director of the Open University Energy and Environment Research Unit and editor of Renew, a journal on renewable energy policy and developments .
D.A.Elliott@open.ac.uk

David Thorpe

David is the Creative Director of Cyberium. For 15 years he has been helping to interpret and popularise the complex issues around sustainable development, via journalism, web sites, multimedia and film/tv. He is the News Editor of Energy and Environmental Management magazine, published by Defra, and other clients have included the Eden Project, the Sensory Trust, Mersey Forest, charities, local government, as well as energy and architecture companies.
david@cyberium.co.uk

Edward Moss

Edward is involved with a community field project which is being developed into community space, incorporating organic farming, permaculture, and natural sustainable building and an open air theatre. Edward lives in Cornwall and has previous architectural and building experience as well as a broad knowledge of sustainable and natural building. He is also developing his hands-on practical skills in this area.
emoss456@yahoo.co.uk

Féidhlim Harty

Féidhlim is director of FH Wetland Systems Ltd., an environmental consultancy company based in West Cork. FH Wetland Systems was started in 1996 with a particular emphasis on designing and planting constructed wetlands for wastewater treatment, and now also offers a range of environmental services including sustained urban drainage systems (SUDs) habitat and catchment management and pollution control consultancy. Féidhlim also does freelance writing and teaches wastewater treatment and stormwater management modules on various courses in Cork city and county. He lives in West Cork with his wife and two children with, predictably enough, a constructed wetland system, solar panels, wood burning stoves and cellulose insulation.
wetland@eircom.net

Gideon Richards

Gideon has, over the past ten plus years, advised companies, organisations and individuals on ways to maximise their resources and profits as a management consultant. With a Diploma in Management Studies and an HND in Electrical and Electronic Engineering, Gideon started his career as a project manager in the passenger lift industry with a portfolio of projects running to £4m after a year. He moved on to have successful posts as a regional sales manager and business development manager, before starting Consulting With A Purpose in 1996. Gideon currently sits on a number of European Standards Working Groups for TC335 Solid Biofuels and TC343 Solid Recovered Fuels and is the chair of the British Standards Institute's PTI/17 mirror committee for TC335 and TC343. He is also on the executive board of The British Pellet Club and a Trustee of the charity CREATE (Create for Research Education and Training in Energy).
gideon.richards@btinternet.com

Jamie Anderson

Jamie is passionate about design, architecture and environmental issues. He studied furniture design at Guildhall University, London after a lifetime of finding products in shops and thinking 'I could make that'. He has undertaken research projects for GLEEN and London Borough of Southwark on eco-construction materials. His discovery of natural paints and desire to be 'hands on' in projects lead him to found ecoartisan, a decoration and design service using natural paints and materials, with Brussels based friend Alec Tortora in spring 1998. Their shared belief in the benefits of natural products and combined skills in decorating and design has imbued their work with a meticulous attention to detail and guaranteed quality of finish. Recent projects have included the refit of the Duffer of St George store in Stockholm, a residential repaint in East London and bespoke furniture and a new bathroom for his demanding wife in central London.
info@ecoartisan.org

Jerry Clark

Jerry has had a long interest in matters environmental, developing a concern for endangered wildlife as a child during the sixties. He spent many years as a cabinet-maker, and injected his environmental concerns into which timbers and finishes were used, often turning down commissions where the customer insisted on the use of an inappropriate timber. Latterly Jerry has gained a first class honours degree in Environmental Sciences and put a lot of his new-found knowledge into practise while creating a super-insulated, eco-home on a smallhold-ing in Wales. He works on a freelance basis that includes work for the Green Building Press. He has recently moved to Cornwall to a multi-generation house with his wife, daughter and father (his son has long since flown the nest). Other interests include listening to music (mostly loud), and kayaking around the estuaries and coasts of Cornwall.
jerry@newbuilder.co.uk

John Garbutt

John has been in the insulation manufacturing industry for fifteen years. He currently works for Kingspan Insulation Ltd. He has worked for manufacturers of mineral wool, extruded polystyrene, rigid urethane and phenolic insulation. He is widely respected in the field for his technical expertise and has played a major role in the government's consultation process for the next revision to Approved Document L of Building Regulations for England & Wales. John sits on the Approved Document L Industry Advisory Groups, and is on three of its seven expert panels. These are the Envelope Expert Panel, which examines the standards for roofs, floors, walls etc. and the Expert Panels for Refurbishment and for Domestic Building Services. He chairs the Roofing Working Group and sits on the Working Group for Masonry Walls and Floors, both of which report to the Envelope Expert Panel. In each of these areas he either represents the Phenolic Foam Manufacturers Association, the British Rigid Urethane Foam Manufacturers Association or Kingspan Insulation. With a BA Hons in Natural Science from Cambridge University, and a Masters in Earth Sciences from the University of Minnesota, John is an avid environmentalist in his private life. He is professionally and personally interested in the topic of sustainability and believes with a passion that manufacturers need to be open and honest about what they do, and that they should be responsible about what they make and how they make it.
john.garbutt@insulation.kingspan.com

John Shore AA Dipl

John Shore graduated from the Architectural Association, specialising in Ecological Design and Renewable Energy. He was responsible for designing, building and monitoring the Integrated Solar Dwelling at Brighton in the 1970's – the UK's first self-sufficient, zero-heat house. He has been involved with pioneering research, development and demonstration with sustain-able buildings and energy systems since the 1960's. As well as writing extensively on self-building and sustainable design and running the wind and solar energy company AERODYN-SHOREPOWER, he has lectured at schools of architecture and worked at Croydon College of Art and Somerset College of Arts and Technology. Current projects include designing low-cost, zero-heat sustaina-ble housing and workspace schemes for the Environment Trust.
esourceresearch@ukonline.co.uk

Keith Hall

Keith completed a three year apprenticeship in carpentry and joinery way back in 1974! In the early '80s he formed his own building business that included general building, renovation and new housing. In 1988 he became concerned about environmental issues, particularly the use of unsustainable tropical timber. From that concern he launched a magazine called Building for a Future and founded the Association for Environment Conscious Building (AECB) in an effort to promote the concept of green and sustainable building. In 1990 he established the Green Building Press, a business dedicated to promot-ing and providing information about eco and healthy building. He is Editor of Building for a Future magazine and the Green Building Bible. He has designed and built many sustainable building projects.
keith@newbuilder.co.uk

Kirk Archibald

Before joining the Energy Saving Trust, Kirk worked for a large housing association in London where he worked in the development and reinvestment department. Kirk was involved in innovative timber frame development projects and large refurbishment programmes in his four years there. Previous to that Kirk worked as a project manager for a small architectural company building one-off timber frame homes in the self-build market. Kirk currently manages the DTI Major Photovoltaic Demonstration Programme.
www.est.org.uk/solar

Dr. Mark Gorgolewski

Mark is an Associate Professor at the School of Architectural Science at Ryerson University in Toronto, Canada, where he recently moved from the UK. Mark is a fully qualified architect in the UK who has worked for many years as an environmental consultant in the UK construction industry. He has worked on a wide variety of research projects for government, local authorities, housing associations, private developers, materials producers and others, focusing on sustainable construc-tion issues and new technologies and processes. He has published widely on construction technology and envi-ronmental issues. Mark is a past chair of the Association for Environment Conscious Building (AECB).
mgorgo@ryerson.ca

Maya Karkour,

Maya is a consultant at EcoConsulting (UK) Ltd, is a BREEAM, BREEAM for Schools, EcoHomes, and NHER assessor, and holds an MSc in environmental policy, planning, and regulation from LSE. EcoConsulting advises architects, developers, and housing associations on cost-effective eco-building solutions to improve energy efficiency, interior health and comfort, and environmen-tal-friendliness. She conducts NHER-certified SAP ratings, and assists in complying with Building Regulations Part L requirements.
maya@ecoconsulting.net

Mike Priaulx

Mike is an Energy and Environmental Advisor at NHBC Services Ltd. Mike has been an EcoHomes assessor almost since the launch of the scheme and has provided advice for a wide range of different projects, including 'very good' and 'excellent' rated developments. He is also a bespoke BREEAM, BREEAM for Offices and NHER assessor.
MPriaulx@nhbc.co.uk

Nanik Daswani

Nanik is director at EcoConsulting (UK) Ltd, a company that advises architects, developers, and housing associations on cost-effective eco-building solutions to improve energy efficiency, interior health and comfort, and environmental-friendliness. Nanik is a BREEAM for offices, BREEAM Retail, EcoHomes and NHER assessor. He holds an MSc in environmental policy, planning, and regulation from LSE.
nanik@ecoconsulting.net

Paul Jennings

Paul studied Engineering Design & Appropriate Technology at Warwick where he developed an interest in energy and sustainability. He provided technical support to the local welfare rights advice centre. He went on to do a Masters in Energy Resources Management at South Bank. He has been testing ever since and has carried out over 10,000 tests upon buildings and parts thereof for a wide range of applications, particularly energy efficiency (both Building Regulations Part L and the more demanding green and eco standards, such as Canadian Super-E housing), checking advanced ventilation systems, testing for fire separation and containment. Paul has tested across the UK and overseas, including Europe, Africa and the Middle and Far East for a vast range of clients. He has also delivered numerous presentations to builders, architects, local authorities and insurance bodies. Specific buildings that he has tested include the AtEIC building at the Centre for Alternative Technology, Sue Roaf's Oxford Solar House and the Nottingham Eco-house.
paul.Jennings@retroteceurope.co.uk

Peter Kaczmar MSc

Peter is Head of TRADA Technology Ltd's chemical and analytical laboratories (Wood Technology) and is responsible for the company's scientific research on surface coatings and timber preservation. His research work on preservatives and woodfinishes has provided in-depth information on the professional and private market sectors within the coatings industry.
pkaczmar@trada.co.uk

Peter Walker

Peter is Senior Lecturer in Dept. Architecture & Civil Engineering, University of Bath. He trained as civil Engineer. He has over 20 year's research experience in earth building, masonry construction and natural fibre construction. he has published over 60 papers and is co-author of 'The Australian earth building handbook'.
p.walker@bath.ac.uk

Richard Handyside

Richard is perhaps best known as the person who, in 1998, established the first ecological building centre in the UK. Concentrating mostly on marketing mainly European eco-building products, Construction Resources, with premises in London, is well established as a centre of expertise and excellence dedicated to the promotion of eco building materials and systems. The centre provides extensive information and education on the application, installation and maintenance of the products it distributes. It also holds seminars for architects and specifiers and training courses for the various trades involved.
www.ecoconstruct.com

Robin Hillier

Robin is a director of Forever Green - architects specialising in timber framed low energy buildings, with a particular interest in community self build, user involvement in design, environmentally friendly design and non-traditional procurement methods.
robin@forevergreen.org.uk

Professor Sarah Sayce BSc, PhD, FRICS, IRRV

Sarah is the Head of the School of Surveying at Kingston University, a post she has held since 1992. She obtained both her first degree and PhD from Reading University and qualified as a Chartered Surveyor whilst working for a small city-based practice. She subsequently worked in the corporate sector before turning to academe. In her current position she is responsible for a range of RICS recognised undergraduate and postgraduate programmes, as well as other mid-career postgraduate courses and PhD students. She also holds University responsibilities notably in respect of Quality Assurance and she lead the Real Estate Research Group within the University. Her research interests range from the appraisal of commercial and leisure to professional standards and she has published widely in both academic refereed journals and national and international conference proceedings. Sarah retains active links with the property profession and she is a committee member of the Leisure Property Forum and a member of RICS South-East Regional Board and the Council for England and Wales.

Stephen Lowndes BEng (Hons) MSc CEng MCIBSE MEI

Stephen is a Chartered Engineer with over 20 years experience working as a Building Services Engineer. During this time he has worked for some of the UK's top services design and energy consultancy organisations and has been involved in a variety of projects in both the private and public sectors in the UK and Europe. Stephen has extensive experience in undertaking designs for low energy buildings that optimise the utilisation of natural ventilation and passive solar heating, as well as engineered schemes encompassing biofueled community heating systems, small-scale combined heat and power (CHP) and solar / wind powered rain water harvesting systems.
s.lowndes@ntlworld.com

Index of advertisers